PLANT LAYOUT
AND
MATERIALS HANDLING

JAMES M. APPLE
Georgia Institute of Technology

Second Edition

THE RONALD PRESS COMPANY • NEW YORK

Library of Congress Catalog Card Number: 63–9241

Preface

This book has been written to meet the need for a comprehensive yet concise single volume showing how to develop the most efficient layouts of equipment and of operating and service facilities, whether in manufacturing plants, warehouses, or other industrial or business applications.

The reception granted the First Edition of this book has been most gratifying. After twelve years of use in colleges, universities, and industry, and many discussions with others in the teaching profession, the author has concluded that the primary reason for its acceptance has been the fact that it was written to be "taught from"—and follows a logical, step-by-step approach to the plant layout and materials handling problem.

In the book, plant layout is presented from an engineering standpoint, but without becoming too involved in the technical features of equipment design and construction. Instead, emphasis has been kept upon the major problem of the essential coordination between plant layout, materials handling, methods engineering, and production planning and control. Such coordination is emphasized throughout the book as a means of integrating the manufacturing facilities and the many related functions to meet today's exacting manufacturing and operating demands. One purpose of the book is, in fact, to show how to take full advantage of all the different interrelated techniques, as the only practical way in which a satisfactory and workable layout can be developed.

The material offered in the volume is the result of close association over a period of twenty years with numerous industries during which time many of the ideas and techniques were developed, tested, and found successful in solving plant layout problems. During this period the author has taught the subject in college and industry, and has practiced it as a consulting engineer and manufacturing executive. From this experience has evolved a "thought pattern" through which the many phases of plant layout planning can be systematically integrated. This pattern is outlined in Chapter 3 and developed fully in the chapters following. It is not claimed it will be a cure-all or formula through which all plant layout problems can be solved, since each plant layout problem is an individual case. But the thought pattern is an effective, organized aid giving assurance that no necessary step will be omitted in the investigation. The pattern aids the tying together of the many interrelated aspects of the problem into a smooth-flowing procedure so that the planning can be carried out in a logical manner in designing the best solution for each case.

In arriving at this result in a practical manner, specific consideration is given to the various means and techniques employed. Thus stress is given the essentials of effective operation planning as the basis for flow process charts used in planning alignment of work flow and working out arrangement of equipment and materials handling services. In connection with materials handling, attention is centered on fundamentals for correct application of each kind of equipment to the particular handling job to be done. The value is shown of plant layout studies and improvements in recovering otherwise inefficiently used floor space for higher production efficiency.

Obviously a book such as the present one could not have been written without help from many sources. My teaching colleagues have been of invaluable assistance in refining the various techniques herein presented. Nearly two hundred companies contributed the illustrations from which those in this book were selected. Engineers from industry have willingly discussed their problems openly and given of their experience; they have tested the techniques and found them practical. Sincere appreciation is expressed to all these persons who have given so generously of their time and experience, whose ideas are included, and whose suggestions have been incorporated in the writing. It is my hope that the publication of this book may in part reward them for their aid.

To my wife and family I owe an especial debt of gratitude for the many household chores and family affairs that were neglected or postponed so that the writing could continue.

Comments and suggestions will be most welcome from any who may make use of this book.

JAMES M. APPLE

Atlanta, Georgia
  January, 1963

Contents

PLANT LAYOUT

AND

MATERIALS HANDLING

1

The Plant Layout Problem

What Is Plant Layout? Plant layout is one of the most interesting and important phases of Industrial Engineering. It deals with the arrangement of the physical facilities and manpower required to manufacture a product. The over-all objective is to plan the arrangement of facilities and personnel so that the manufacturing process may be carried out in as effective a manner as possible. This objective calls for a minimum of movement on the part of both materials and personnel and a minimum of time in process for any individual part. The shorter the amount of time a piece of material spends in the plant, the less opportunity it has to collect charges against it in terms of labor and overhead costs.

Plant Layout may be defined as *planning* and integrating the paths of the component parts of a product to obtain *the most effective and economical* interrelationship between men; equipment; and the *movement of materials from receiving, through fabrication, to the shipment of the finished product.*

It will be noted that the italicized words are a definition of materials handling, and removing it from the complete definition actually makes plant layout meaningless. This is of course a fact—since no two fields are so closely related as plant layout and materials handling.

The term "plant layout" may refer to an existing *installation;* a two- or three-dimensional *plan;* or the *work involved* in designing the most effective interrelationship between operating equipment and personnel, materials movement, storage facilities, service functions, and auxiliary equipment.

Scope of the Plant Layout Problem. Plant layout is frequently thought of as dealing only with the careful and detailed planning of production equipment arrangement. However, this is really only one phase of a very extensive series of interrelated activity areas making up a typical industrial plant layout project.

The complete scope of plant layout work should include a careful study of the following:

1. External transportation facilities
2. Receiving operations (unloading, inspection, stores)
3. Production activities
4. Service and auxiliary operations
5. Quality control and inspection areas
6. Packaging operations
7. Storage operations
8. Shipping operations

The work of designing a layout starts with an analysis of the product to be made and a consideration of the over-all flow of materials. It progresses step-by-step through the detailed planning of the arrangement of equipment in each individual work area. Then the interrelationship between work areas is planned; related areas are coordinated into departments, sections, or units, which then are woven into a final layout.

The detailed steps by which this work is accomplished are explained in subsequent chapters.

Importance of Plant Layout. The importance of plant layout to the efficient operation of an enterprise cannot be overemphasized. It should be recognized that the flow of materials represents the "backbone" of a production facility. As such, it should be very carefully planned and not allowed to grow or develop into an unwieldy octopus of confused traffic patterns. Perhaps the concept can be summarized as follows:

1. A primary requisite for economical production is an efficient plan for the flow of materials.
2. The materials flow pattern becomes the basis for an effective arrangement of physical facilities.
3. Materials handling converts the *static* flow pattern into a *dynamic* reality —by providing the means by which the materials are caused or permitted to flow.
4. Effective arrangement of facilities *around* the materials flow pattern should result in efficient operation of the various related processes.
5. Efficient operation of the processes should result in minimum production costs.
6. And . . . minimum production costs should result in maximum profit.

The materials flow pattern, then, becomes the basis for the entire plant design as well as for the success of the enterprise. All too frequently, insufficient emphasis is placed on determining the most efficient plan for the flow of materials through the production facilities.

It should be our conclusion then, that plant layout comes *first*. No industrial building should be erected without having first completed a plant layout study. This will determine the desired flow of materials, the most economical arrangement of physical facilities, and will serve as the *basis* for the building design. Of course, the architect should be consulted in the early planning stages for advice on general building construction information, but his actual design work should *follow* that of the plant layout engineer.

Plant Layout Problems. Ordinarily when one thinks of plant layout, there comes to mind the problem of planning a complete layout for a new part or product, that is, of planning an entirely new plant, starting from scratch. This, however, is usually not the case. More frequently the problem involves the re-layout of an existing process or an alteration of some sort in the arrangement of certain equipment. Plant layout problems are of several types.

1. *Design Change.* Frequently a change in the design of a part calls for changes in the processes or operations to be performed. This change may require only minor alterations of the existing layout, or it may result in an extensive re-layout program, depending on the nature of the change.

2. *Enlarged Department.* If, for one reason or another, it becomes necessary to increase the production of a certain part or product, a change in the layout may be called for. This type of problem may involve only the addition of a few machines for which room can easily be made, or it may call for an entirely new layout if the increased production calls for a process different from the one used before. For example, if compressors were being made in hundreds, ordinary toolroom equipment might be used. However, if the schedule were changed to thousands it might be expedient to install a related group of special-purpose machines.

3. *Reduced Department.* This problem is nearly the reverse of that stated above. If production quotas were reduced drastically and permanently, it would be necessary to consider using a process different from that previously used for high production. Such a change would probably require the removal of present equipment and planning for the installation of other types of equipment.

4. *Adding a New Product.* If a new product is added to a line, and it is similar to the products already being made, the problem is primarily one of enlarging a department. If, however, the new product differs considerably from those in production, a different problem presents itself. The present equipment may be used by adding a few new machines here and there in the existing layout, with a minimum of rearrangement; or it may be found necessary to set up a completely new department or section of the plant—possibly a new plant.

5. *Moving a Department.* Moving a department may, or may not, present a major layout problem. If the present layout is satisfactory, it is necessary only to shift to another location. If, however, the present layout has not been satisfactory, an opportunity presents itself for the

correction of past mistakes. This may amount to a complete re-layout of the area in question.

6. *Adding a New Department.* This problem may arise from a desire to consolidate, let us say, the drill press work from all departments into one central department; or it may result from the need for establishing a department to do work never before performed in the plant. Such a case would arise if it were decided to make a part which had previously been purchased from an outside firm.

7. *Replacing Obsolete Equipment.* This may require movement of adjacent equipment to provide additional space.

8. *Change in Production Methods.* Anything more than a small change in a single workplace is very likely to have an effect on adjacent workplaces or areas. This will require a re-working of the area involved.

9. *Cost Reduction.* This, of course, could be the cause or result of any of the above situations.

10. *Planning a New Plant.* This presents the biggest problem in plant layout. Here the engineer generally is not limited by restrictions of existing facilities. He is free to plan the most effective layout he can devise. Buildings can then be designed to house the layout after it has been completed. This is where the ideal in layout can be attained. The plant can be completely laid out for the most efficient manufacturing. Then walls can be planned around the layout and the proper form of physical structure decided upon.

Each of these situations may present itself to the plant layout engineer. Each is as fascinating as another. Each presents its own peculiar problems to be solved; and though the engineer may have done his best on a completed layout, he always feels that a better way might possibly have been discovered.

And in addition to the above "normal" reasons for plant layout problems or projects, there are many "abnormal" situations or difficulties which may indicate the need for a study of an existing layout. Some of these indicators are:

1. Building not suited to requirements
2. Failure to apply "line" production techniques when applicable
3. Product design or process changes made without making necessary changes in the layout
4. Installation of additional equipment without considering relationship to existing flow pattern
5. Unexplainable delays and idle time
6. Stock control difficulties
7. Decreased production in an area
8. Crowded conditions
9. Large numbers of men moving materials

10. Bottlenecks in production
11. Backtracking
12. Excessive temporary storage
13. Obstacles in materials flow
14. Scheduling difficulties
15. Wasted "cube"
16. Idle people and equipment
17. Excessive time required in process
18. Poor housekeeping

Stable vs. Changing Products. These two widely different situations call for entirely different treatments of the plant layout function. In a steel mill, there may be no such thing as a Plant Layout Department. This is due to the enormous size and relative immobility of steel mill equipment. So long as there are no major changes in the process, plant layout problems are relatively few; and plant layout may be a dormant or non-existent function.

In an automobile plant, the plant layout function is far from dormant. Every year models are changed in some details. Each change calls for layout shifts. Major changes made every few years may warrant entire re-layout of large areas.

Between these two extremes fall the types of problems listed above, so that the complete scope of plant layout problems will range from a fairly well-established layout in the case of the steel mill to a complete layout in the case of a proposed plant.

Objectives of Plant Layout. If a finished layout is to present an effective arrangement of related work areas, in which goods can be economically produced, it must be planned with the objectives of plant layout well fixed in mind. The major objectives are to:

1. Facilitate the manufacturing process
2. Minimize materials handling
3. Maintain flexibility of arrangement and of operation
4. Maintain high turnover of work-in-process
5. Hold down investment in equipment
6. Make economical use of floor area
7. Promote effective utilization of manpower
8. Provide for employee convenience, safety, and comfort in doing the work

A brief discussion of each of these objectives will guide the plant layout engineer in attaining them.

Facilitating the Manufacturing Process. The layout should be designed in such a way that the manufacturing process can be carried on in the most efficient manner. Some specific suggestions are:

    a) Arrange machines, equipment, and work areas so that the material is caused to move smoothly along in as straight a line as is possible. This does not necessarily mean that the flow line must be "straight." It merely indicates that there should be a minimum of backtracking. The flow might well be **U**-shaped, circular, or one of many other forms, as indicated in a later section on planning materials flow.

    b) Eliminate all delays possible. It has been said that during 80 per cent of the time a part is in the plant it is either being moved or stored—only 20 per cent of the time is productive.

    c) Plan the flow so that the work passing through an area can be easily identified and counted, with little possibility of becoming mixed with other parts or batches in adjacent areas.

    d) Plan for the maintenance of conditions which will maintain quality of work. This planning may involve capital expenditures, such as air conditioning of certain areas; or it may call only for planned good housekeeping to prevent damage of parts in process, movement, or storage.

These and many other suggestions will be more completely explained as the following chapters present the plant layout planning procedure.

Minimizing Materials Handling. A good layout should be planned so that materials handling is reduced to a minimum. Wherever practicable, handling should be mechanical; and all movement should be planned to move the part toward the shipping area. Where possible, the part should be "in-process" while in transit, as in painting, baking, degreasing, etc. Materials handling will be dealt with in greater detail in later chapters.

Maintaining Flexibility. Although a plant or department may be planned for the production of a certain quantity of a certain item, there are many occasions when it will be necessary to alter its production capabilities.

Many of the changes thus called for may be more easily made if they are anticipated in the original planning. A common way to facilitate the rearrangement of equipment is to install utility systems into which service connections can be easily tied when the building is constructed. Good examples are the electrical ducts and the cutting-compound pipe lines which are installed overhead, down the centers of bays. Such arrangements permit machines to be "plugged-out," moved into new locations, and "plugged-in" again, almost at will.

Maintaining High Turnover of Work-in-Process. The greatest operating efficiency is attainable only when the material used in a plant is moved through the necessary processes in the shortest possible time. Every minute a part spends in the plant adds to its cost through the tie-up of working capital. The nearest to an ideal situation exists in the process-type industry where, by its nature, the material passes, sometimes without stopping, from the start to the finish of the process. If in-process storage of materials is reduced to a minimum, over-all material turnover (manufacturing) time is reduced, the amount of work-in-process is reduced, inventory is decreased, and a lower amount of working capital is tied up therein. These savings, in turn, reduce production costs.

Reducing Investment in Equipment. The proper arrangement of machines and departments can aid considerably in reducing the quantity of equipment required. For example, two different parts, both requiring the part-time use of an internal grinder, may be routed through the same machine, thus eliminating the cost of a second machine. Foresight in selecting the method of processing may sometimes save purchasing a machine. If it is found that one part, as processed, calls for broaching, and will use only part of the capacity of a machine, a switch to drilling and reaming might be effected and the job done on equipment already available.

Making Economical Use of Floor Area. Each square foot of floor area in a plant costs money. One manufacturer, for example, has calculated his floor area cost to be $1.00 per square foot per month. This amount includes all overhead costs. Only if each square foot is used to best advantage can the attending overhead costs per unit of product be kept down. Floor area occupied by equipment in operation pays its own way. Unoccupied, wasted, or idle floor area is a burden on the rest of the plant.

Proper layout dictates minimum spacing between machines, after the necessary allowances for the movement of men and materials have been made. With proper consideration of machine spacing in relation to other factors, much floor area can be saved. At that, many manufacturers find that only about 50 per cent of their floor area is occupied by production equipment.

Promoting Effective Use of Manpower. A large amount of productive manpower may be wasted through poor layout practices. Proper layout, on the other hand, may increase the effective utilization of labor. Suggestions such as the following should lead to increased labor utilization:

a) Reduce manual handling of materials to a minimum, especially all avoidable rehandling.
b) Minimize walking. One plant found that 20 per cent of the time spent on the assembly line was occupied by men walking to and from material supplies and keeping up with the assembly conveyor as it moved along. This time loss was reduced considerably by bringing materials closer to the workers with specially designed racks, hoppers, and conveyors, and having the conveyor index at predetermined intervals, instead of moving continuously. Such improvement obviously requires high production and the ultimate in good planning.
c) Balance machine cycles, so that, as nearly as possible, machines and workers are not unnecessarily idle. Well-balanced operation necessitates good ma-

terials handling, good production control, good methods engineering, and good supervision.

d) Provide for effective supervision. In theory, the supervisor might stand in the midst of his group, so that he would be in immediate contact with each employee.

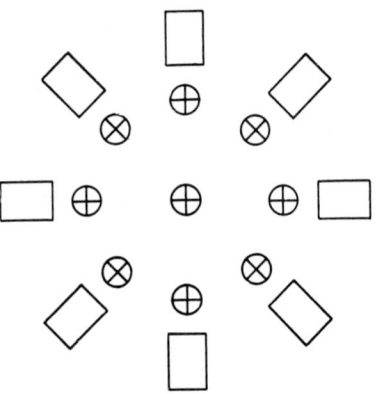

Fig. 1–1. Theoretical supervisory situation.

Such a plan seems hardly possible. It is necessary to emphasize, however, that a properly laid-out department is easier to supervise than one which is spread out over too large an area, or is too congested, or otherwise hinders the relationship between the supervisor and his men. A well-laid-out department makes it easier for a supervisor to handle more employees, keep work moving, and conserve his time for his more important duties.

Providing for Employee Convenience, Safety, and Comfort. Satisfying this objective requires attention to such items as light, heat, ventilation, safety, removal of moisture, dirt, dust, etc.

Equipment causing excessive noise should be isolated as much as possible or enclosed in an area with sound-deadening walls and ceiling. Equipment which vibrates should be cushioned or specially mounted to prevent the transmission of vibration to the floor or surrounding objects. Safety must also be assured by proper planning of the layout. Machines and auxiliary manufacturing equipment must be so placed as to prevent injury to personnel and damage to material and to other equipment. Safety may be incorporated into the layout by a careful study of workplace arrangement, materials handling methods, storage techniques, ventilation, lighting, fire protection, and all other factors involved in plant operation.

It will be noted that in many cases it is impossible fully to achieve these objectives. In fact, some of them are rather almost in opposition to each other. Nevertheless, each represents an important goal toward which the plant layout engineer must strive. When objectives in a particular situation seem to be opposed, an equitable solution must be reached that will be most effective in light of all factors considered.

Marks of a Good Plant Layout. In view of the preceding discussion, it would appear that efficient plant layout has certain desirable characteristics which should be evident from even a casual survey or observation. Among the most important of these are:

1. Planned materials flow pattern
2. Straight-line layout (or an adaptation thereof)
3. Building constructed (or altered) around a preplanned layout design
4. Straight, clear, marked aisles
5. Backtracking kept to a minimum
6. Related operations close together
7. Production time predictable
8. Minimum of scheduling difficulties
9. Minimum of goods-in-process
10. Easy adjustment to changing conditions
11. Plans for expansion
12. Maximum ratio of actual processing time to over-all production time
13. Good quality with minimum inspection
14. Minimum materials handling distances
15. Minimum of manual handling
16. No unnecessary rehandling of materials
17. Materials handled in unit loads
18. Minimum handling between operations
19. Materials delivered to production employees
20. Materials efficiently removed from the work area
21. Materials handling being done by indirect labor
22. Orderly materials handling and storage
23. Good housekeeping
24. Busy employees, working at maximum efficiency

Subsequent chapters will present the procedures and techniques for accomplishing the objectives and philosophies set forth above.

QUESTIONS

1. What is the over-all objective of plant layout?
2. Define plant layout.
3. Name and briefly describe the ten types of layout problems.
4. Name the objectives of plant layout.
5. Indicate some ways in which each objective can be met.
6. Why is materials handling an integral part of plant layout?
7. What are some of the advantages of an efficient plant layout?
8. What are the marks of a good plant layout?

2

The Plant Layout Function

Varying Situations. The plant layout function is a staff service, usually associated with the manufacturing or production activity. However, there are several organization levels at which plant layout work is performed, depending upon the relative size of the company and the relative importance of the plant layout function to the operation of the enterprise.

In the small plant, there is usually no formal Plant Layout Department. The layout work which must be done will be the result of the combined efforts of one or more foremen, the general manager, sometimes the company president, and the engineer and draftsman, who will all be in on the planning.

In a large plant, where there is much layout work to be done, a staff, perhaps of a dozen or more people, will spend full time working on problems in plant layout. Each person will be skilled in certain areas of layout work. Tasks will be subdivided, the individual parts being performed by trained experts; and a coordinated layout will finally be built up from their combined contributions.

There are certain large plants which require little in the way of repeated layout work because of the nature of their processes. Plants of this kind are those in the process industries field—steel, rubber, petroleum, glass, etc.—where the plant, once satisfactorily laid out, remains relatively unchanged for long periods of time.

Plant Layout Activities. The specific activities assigned to the plant layout group vary considerably from one plant to another, depending on the size of the plant, the importance of the layout function in the particular plant, and the organizational plan of the enterprise. The following are duties which may be performed by this group in approximately the order in which they would be carried out in a plant layout project.

1. Procure and analyze basic data.
2. Plan materials flow pattern.
3. Consider general materials handling plan.
4. Plan individual work stations.

5. Select specific materials handling equipment.
6. Determine storage requirements.
7. Coordinate groups of related operations.
8. Plan service areas.
9. Allocate all areas to over-all space allowance.
10. Construct master layout plan.
11. Check layout with appropriate persons.
12. Obtain approvals of layout.
13. Participate in building design.
14. Supervise construction and installation of layout plan.
15. Follow up on implementation of layout plans.

Details of the above activities will be covered in the following chapters.

Position of Plant Layout Department in Different Organizations. As was indicated above, the small plant will probably not have a Plant Layout Department, the responsibility for the function resting with the president or general manager, engineer, or foreman. When special problems arise, the man responsible for the project will solicit aid from whichever persons in the plant seem able to contribute to their solution.

In the plant where a regular layout group has been organized, this group will be assigned a definite place in the organization plan.

The position of the Plant Layout Department in the organization varies, as do the duties, with the size of the plant, the nature of the product, the importance of the plant layout function, and the organizational plan.

In a survey of 70 plants in the United States, the author found that 35 or more different titles were given to the person actually in charge of plant layout. The plants surveyed ranged in size from 600 to 102,000 employees. The average plant had 2,500 employees.

With slight alterations in the specific titles as reported, the following list indicates typical titles assigned, from most common to least common.

1. Plant Engineer
2. Plant Layout Engineer
3. Supervisor of Plant Layout
4. Methods and Equipment Engineer
5. Master Mechanic
6. Industrial Engineer
7. General Superintendent
8. Foreman
9. Superintendent of Maintenance
10. Manager of Production Engineering
11. Engineer
12. Technical Assistant
13. Manufacturing Analysis Engineer

14. Manager of Engineering Design and Construction
15. Superintendent of Planning
16. Chief Engineer
17. Process Engineer

Likewise, the title of the person to whom the above individual reports varied widely. Again with slight changes in titles reported, that person is:

1. Works, Plant, Factory, or General Manager
2. Vice-President
3. Works or Plant Engineer
4. Plant or General Superintendent
5. Chief Engineer
6. Master Mechanic
7. Methods Engineer
8. Manager of Industrial Engineering
9. Production Engineer
10. President
11. Manufacturing Engineer
12. Tool Engineer
13. Supervisor
14. Standards Head
15. Planning Engineer
16. Department Manager

In two other surveys of the Industrial Engineering function, results showed that in about 62 per cent of the cases, the plant layout group is a part of the Industrial Engineering Department. It would appear that the increased emphasis on plant layout has tended to place the activity in closer proximity to other related functions.

Assuming the organization chart of a typical industrial enterprise of 2,500 employees to be as shown in Figure 2–1, the position of the plant layout group is most commonly located as shown on the diagram.

Relationship Between Plant Layout and Other Departments. If the finished plant layout is to represent the best possible arrangement, the whole-hearted cooperation of many individuals is necessary. Included in this group of individuals who can contribute information or offer suggestions will be not only members of the Plant Layout Department, but also persons from practically every other department and division in the plant. The departments and divisions thus concerned, and the areas in which their cooperation is needed, are as follows:

1. Sales Department
   a) Determining quantities for production runs
   b) Determining quantities to manufacture for replacement parts

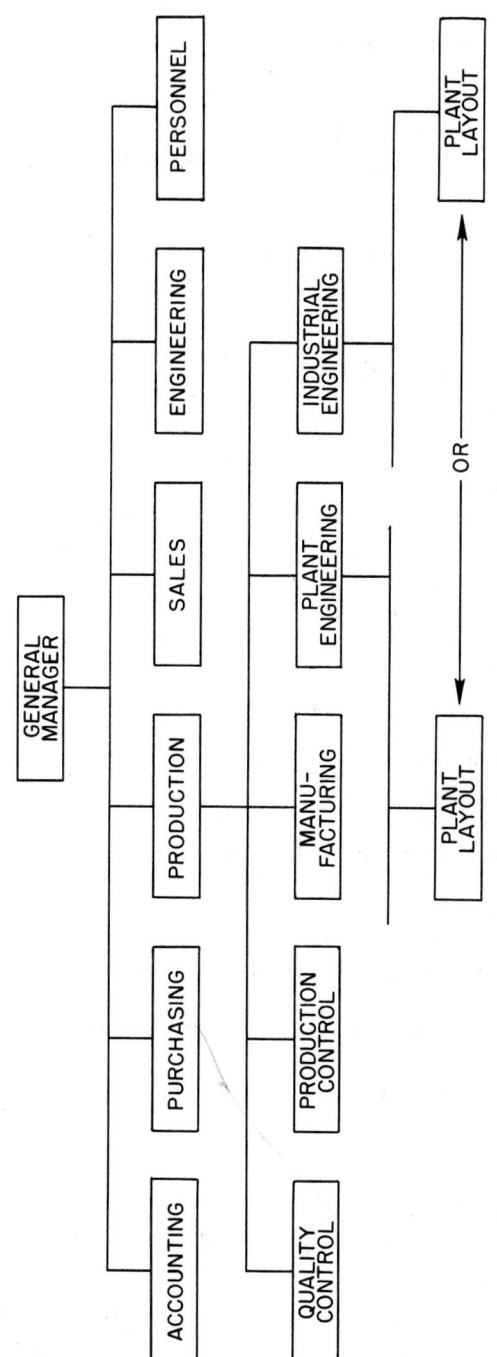

Fig. 2–1. Position of the plant layout function in the organization.

2. Purchasing Department
   a) Finding necessary factory equipment
   b) Procuring equipment at lowest practicable cost
3. Engineering Department
   a) Providing blueprints and parts lists
   b) Offering information on manufacture, as gained in research and development work
4. Personnel Department
   a) Helping to design safety into the layout
   b) Looking after employee comfort and services in layout
   c) Training personnel for new jobs necessitated by new layouts
5. Accounting Department
   a) Aiding in determining cost of layout
   b) Aiding in keeping equipment records
6. Industrial Engineering Division
   a) Determining production standards for all operations
   b) Determining work methods for each work area
   c) Determining machine capacities and number of machines needed
   d) Aid in comparing effectiveness of methods between alternate layouts
   e) Suggestions on processing and methods
   f) Design of special tools and equipment
   g) Planning operation sequence
   h) Specifying machines and equipment
   i) Trying out tools, etc.
7. Production Control Division
   a) Supply routings or operation lists
   b) Determine production schedules
   c) Aid in planning materials flow
   d) Offer suggestions on materials handling methods
   e) Plan storage methods and space requirements
8. Production Division
   a) Suggestions on machine arrangement
   b) Suggestions on human relations problems involved in layout
   c) Ideas on materials handling
9. Plant Engineering Division (other than plant layout group)
   a) Aid in planning for utilities
   b) Plan for building changes or construction
   c) Move machinery and equipment
   d) Install machinery and equipment
10. Inspection Division
    a) Help plan layout to maintain quality in processes
    b) Assure proper handling to protect product from damage
    c) Plan scrap disposal

These are only a few of the ways in which other departments and divisions can be of invaluable aid to the plant layout group. The utmost in cooperation is needed among all concerned if a project as large as a

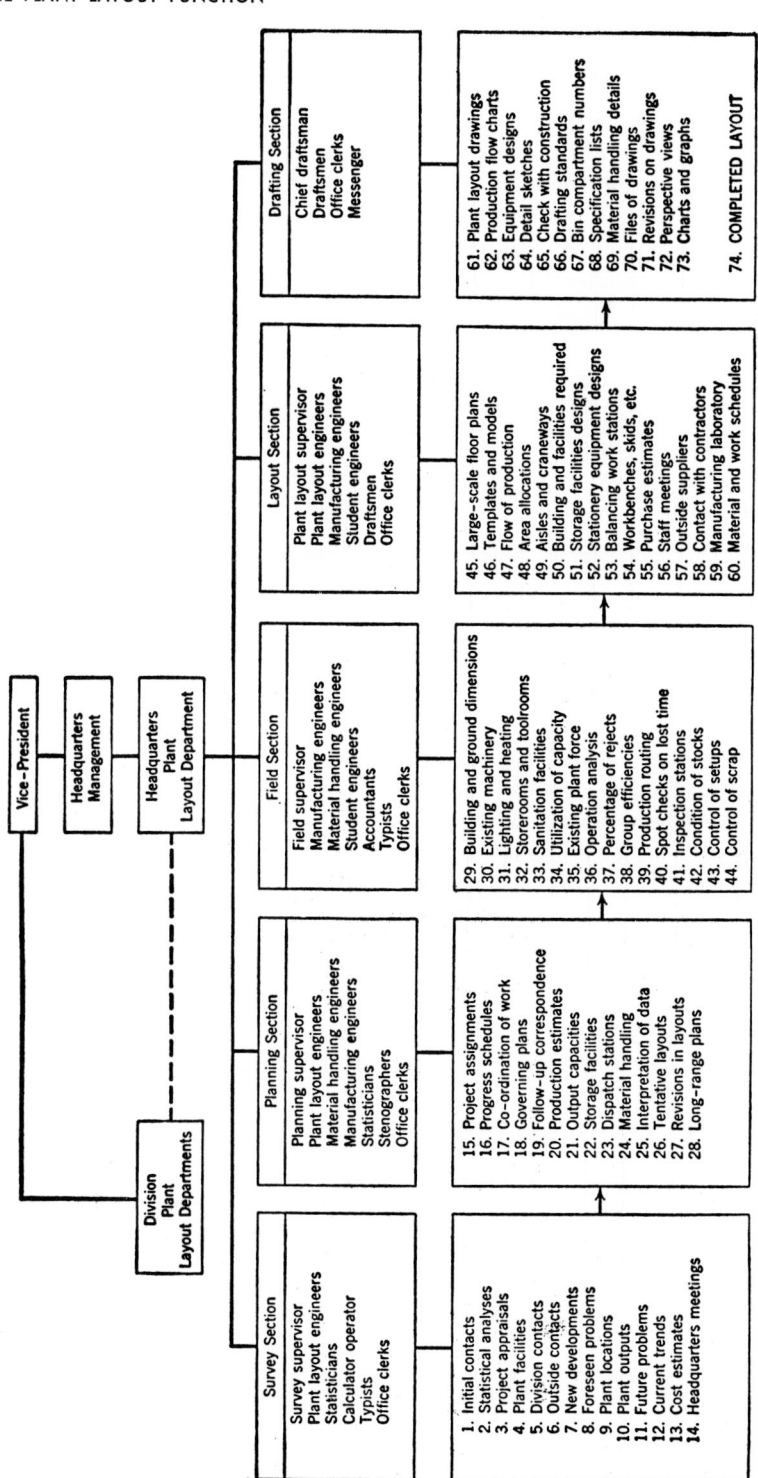

Fig. 2-2. Organization of the plant layout function.

plant layout is to be successfully completed. This subject is considered further in Chapter 16.

Organization of the Plant Layout Department. Where a Plant Layout Department exists, it will probably handle such activities as those indicated in the listing at the beginning of this chapter. Its organization would be similar to that shown in Figure 2–2.

Functions, of course, will vary from plant to plant. In the smaller plant, activities indicated above would be grouped together. In larger plants they might be subdivided, depending upon the amount of work to be done, the number of people involved, functions performed by other departments or divisions, etc.

Nevertheless, all these activities exist in every plant. It is the degree to which they are necessary that varies. In a small manufacturing plant of 50 to 100 employees, one person may be responsible for all the activities indicated. In a plant with 8,000 to 10,000 employees, making automobiles, household appliances, etc., as many as 35 men might be required to handle the same range of activities.

QUESTIONS

1. Why does the plant layout function vary in scope and size from one plant to another?
2. What are the most common activities of a Plant Layout Department?
3. In what functional area is plant layout usually found in the organization?
4. Indicate several ways in which the plant layout function is related to other departments and divisions in the organization.

3

General Plant Layout Procedure

Plant Layout—a Coordinating Function. This chapter will present a "preview" of the entire plant layout planning procedure as a means of orientation and introduction to the detailed discussion in later chapters.

The design of an efficient plant layout can best be achieved if the problem is attacked in a logical and orderly manner. The following step-by-step "procedure" is presented as a guide or basic thought pattern to assure proper consideration of all aspects of the over-all problem. It is obvious that the steps may not be followed in chronological order, as much interaction of suggested activities will occur. This is necessary because of the complex functional interrelationship existing between plant layout personnel and other members of the organization. For example, planning the general flow pattern (step 2) cannot be properly completed without giving some consideration to proposed individual work stations (step 6) and the direction of flow through them, which is not considered in detail until later in the planning process.

It should be pointed out also, that conclusions reached at any step in the procedure are subject to revision when conditions are changed as a result of later findings or after more detailed consideration in subsequent stages of the planning process.

With this brief note of caution, the design of an effective layout might proceed somewhat in the following manner:

1. *Procure and Analyze Basic Data.* Before any work can be done on a plant layout project, much data must be accumulated. Among the items of information required are:

    a) Sales potential
    b) Product model or prototype
    c) Engineering drawings
    d) Engineering specifications
    e) Process engineering plans
    f) Production routings
    g) Equipment requirements
    h) Production schedule

    i) Inventory policies
    j) Investment policy
    k) Space available

These items and many others will be taken up and related to the over-all plant layout project in Chapter 4, Production Planning.

    2. *Determine Preliminary Materials Flow.* A careful study of the basic data and especially the production routings and bills of materials will permit the construction of an Assembly Chart. This technique graphically relates each part of the product to all others and provides a preliminary basis for determining the flow of materials. The Assembly Chart is presented in Chapter 4.

    3. *Consider Factors Affecting the Materials Flow Pattern.* After a preliminary idea of the flow of materials has been obtained, it becomes necessary to consider the many factors having an important bearing on the final flow pattern. A carefully planned flow pattern follows certain principles and general methods of materials flow in the integration of materials movement with the related factors. Some of these factors are covered in Chapter 4, Production Planning, and Chapter 5, Automation. Others taken up in Chapters 6, 7, and 8 are:

    a) Levels of activity
    b) Movement of personnel
    c) Working conditions
    d) Required flow between work areas
    e) Receiving, shipping, storage, and warehousing
    f) Aisles
    g) Employee services
    h) Flexibility
    i) Building type
    j) External transportation facilities
    k) Production services

    4. *Plan Detailed Materials Flow Pattern.* After a careful consideration of the various factors affecting the flow pattern, the product itself must be analyzed in detail. The sequence of the various operations and activities performed in the plant is usually determined by the process engineer, who studies each part, subassembly, and assembly; determines the order in which the various operations are to be performed; and lists them on a Production Routing or Operation Sheet. The order or orders thus prescribed becomes the basis for the actual arrangement of physical facilities. It is also necessary to correlate the activities involved in the processing of the various product components into one over-all master flow pattern.

However, the final flow pattern must not be so rigid that future changes in plans cannot be accommodated. Flexibility is a highly desirable characteristic of a good layout. Here a compromise must be worked out to balance the objectives of the present layout and still permit future changes without too much interference with the existing layout.

The Assembly Chart mentioned above will aid in visualizing a general materials flow pattern. The Operation Process Chart, Activity Relationship Chart, From–To Chart, and other related techniques in Chapter 9 will aid in the final development of the materials flow pattern.

5. *Plan Materials Handling Methods.* On the basis of the flow pattern developed above, some decisions should be made as to the general methods that will be used in handling the various materials and, in some cases, the types of equipment that will be selected. The three general types of materials handling equipment are:

  a) Conveyors
  b) Cranes and hoists
  c) Industrial trucks

Frequently some combination of these basic types works out to be most practicable.

Next to the method of processing, materials handling is probably the most important factor to be considered in planning a layout. Because of the need for discussing the handling problems in some detail, Chapters 11, 12, and 13 are devoted to this subject.

Eventually, specific methods of materials handling must be decided upon for each move of each material or item in the entire manufacturing process. Many factors must be considered in the selection of each separate handling method. These factors and methods of relating them to other phases of the layout planning process will be covered in Chapter 13.

6. *Operation and Work Area Planning.* At this point, each work station, area, process, etc., must be planned in detail. The interrelationships between machines, operators, and auxiliary equipment must be planned. Consideration must also be given to operator cycling, multiple machine operation, principles of motion economy, work place materials handling, etc.

The details involved in operation and work area planning will be presented in Chapter 14.

7. *Coordinate the Planning Activities.* At this point, plans should be fairly complete for individual operation and work stations; but proper consideration may not have been given to work station interrelationships. The Layout Planning Chart is a technique which has been found useful

as an aid in pointing out such omissions in planning and guides the further development of the integration of operations.

Here again, this step may have been started, or partially worked out, during consideration of the individual work stations (step 6) or earlier, under flow patterns (steps 3 and 4). If not yet complete, then the activity in each work area, production center, department, or process should now be integrated with related activities and "tied together" with a final master flow diagram. A start can be made at this time toward coordinating the individual flow patterns or diagrams of each process, etc., into the master flow pattern, as originally conceived in step 4.

On the basis of the flow diagram for each process and plans for service areas, space for each activity should now be allocated on a combined flow pattern and plot plan. Proper consideration must be given to aisles, column spacing, storage space, etc., in order to assure the attainment of the original objectives. Ground work for this step may have been laid in preliminary sketches made in conjunction with plans for previous steps. The Layout Planning Chart and Area Allocation Diagram will be demonstrated in Chapter 14 as means of accomplishing this coordination.

8. *Making the Master Plant Layout.* This step is the consummation of the detailed work and planning which has been done in steps 1 to 7. It is here that the master layout is prepared with the aid of templates, scale models, etc. Three-dimensional scale models of physical facilities are gradually replacing the more traditional templates, or two-dimensional cut-outs. With the completion of the master layout, the plant layout engineer should have accomplished the design of the efficient production facility, as envisioned at the start of the project. The various techniques and procedures in making the final plant layout are detailed in Chapter 15.

9. *Evaluating the Plant Layout.* It is only proper that the plant layout engineer and his associates check over their work at this stage, prior to submitting it to company officials for examination. Preliminary checks are also made with representatives of those staff functions which have aided in the layout planning, such as personnel, safety, etc.

Many of the staff specialists will have worthwhile suggestions to offer on matters which may have been overlooked by the plant layout engineer because "he was so close to the forest he couldn't see the trees." In the final stages, the layout must be formally approved by certain company officials, depending on plant policies and procedures. Such persons may have either special knowledge of certain phases of the proposed operation, or a broad understanding of the over-all relationship between various phases of the operation. Evaluation of the plant layout is covered in Chapter 16.

10. *Installing the Plant Layout.* Because the plant layout engineer has designed the layout, it is logical that he should closely supervise the necessary work involved in the "installation" of the layout. He should be sure all work done is according to the plans set forth in the approved layout. Any changes found to be desirable as construction work progresses should be thoroughly investigated by the plant layout engineer and, if made, approved by the proper persons.

The layout engineer should cooperate with the architectural and construction engineers to see that the planned layout is properly incorporated into the building itself.

No plant layout is ever perfect, and the plant layout engineer must be continually appraising the layout as it affects the production operations. When opportunities for improvement are observed, they should be properly evaluated and changes made if they are found to be desirable. Some of the details to be considered in installing the layout are discussed in Chapter 16.

CONCLUSION

It should be emphasized again that the above procedure is intended only as a guide or thought pattern to be followed in approaching a plant layout problem. Much skipping back and forth between the steps is to be expected. Many changes will be made as work progresses, and the procedure should not be considered a rigid plan for work.

In many types of layout problems, the project may not require all of the planning work suggested here. In such cases then, it is for the plant layout engineer to decide what work must be performed to satisfactorily carry out the project. No layout project is routine, no two are alike, and each calls for careful and thorough consideration of all its aspects by the plant layout engineer.

Subsequent chapters will present detailed considerations and instructions for carrying out the above suggested procedure.

QUESTIONS

1. What is the necessity for following a predetermined plant layout procedure?
2. What are some examples of situations in which the procedure might not be followed?
3. What are some of the basic data required for production planning? Why? What does each contribute?
4. What is meant by a materials flow pattern?
5. What are the three basic types of materials handling equipment?
6. Show by a sketch the relationship between the over-all flow pattern and

an individual work place.
7. What persons in an organization should be consulted prior to finalizing the plant layout? What does each contribute to the final plan?
8. What are some of the relationships between the plant layout and the building which will house the layout?
9. Why should the plant layout engineer be interested in the actual construction of the plant building?

4

Production Planning

Preliminary Activities. The previous chapters have presented the over-all objectives of plant layout and a brief preview of the layout planning process or procedure. The next area for consideration is a detailed presentation of the preliminary steps involved in the manufacture of a typical product.

In order to provide the essential basic data for a layout project, it is necessary to consult with other departments of the organization—or at least to get information from them. These departments and their necessary contributions are as follows:

1. Sales Department
   a) Market research
   b) Sales forecast
2. Top Management
   a) Desired production date
   b) Inventory policy
   c) Investment policy
3. Product Engineering
   a) Research and development
   b) Design and test
   c) Drawings and specifications
   d) Parts lists, or bills of materials
4. Industrial Engineering
   a) Product analysis ⎱ Value analysis
   b) Process analysis ⎰
   c) "Make or buy" decisions
   d) Production routing
   e) Preliminary time standards
   f) Tool design
   g) Equipment selection and specification
   h) Methods analysis and specifications

The above functions and items will be covered later in this chapter. However, let us first review what the plant layout personnel will do with the above data.

5. Plant Layout (from Chapter 3).
   a) Procure and analyze basic data
   b) Determine preliminary materials flow
   c) Consider factors affecting the materials flow pattern
   d) Plan detailed materials flow pattern
   e) Plan materials handling methods
   f) Plan operations and work areas
   g) Coordinate the planning activities
   h) Make the master plant layout
   i) Evaluate the plant layout
   j) Install the plant layout

In addition to the information provided by the organizational areas listed above (1 through 4), the plant layout group will obtain much data from its own files. These data will be on the building (existing or proposed), on production equipment, on operating conditions, etc. They will be covered later in this chapter.

After a consideration of the contributions of top management, sales, product engineering, and industrial engineering, the balance of this chapter will be devoted to the plant layout function of analyzing basic data. Subsequent chapters will deal with the other plant layout functions listed under 5, above.

Sales Department Contributions. The Sales Department will have made an extensive study of the potential market for the new product. They will have decided that it is worthwhile putting it on the market, as an addition to the present line of products.

By means of their market research activities, they will have established an estimated sales volume. This will most likely be broken down by monthly requirements and will be projected ahead for several years. Such decisions are a necessity if product engineering, industrial engineering, and plant layout are to properly carry out their planning functions. At the same time, it will be necessary for Sales to predict the effect of the new product on any of the existing products in the line.

The sales forecast must include not only the total predicted demand for finished products, but must also indicate seasonal fluctuation, if any, as well as service requirements for parts or assemblies.

Top Management Contributions. One of the first decisions which top management must make is the date on which the new product is desired for introduction to the market. This decision must be predicated on the work to be done in preparation for production. Usually a schedule is established which lists all the phases of preparatory work, along with estimates of the time involved in performing each phase. Figure 4–1 shows an actual schedule for a proposed product.

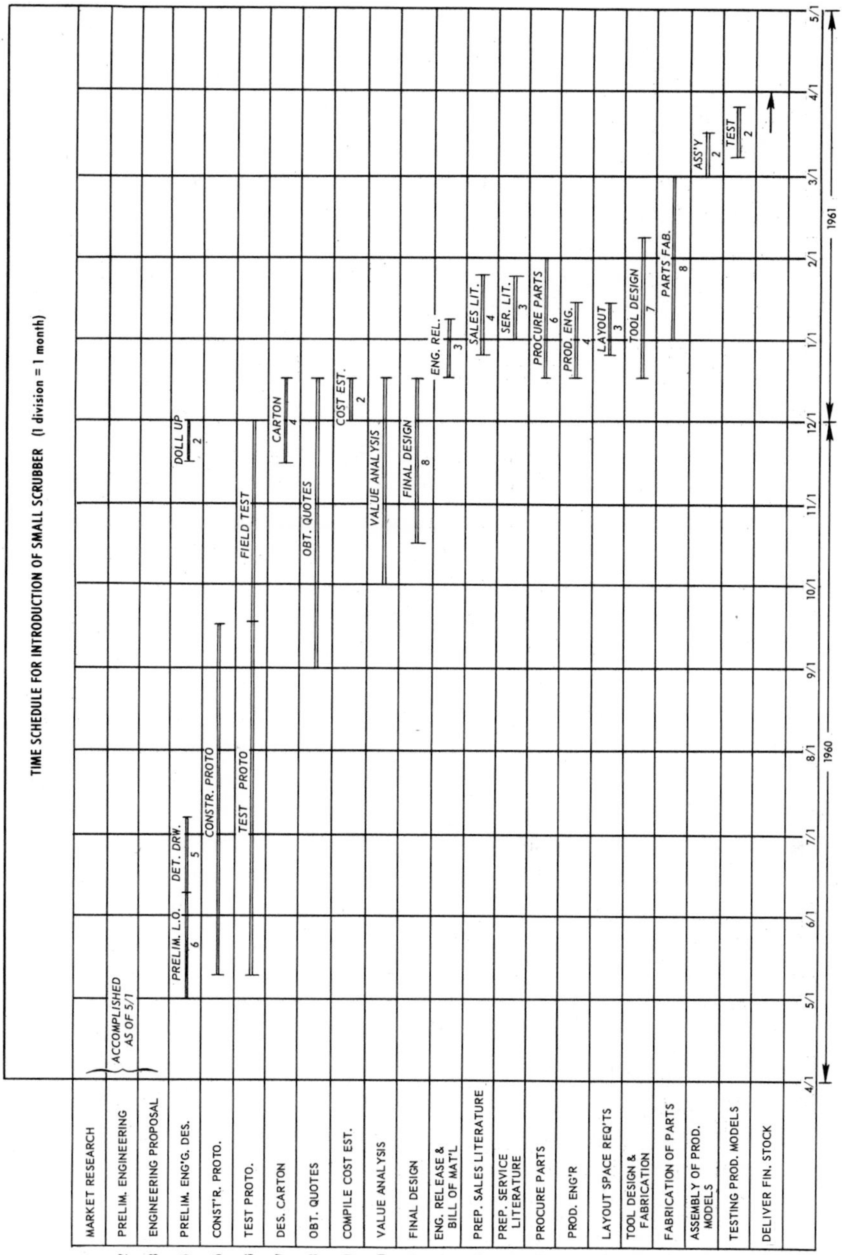

Fig. 4-1. Time schedule for a typical new product. (By permission of Clarke Floor Machine Co.)

Top management should also indicate the desired inventory policy for the new product—that is, how much of a "stock-pile" they desire to have on hand at any one time. This is especially important if the product sale is seasonal. Figure 4–2 shows a typical annual sales curve for a seasonal item. Figure 4–3 tabulates the necessary relationships between sales, production, and inventory. These two figures will indicate the nature of the problem. The details of such decisions and calculations are beyond the scope of this book.

Another item for decision by top management is the investment policy they intend to follow in putting the new product into production. A budget must be formulated that will cover the manpower costs, equipment, and other expenses incident to developing the product and getting initial production underway.

Product Engineering Contributions. The product engineering function is the source of the most important basic data required for production planning—the production drawings, specifications, and parts lists or bills of materials. However, before these items can be provided, much preliminary work will have been done.

First, of course, was the basic research and development work preliminary to the final design of the product to be produced. This most likely began with an idea—from management, sales, or other source—for a new product, model, or modification. Preliminary decisions between management, sales, and product engineering most likely resulted in establishing a list of design characteristics and/or functional requirements of the proposed product.

This was followed by experimenting with basic product components by the experimental group. Then, after satisfying themselves that basic functions were workable, a prototype was constructed. This became the first "working model" of the new product and was built from sketches and preliminary drawings in the experimental shop or tool room.

Next came a series of tests, trials, and modifications of the original prototype. Following further tests in the laboratory or in the field, probably came the construction of a small lot—two to six—of the redesigned prototypes. These, in turn, were tested, until all concerned agreed that the basic product design was sound, and it was ready for the final design stage—upon which manufacturing would be based.

However, at this point, the manufacturing people were called in to conduct what is commonly called a "value analysis." Involved at this stage were representatives of production (sheet metal, machining departments, assembly, etc.), quality control, methods, purchasing, and possibly others. This group "attacked" the proposed product from a manufacturing point of view, looking for any changes which might make it easier or less costly to build the product. Piece-by-piece they analyzed the product, looking

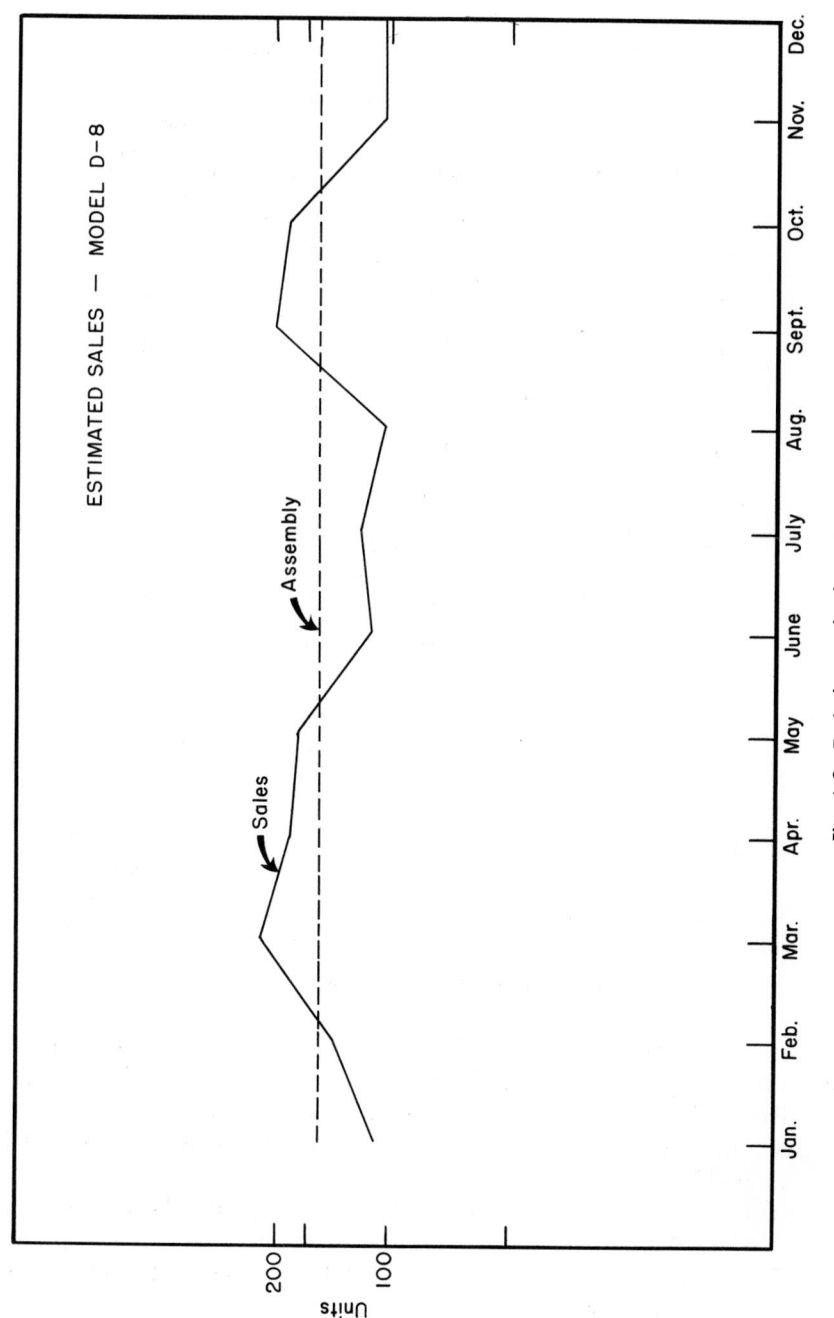

Fig. 4-2. Typical annual sales curve.

SALES, ASSEMBLY & INVENTORY — MODEL D-8

	Sales	Assembly	Balance	Cumulative inventory (100 starting inventory)
JAN	106	143	+37	+137
FEB	134	143	+9	+146
MAR	210	143	−67	+79
APR	179	143	−36	+43
MAY	170	143	−27	+16
JUNE	110	143	+33	+49
JULY	116	143	+27	+76
AUG	103	143	+40	+116
SEPT	200	143	−57	+59
OCT	180	143	−37	+22
NOV	102	143	+41	+63
DEC	104	143	+39	+102 (for carry over to next year)
TOTALS	1714	1716	−	−

Fig. 4–3. Sales, assembly and inventory relationships.

for less expensive materials or processes, unnecessarily close tolerances, sharp corners, parts of too high a quality for the function required, points of difficulty in assembly, etc. Suggestions from this value analysis were considered by product engineering and, whenever possible, incorporated into their thinking.

Now—and only now—was the new product ready for the final design stage. The actual production or working drawings were made and prints issued, along with bills of materials—a complete listing of all components making up the product.

The Production Drawings. Each major component of the new product must be represented in the form of a drawing. This drawing is most commonly made on a type of tracing paper and prints made from it. It is these prints which are used as the basis for making or buying the various parts. The print is the "Bible" to the planning and production personnel.

In general, prints are issued for every part—with the possible exception of "standard" hardware items, such as screws, nuts, washers, etc. Occasionally, if a component is a standard product of some other manufacturer, the print may be general in nature containing only enough detail to identify the product—but with specifications listed to positively identify it as the one that is wanted.

Figures 4–4 and 4–5 are typical production drawings.

The Parts List, or Bill of Materials. The Parts List is a complete listing of all components of the new product. It serves as a convenient reference to all concerned in the planning and production activities. The Parts List should contain at least the information shown in Figure 4–6. In some cases, additional information will be desired. The Parts List is generally furnished, with the drawings, by the Product Engineering Department. As the Parts List is the basis for the layout, the information it contains should be as complete as is possible. Many companies find it desirable to place additional information on the Parts List concerning:

1. Detailed specifications
2. Source of purchased parts
3. Cost of parts
4. Part numbers of similar parts in other products

Another typical Parts List is shown in Figure 4–7. This was reproduced from punched cards on standard tabulating equipment.

The Parts List, along with the assembly drawings, is the first item with which the plant layout group will work in their preliminary layout planning activities.

Industrial Engineering Contributions. The industrial engineering group also furnishes basic data for use by plant layout in the early planning stages of a layout project. They will already have participated in the value analysis mentioned earlier in this chapter. Members of this group, along with product engineering and purchasing, will also decide which components of the new product should be made in the plant—and which should be bought from outside sources. This is frequently a complex problem with much study required by all three groups. However, it is usually common practice to purchase complete, such items as:

1. Standard hardware
2. Components that are specialized products of another manufacturer, such as shock absorbers, electric motors, and wheels
3. Parts that others can make cheaper in larger quantities than our production would require, such as gears and relays

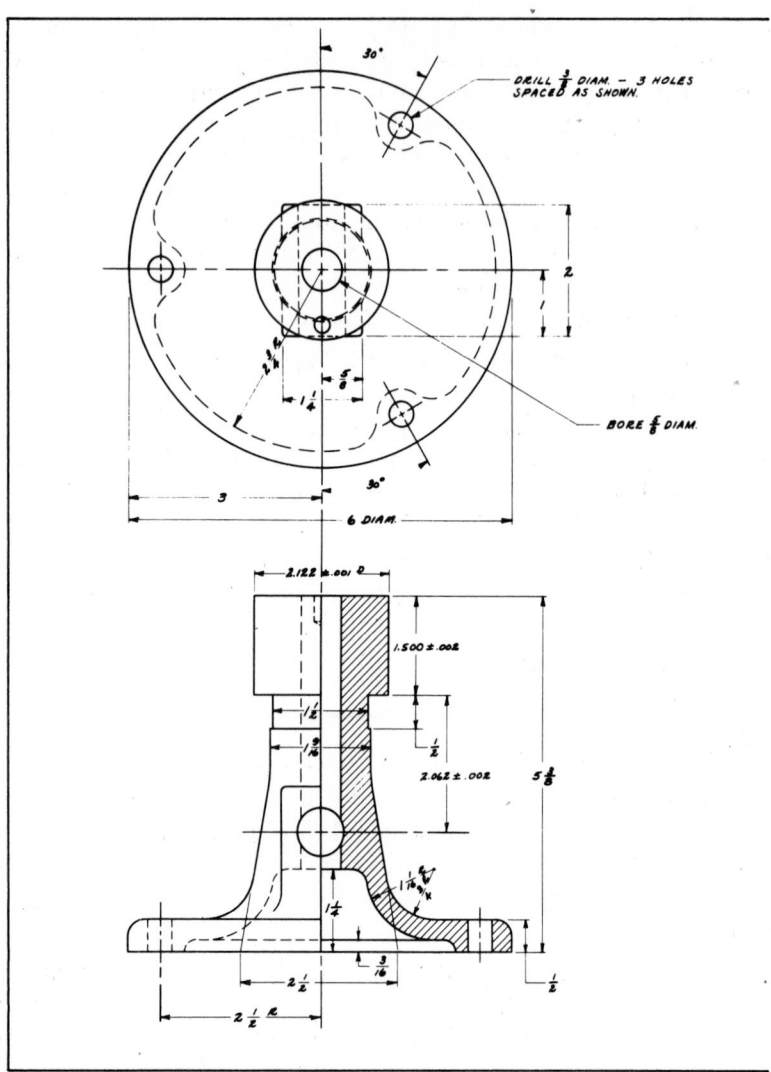

Fig. 4–4. Typical production

4. Parts requiring processes not available or economical in our plant, such as die castings, plastic parts, and metal tubing

The Production Routing. The process engineers must now analyze the drawings for the parts to be made in the proposed plant or department. This analysis involves:

1. Determination of work elements to be performed on the material
2. Selection of processes to be used in performing the work elements

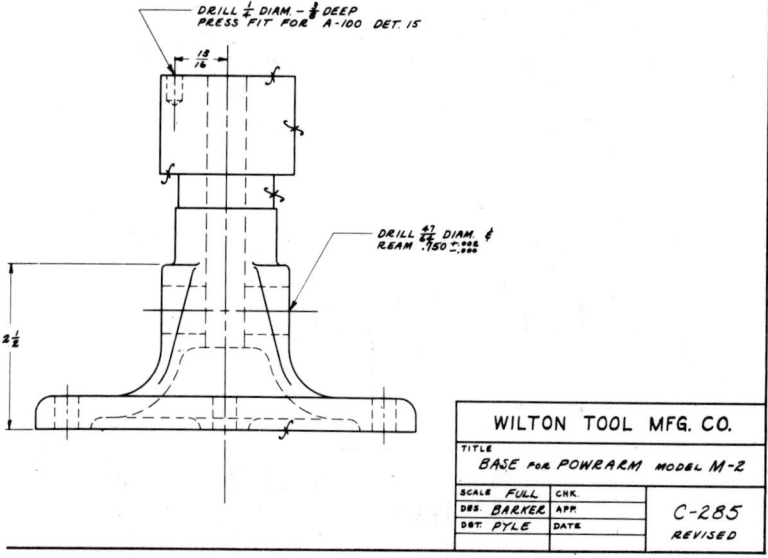

MATERIAL
ALUM. ALLOY CASTING

DRILL ¼ DIAM. – ⅜ DEEP
PRESS FIT FOR A-100 DET. 15

DRILL ⁴⁷/₆₄ DIAM. ¢
REAM .750 ⁺·⁰⁰⁵

WILTON TOOL MFG. CO.

TITLE		
BASE ꜰᴏʀ POWRARM ᴍᴏᴅᴇʟ _M-2_		
SCALE _FULL_	CHK.	
DʙS. _BARKER_	APP.	_C-285_
Dʀᴛ. _PYLE_	DATE	_REVISED_

drawing—Powrarm base.

3. Combining the processes into manufacturing operations
4. Deciding upon the sequence of operations
5. Selecting the production and auxiliary equipment desired
6. Specifying tools and related equipment

The results of this analysis are recorded on a sheet commonly known as a Production Routing, Process Sheet, Operation Sheet, etc.

Basically, the Production Routing is a tabulation of the steps involved

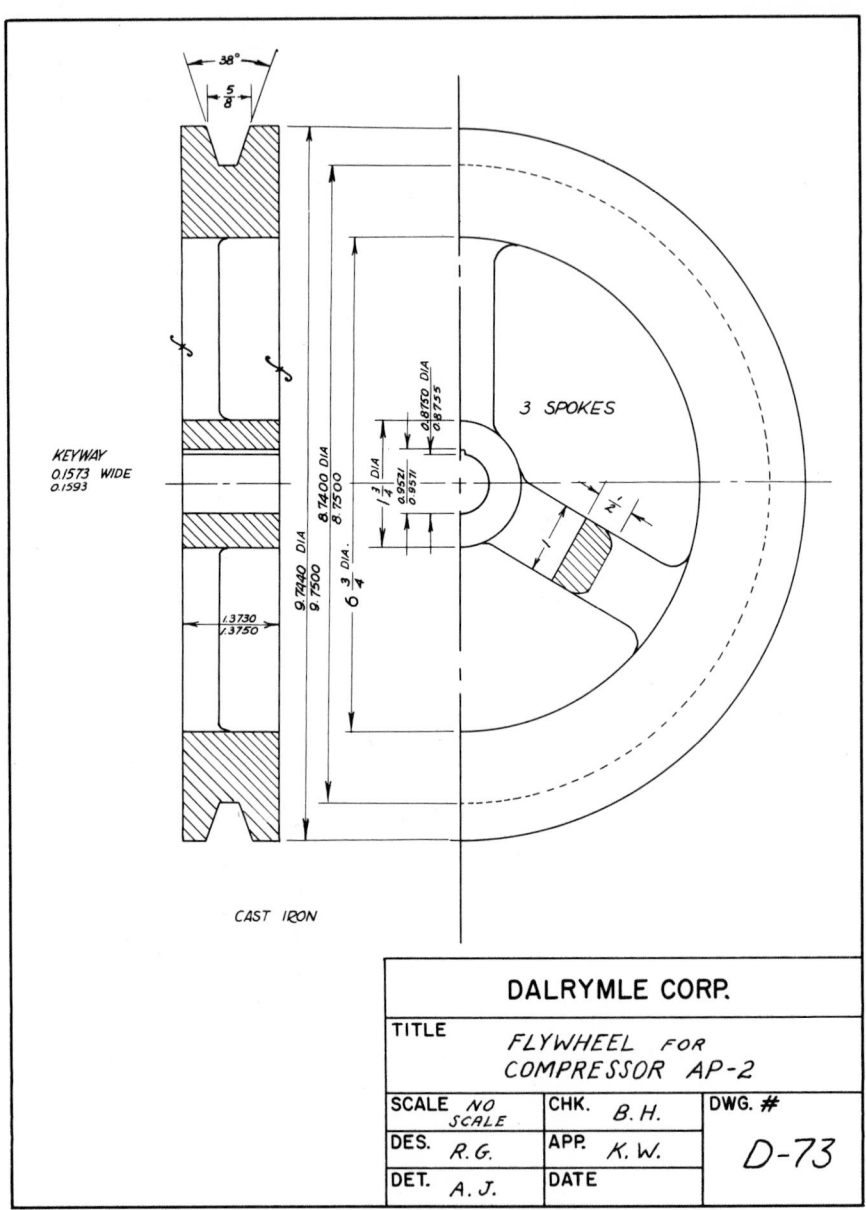

Fig. 4–5. Typical production part drawing.

| \multicolumn{7}{c}{A. B. C. Manufacturing Co.} |

| \multicolumn{7}{c}{PARTS LIST} |

For: _____ Powrarm Model M-1 _____ Dwg. No. __D-442__

Part No.	Part Name	Dwg. No.	Quant. per Unit	Material Spec.	Remarks
1	Base	C-285	1	Cast Alum.	
2	Eccentric Rod	A-143	1	C.R.S.	
3	Handle	A-143	1	C.R.S.	
4	Knob	A-143	1	Plastic	purchased
5	Plunger	A-163	1	C.R.S.	
6	Hex. Head Screw	--	4	--	$\frac{1}{4}$-20x$\frac{3}{4}$ purchased
7	Cover	A-95	1	C.A.	
8	Cap	B-111	1	C.A.	
9	Pin	A-100	1	C.R.S.	
10	Pressure Pad	A-97	1	C.I.	
11	Ball Swivel	A-98	1	C.R.S.	
12	Washer	--	2		purchased
13	Hex. Head Screw	--	2		$\frac{1}{4}$-20x1 purchased
A-1	Eccentric Assembly	A-143			pts. 2, 3, 4
A-2	Ball Swivel Assembly	D-442			pts. 11, 12, 13
A-10	Final Assembly	D-442			

Fig. 4–6. Parts list, or bill of materials, for the Powrarm.

in the production of a particular part and necessary detail on related items. Information on the Routing may include:

1. Part names and numbers
2. Operation numbers and sequence
3. Operation names

FORM NO. 701 REV.

CLARKE FLOOR MACHINE COMPANY
BILL OF MATERIAL

785450	9	15	61	HDS36 SWEEPER	COMMON	785450
WHERE USED	CHANGE DATE			MODEL NAME		BILL OF MTRL. NO.

		EFF. DATE		LATEST E.C.N. NO.		ISSUED BY
PART CODE	QTY. REQ.			PART OR ASSEMBLY NAME	ASSY	SHEET NO.
782820	1			HDS36 EL SPECIAL 3/8 PT		
782821	1			HDS36 ELBOW MALE 8 12		
782822	1			HDS36 EL SPECIAL 1/4 PT		
782823	1			HDS36 ELBOW 90 ST 12		
782824	1			HDS36 ELBOW 90 ST 8 12		
783001	1			HDS36 FAN BLOWER		
783301	1			HDS36 FILTER HDY OIL		
783302	8			CS27 FLANGE BRG MOUNT		
783303	1			HDS36 FILTER FILLER CAP		
783304	14			HDS36 FLANGE BRG MOUNT		
783305	8			HDS36 FLANGE BRG MOUNT		
783306	2			HDS36 FLANGE BUSHING		
783310	1			HDS36 FILTER AIR		
783401	1			HDS36 GASKET FC602		
783402	1			HDS36 GASKET FC 603		
783403	1			HDS36 GASKET TANK COVER		
783615	1			HDS36 GUARD STEERING		
783623	1			HDS36 GUARD DRIVE		
783626	1			HDS36 GUARD BATTERY		
783635	1			HDS36 GUARD CHAIN		
783636	1			GUARD MUFFLER		
783701	1			HDS36 GAUGE OIL PRESSURE		
783803	1			HDS36 GAUGE AMMETER 6V		
783805	1			HDS36 GAUGE TEMPERATURE		
783806	1			HDS36 GAUGE SIGHT		
784001	1			HDS36 HOLDER REAR APRON		
784002	12			HDS36 HOLDER MAIN BROOM		
784003	2			HDS36 HOLDER SIDE APRON		
784101	2			HDS36 HOSE ASSY 12 42		
784105	1			HDS36 HOSE ASSY 6 36		
784108	1			HDS36 HOSE ASSY 6 23		
784109	1			HDS36 HOSE ASSY 6 11		
784114	2			HDS36 HOSE EXHAUST		
784117	1			HDS36 HOSE ASSY 4 34		
784118	1			HDS36 HOSE ASSY 4 38		
784119	1			HDS36 HOSE ASSY 4 17		
784120	1			HDS36 HOSE RAD TOP		
784121	1			HDS36 HOSE RAD BOT		

SHEET NO.

Fig. 4–7. Parts list produced from punched cards of individual components. (By permission of Clarke Floor Machine Co.)

4. Operation descriptions
5. Machine names and numbers
6. Tool, jig, and fixture numbers and sizes
7. Department numbers

8. Production standards (time and/or pieces)
9. Number of operators
10. Space requirements
11. Speeds and feeds
12. Effective date
13. Group numbers
14. Labor classifications required
15. Materials

Typical Production Routings are shown in Figures 4–8, 4–9, and 4–10.

PRODUCTION ROUTING

PART NAME   Powrarm Base

DRAWING NO. ___C – 285___
PART NO. ___1___

Oper. No.	Operation Description	Machine Name	Jigs, Fixtures, Tools, Etc.	Dept. No.	Std. Time (Hrs.)	Hourly Mach. Cap'y	No. Machs.	No. Oper.	Floor Space Req'd
1.	Face bottom.	14" LeBlond Engine lathe	Special chuck Turning tool		.0167	60	1.46		
2.	Face top, turn O.D., neck, drill & ream 5/8" hole.	Warner & Swasey turret lathe	Special chuck Face Turn-neck Drill Ream		.042	23.8	3.45		
3.	Drill 3 bolt holes	21" Cleereman drill press	Box jig 3-spindle head		.0120	83.4	.96		
4.	Drill pin hole	Delta drill press	Plate jig		.0042	238.0	.33		
5.	Drill & ream 3/4" ecc. hole	#4 Fosdick 2 spindle drill press	Box jig		.0153	65.4	1.18		
6.	Inspect				.018	55.5	1.34		
7.	Degrease	Detrex			.0070	143.0	.52		

IE – 17

Fig. 4–8. Production routing for Powrarm base.

An idea of the extent of the process engineer's task may be gained from an example based on an automobile part, a spindle used in the transmission. It is a steel shaft about 8 inches long, slotted at one end, and with two gears near the center.

In one modern automobile plant, it takes 39 machines to make that spindle, including power hammers, centering machines, lathes, grinders, gear cutters, gear finishers, and many more. The process engineer must plan how to perform each operation in the easiest way and specify on what machine it should be done. Besides the 39 machines, there must be

ROUTING

Part Name Blade Piston Models AD7562-A1 Part No. 6510777

Material Bronze Forging A29 Date No. of Sheets 1 Sheet No. 1 Issue No. 9

Operation	Equipment	Oper. No.	Dept. & Group	Standard Time: Regis. No.	Standard Time: Minutes	Standard Time: Hours	No. Men	Group Standard Hours
Face, turn, chamfer & form groove in small O. D.	(#5 W & S)	27A	44A3	2776		.1530		.2202
Face & turn large end	(#5 W & S)	27B	44A3	2806		.0672		
Inspect & credit Group 44A3		24	33	Ind. Labor				
Drill (2) 21/64 holes & (2) 7/32" holes & drill burr (4) holes	(4 Spdl. L. G.)	13	44B1	3539		.0730		.0730
Inspect & credit Group 44B1		24	33	Ind. Labor				
Mill slot 3/32 x 7/64" deep	(Kent Owens)	31A	44B2	2883		.0237		.0237
Inspect & credit Group 44B2		24	33	Ind. Labor				
Mill threads	(Lees Bradner)	31B	44B5	2897		.0721 (1 Oper.	2	.0721 Mach.)
Inspect & credit Group 44B5		24	33	Ind. Labor				
Burr slots, groove, & threads	(Burr Room)	7A	44D	3255		.0330		.0467
Scratch brush slotted end	(Burr Room)	7B	44D	3389		.0090		
Wash	(Burr Room)	10	44D	3390		.0047		
Inspect & credit Group 44D		24	30	Ind. Labor				
MOVE TO BOND ROOM								
(Used on Piston Assembly - 6500386)								
TOTALS								

Fig. 4–9. Typical production routing. (By permission of Aeroproducts Div., General Motors Corp.)

ASSEMBLY PROCESS ESTIMATE
METHODS ENGINEERING

| SHEET | STATION 16 STATION 17 | | MODEL | 1950 98 88 76 CS | PART NO. 839855 |

PART NAME	CAR ASSEMBLY – BODY LINE			
DEPT. NO. 5-52-6	SUPERSEDES ESTIMATE		ENGR. ORDER NO. 6662	DATE

OPER. NO.	OPERATION NAME — TOOL AND EQUIPMENT DESCRIPTION	98 S.M.	98 H.T.	88 S.M.	88 H.T.	76 S.M.	76 H.T.	CS S.M.	CS H.T.	TOOLING COST	EQUIPMENT COST
6230	LOOSE ASSEM. GRILLE. ASSEMBLY #917585 ON										
	RADIO JOBS (1) RADIO GRILLE SCREEN #887885 &										
	(1) RADIO SPEAKER SHROUD #6188527 TO INSTRU-										
	MENT PANEL WITH (6) F.W. #583021, (6) L.W.										
	#794601 & (6) NUTS #163021. 76 & 88 GRILLE										
	#179355	.0113		.0113		.0113		.0113			
	(2) OPERATORS L. SIDE										
	(1) COMP. TRAY										
	(4) LENGTHS OF 12" ROLLER CONV. –6' LONG										
	SUPPORTED 30" FROM FLOOR										
	(3) #8 HOPPERS										
	(3) #8 HOPPER STANDS										

PROCESSED BY ___R. W. BOOS___   PART NO.___839855___

Fig. 4-10. Typical production routing. (By permission of Oldsmobile Division, General Motors Corp.)

194 dies, jigs, fixtures, tools and arbors. And on top of all this, **157** precision gages are needed to make sure that the work is done accurately. The spindle, moreover, is one of the simpler of the more than 10,000 parts making up a modern automobile.

Production Standards. The time standards personnel in the Industrial Engineering Department will also furnish estimated production standards, or standard times. These will be determined on the basis of past experience; standard data; or predetermined time standards such as MTM, BMT, and Work Factor. These production standards are shown on the accompanying Production Routings.

Each production standard is the estimated time it will take to perform a given operation on the machine or equipment specified. The standards are, of course, subject to revision if machines and/or methods should be changed in later steps of the planning program. Since this is quite likely, these standards are usually used only as guides in planning and until more accurate standards can be developed.

Plant Layout Functions. Only after all the above described work has been accomplished will the plant layout group have enough "basic data" available to properly start in on the layout planning itself. Their immediate task is to "procure and analyze the basic data." They may now gather together such items and data as the following:

1. From other departments:
    a) Production drawings—Product Engineering
    b) Parts lists—Product Engineering
    c) Prototype (if available)—Product Engineering
    d) Production volume—Top Management
    e) Production routings—Process Engineering
    f) Production standards—Time Study
    g) Assembly routing—Methods
2. From their own files:
    a) Existing layouts of space involved
    b) Plans for utilities (heat, ventilating, steam, air, sewage, water, air conditioning)
    c) Lighting layouts
    d) Building elevations and dimensions
    e) Machinery data
    f) Machine load data
    g) Scrap percentage
    h) Rework percentage
    i) Floor load limits
    j) Ceiling and/or truss heights
    k) Area available for current project

Now, with much of the necessary information on hand, the plant lay-out engineer is at last ready to start the task of analyzing the basic data.

Analysis of Basic Data. As pointed out previously, much basic data is required before the actual layout planning activity can proceed. Specific items required at this time will include:

1. Blue prints
2. Bills of material, or parts list
3. Production routings
4. Production standards
5. Production volume data

With the blue prints and bill of materials at hand for reference, the production routings should now be examined. The production standards, usually found on the routings, must now be combined with the production volume data to determine the quantity of production equipment required. Although the quantity of equipment is not required in the use of all the layout planning techniques, it is required for some. It should also be pointed out that in many cases, these figures (at this point in the planning process) may be no more than rough estimates. Their true value may not be known until after detailed work plans have been developed. This phase of the layout planning project is discussed in Chapter 14. However, for the sake of orderly procedure, it will be assumed here that *some* estimates are available. If they are *not,* variations of the techniques described in Chapter 9 will permit the planning process to proceed, with the detailed calculations made later, as discussed in Chapter 14.

Referring to Figure 4–8, note the column headed "Std. Time (Hrs.)." These figures represent the time required to produce one piece; that is, on Operation 1, Face Bottom, it will require .0167 hrs. for the operator to produce one piece on the 14″ LeBlond engine lathe.

Fundamentally the number of machines to be used is based on the required production for a unit of time. There are two major factors, how-ever, which will combine to reduce the established production rate. One is the loss through scrap or rejects, and the other is production efficiency.

It is now necessary to refer to the basic data previously accumulated for the production volume estimated by the Sales Department and/or top management. For purposes of illustration, let us assume that sales fore-casts show estimated sales of the Powrarm of 134,000 units per year.

If there are 2,000 hours per year, then the required production of fin-ished *good* units is 134,000 ÷ 2000 = 67 per hour.

First it is necessary to allow for the scrap that will be produced at each operation on each part of the product, so that when the parts all reach assembly, there will be 67 good pieces of each part.

In order to assure this, it is necessary to start at the last operation on each part that will result in any scrap, and work back up to the first operation, figuring the scrap on *each* operation and "compounding" it into the total number of pieces required at the first operation. This can be determined as shown below, where the calculations were started at the last operation, and the material requirements for each operation divided by 1 minus the scrap expected at that operation. The illustration is from Fig. 4–8, the Powrarm base.

Oper. No.	Machine	Good Pieces Desired	Expected Scrap %	Pieces Actually Started
7	Degrease	67.0	0	67.0
6	Inspect	67.0	0	67.0
5	#4 Fosdick D. P.	67.0	2	68.3
4	Delta D. P.	68.3	3	70.5
3	Cleereman D. P.	70.5	2	72.0
2	W & S Turret Lathe	72.0	5	75.8
1	LeBlond Eng. Lathe	75.8	4	78.9

These calculations show that it will be necessary to purchase 78.9, or 79 pieces of material to start through operation 1. If the "expected" scrap is made, 67.0 good pieces will be available *after* operation 7.

This takes care of the material requirements, but it assumes that the plant is operating at 100% efficiency—which is highly improbable. If it is estimated that the plant will operate at 90% efficiency, then plant space, machinery and manpower must be provided to make up for the loss in efficiency. This calculation is made by dividing the required work output of each operation by the efficiency of the plant (or operation), as follows:

Oper. No.	Req'd Work Output	Basis for Planning Facilities & Manpower
1	78.9	87.7
2	75.8	84.2
3	72.0	80.0
4	70.5	78.3
5	68.3	76.0
6	67.0	74.5
7	67.0	74.5

The above calculations indicate that if a plant is built, equipped, and staffed to produce 74.5 units per hour at operation 7, and works at 90% efficiency, it will turn out 67 units. Referring to operation number 1, if plans are made to produce 87.7, then 90% efficiency will result in 78.9 pieces and 4% scrap will reduce the total to 75.8—which is what is required for operation number 2, etc. Or, the calculations can be shown as follows:

> 87.7 units *planned* for
> − 8.8 units lost due to inefficiency
>
> 78.9 units for which *material* must be purchased
> − 3.1 units scrapped
>
> 75.8 units to go into operation number 2

It should be pointed out here that there is a difference between "operation" efficiency and "department" or "plant" efficiency. Even though an individual operation may be running at over 100 per cent of its assumed efficiency, other operations in the same department may be running at lower efficiencies. The efficiency of the department then is the average efficiency of all units in the department. The plant efficiency is the average efficiency of all departments in the plant. The 90 per cent used in the above calculation is a plant efficiency. In some companies, the plant figure is used in all cases; in others, the individual departmental figures are used; and in still others, the operation efficiencies are used.

Now, if 87.7 units must be planned for, equipment must be available to produce that number. The standard time for operation number 1 (Fig. 4–8) is .0167 hr./pc., and the hourly production is 60 pc./hr. Therefore, 87.7 ÷ 60 = 1.46 machines will be required to produce 75.8 good units.

The entire procedure can be recapped as follows:

Oper. No.	Good Pieces Desired	Expected Scrap %	Pieces Actually Started	Basis for Planning Facilities & Manpower at 90% Eff'y	Mach. Prod'n Per Hr.	Theor. No. of Mach. Req'd
1	75.8	4	78.9	87.7	60.0	1.46
2	72.0	5	75.8	84.2	23.8	3.54
3	70.5	2	72.0	80.0	83.4	.96
4	68.3	3	70.5	78.3	238.0	.33
5	67.0	2	68.3	76.0	65.4	1.18
6	67.0	0	67.0	74.5	55.5	1.34
7	67.0	0	67.0	74.5	143.0	.52

As in this situation, there are many cases where the number of machines will not come out as an even number. If, instead of 1.46 machines, the above calculation had resulted in 1.25, 3.68, or 6.42 machines, there would be a question as to the number of machines to provide.

Such decisions are largely a matter of judgment based on such factors as:

1. How much of the machine cycle is man-controlled and might yield more pieces per hour with more favorable conditions, i.e., less scrap, better over-all efficiency, or a better than average operator?
2. Can the method be changed to reduce the standard time?
3. Is overtime cheaper than an additional machine?
4. Would a breakdown of a single machine shut down the line?

It would be much harder for 1 machine to turn out production for 1.25 machines than it would be for 6 to turn out production for 6.42. In the first instance the single machine must bear a .25 overload; while in the latter each machine must bear only $.42 \div 6$, or a .07 overload. Actual decisions in such cases are made on the basis of past experience and detailed knowledge of plant conditions.

It must also be remembered that if the engine lathe used as an example here is to be used to produce *other* parts too, then these work loads must be added. That is, the equivalent machine requirements of the other parts must be added to the 1.46 machines determined above.

The Assembly Chart. Probably the next step in the planning process is the construction of an Assembly Chart. This is a graphical portrayal of the sequence in which parts and subassemblies flow into the assembly of a product. A typical Assembly Chart is shown in Figure 4–11.

It will be seen that the Assembly Chart shows in an easily understandable way:

1. How the parts go together
2. What parts make up each subassembly
3. The flow of parts into assembly
4. The relationship between parts and subassemblies
5. An over-all picture of the manufacturing process
6. The order in which the parts go together
7. An initial impression of the over-all material flow pattern

An Assembly Chart may be made as follows:

1. From the Assembly Routing, decide what would be the last operation in the production or assembly of the product. (It has been found most convenient to tackle the problem of making the Assembly Chart in reverse— that is, disassembling the product as the chart is made.)
2. Designate this operation by a ½-inch circle near the lower right-hand corner of a sheet of paper. Indicate briefly the description of the assembly operation.

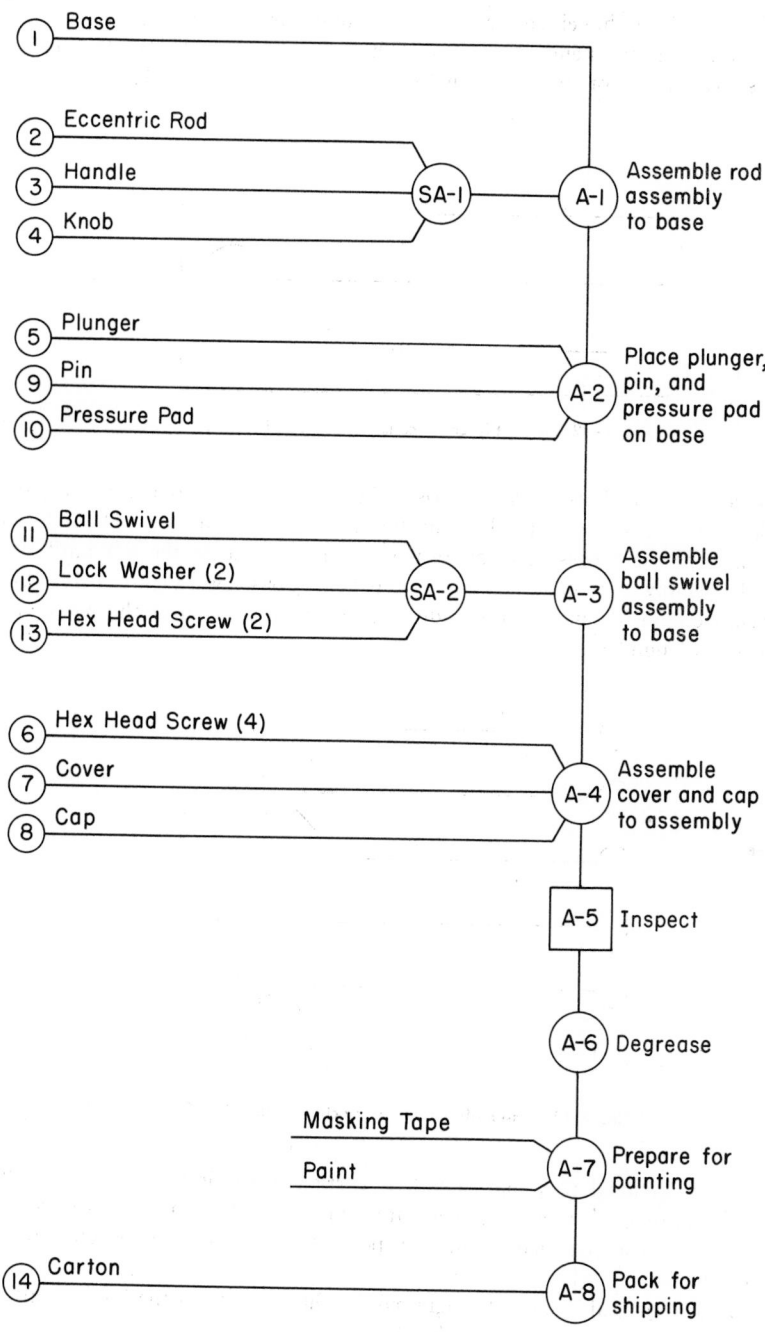

① Base

② Eccentric Rod
③ Handle
④ Knob

SA-1 ── A-1 Assemble rod assembly to base

⑤ Plunger
⑨ Pin
⑩ Pressure Pad

A-2 Place plunger, pin, and pressure pad on base

⑪ Ball Swivel
⑫ Lock Washer (2)
⑬ Hex Head Screw (2)

SA-2 ── A-3 Assemble ball swivel assembly to base

⑥ Hex Head Screw (4)
⑦ Cover
⑧ Cap

A-4 Assemble cover and cap to assembly

A-5 Inspect

A-6 Degrease

Masking Tape
Paint

A-7 Prepare for painting

⑭ Carton

A-8 Pack for shipping

Fig. 4–11. Assembly chart for Powrarm.

3. To the left of this circle, draw one horizontal line to represent each part, material, or subassembly involved. The bottom line should represent the last part added or item used on the product. See Figure 4–12.

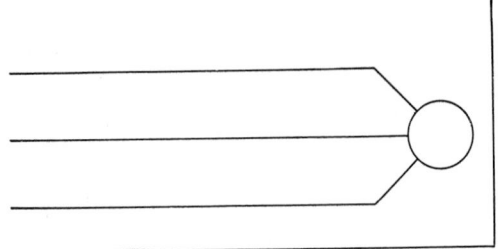

Fig. 4–12. Assembly chart construction, detail No. 1.

4. When subassemblies or "sub-subassemblies" are encountered, run the part lines only part way to the left and terminate them with a ⅜-inch circle to represent the subassembly operation. Then continue to the left until the subassembly is resolved into its component parts. See Figure 4–13. Assemblies can be numbered as indicated in Figure 4–11, after the Assembly Chart is complete.

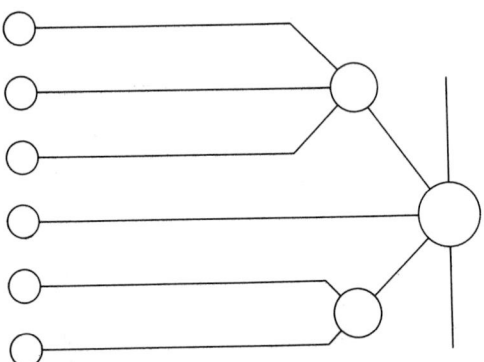

Fig. 4–13. Assembly chart construction, detail No. 2.

Each individual part line should be carried to the left side of the paper and terminated with a ¼-inch circle in which the part number can be entered. The part name, number per assembly, etc., can be entered on the line.

5. Draw a vertical line up the right side of the sheet, from the last operation, to represent the assembly, or flow line.

6. Place another ½-inch circle above the first to represent the next to last operation and record its components to the left.

Fig. 4–14. "Exploded" photograph for use in planning work. (By permission of Walworth Valve Co.)

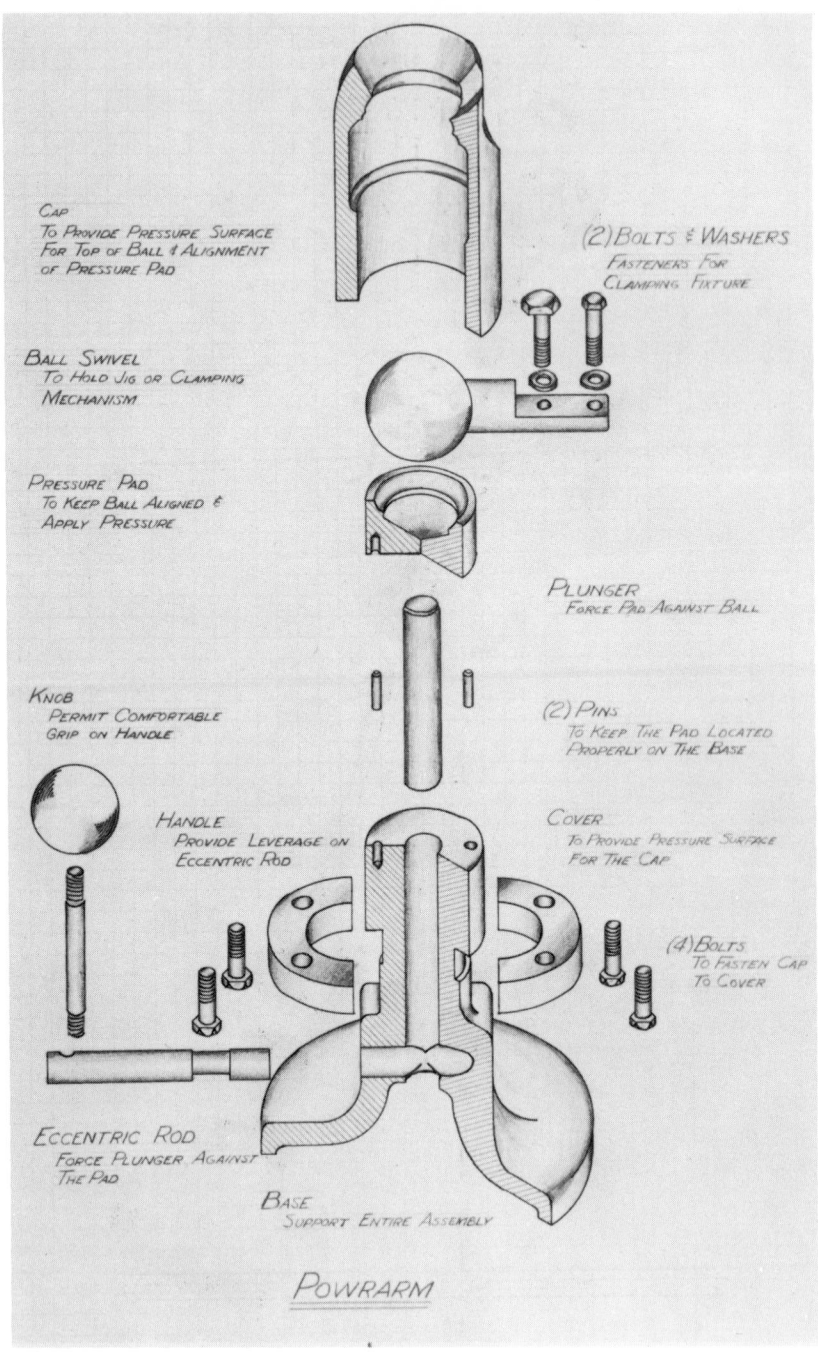

Fig. 4–15. Exploded drawing of Powrarm.

7. Continue this procedure until the object has been completely "disassembled" and each component of the product has been listed on the left-hand side of the paper.
8. Check the Assembly Chart against the Parts List to make sure that all parts have been included.
9. When completed, the items listed on the left should be in the order in which they are actually used or assembled to the product—from top to bottom.

Circles representing assemblies or subassemblies do not necessarily indicate stations on the assembly line, nor persons, but merely operations to be performed. The time required by each operation will determine what is done by each worker. The objective of the Assembly Chart is to show the interrelationship of parts.

Another technique for performing the function of the Assembly Chart is the "exploded" drawing or diagram, such as that shown in Figures 4–14 and 4–15. This technique is also widely used as an aid in teaching inexperienced workers how to assemble complicated objects.

CONCLUSION

Now that the Assembly Chart has been completed, the plant layout engineer has his first "glimpse" of what the over-all material flow pattern may look like. And as a result of the activities discussed in the early part of this chapter, he has the basic data required to proceed with the layout planning. The next step in the layout procedure will be discussed in Chapter 6 after a brief consideration of automation and its effect on plant layout.

QUESTIONS

1. Before plant layout work can be started, what information must be contributed by
   a) Sales Department
   b) Top Management
   c) Product Engineering
   d) Industrial Engineering
   Briefly describe each contribution and indicate its importance in the layout planning.
2. What sources might such information, as referred to above, come from in a smaller plant—of say 15 to 25 *total* employees?
3. How does a seasonal sales pattern affect production?
4. How does one ascertain the time required to get a new product into production?
5. How might the financial policies of a company affect the introduction of a new product?

6. Why is it important to test a new product before going ahead with production? What kinds of things might one find? Discuss examples you are familiar with.
7. What is value analysis? Why couldn't it be done by product engineering?
8. Briefly describe a:
   a) Production Routing
   b) Parts List, or Bill of Materials
9. What kinds of components would we usually buy, rather than make? Name several and indicate why.
10. What are production standards? Where do they come from? What purpose do they serve in production planning?
11. What are some of the kinds of information that plant layout must "pull" from its own files for use in planning? Where do they get it?
12. What is an Assembly Chart? What purposes does it fulfill?
13. What is an "exploded" drawing?

5

Automation

Introduction. Automation was not considered in the previous chapter since the large majority of "typical" plants are too "small" to become involved in more than a token amount of such "automatic manufacturing." When one hears the word "automation," or the term "automatic manufacturing," the image brought to mind is usually of a "large" plant producing a high volume of a relatively "standard" item. While this is not a completely true concept, it is more typical than not.

As far as plant layout is concerned, automation is primarily a process engineering or machine design function. The equipment is usually very specialized and rather large. The plant layout personnel would frequently have little to do with the design or procurement but would be concerned with the materials flow to and from the "machine" and with the building, facilities, utilities, etc., required.

One further word of explanation—many instances of automation are found in most any plant. These are commonly isolated or specialized operations, performed on a relatively small piece of equipment. This will be discussed later on, since it more closely affects the plant layout engineer in his planning efforts.

However, automation is of importance to the plant layout engineer. More and more of it will be taking its place in more and more plants.

In a recent survey [1] of nearly 3,000 plants, the following tabulation shows the extent of automatic equipment and controls currently in use.

Type of Equipment	Per Cent of Plants
Drive and speed regulation	72.7
Interlocked control of operations	59.6
Automatic measuring and gaging	42.6
Automatic weighing	28.3
Process sensing and control	41.5
Tape and punched card control	23.2
Computer control	4.6
Automatic data processing	16.6
Remote control	8.2

[1] "Survey Report and Automation Forecast," *Automation,* Jan. 1959.

As for the operations they planned to make more automatic, 1,700 plants reported as follows:

Per Cent Now Used	Operation	Per Cent Planned for Current Year
26.0	Assembly	17.9
6.3	Casting, forging, rolling	3.6
20.0	Cutting, shearing, forming	9.3
17.4	Data Processing	8.8
23.6	Finishing, painting, etc.	10.4
48.0	Handling, conveying, etc.	26.2
15.5	Inspection	12.0
19.8	Machine tools	9.8
27.8	Packaging, etc.	17.2
16.6	Testing	10.3
18.9	Washing, cleaning, etc.	9.2
23.0	Weighing, mixing, blending	12.0

The above two tabulations will give an idea of what types of functions and operations are commonly being automated.

This chapter will be devoted to a brief presentation of automation in its various forms—some of which will be familiar to the plant layout engineer. A general understanding of the subject will stand him in good stead for such developments as they may appear in the future.

Definitions. The original concept of what is now known as automation was merely the application of work-feeding devices to the large, integrated "transfer" machines. The concept was later broadened to include work-removal devices. Several more complete definitions—which will help in understanding automation—are quoted here.[2]

. . . the art of applying mechanical devices to manipulate work pieces into and out of equipment, turn parts between operations, remove scrap, and to perform these tasks in timed sequence with the production equipment so that the line can be put wholly or partially under push-button control at strategic stations. [Le Grand]

. . . a new word denoting both automatic operation and the process of making things automatic. In the latter sense it includes several areas of industrial activity, such as product and process redesign, the theory of communication and control, and the design of machinery. . . . [Diebold]

. . . significantly more automatic than previously existed in that plant or location. [Bright—based on connotations of current usage]

Summing all of these up, we find that "true automation" might be the process of completely manufacturing a product by automatic means. This

2 Bright, James R. *Automation and Management,* Harvard Business School, 1958, Chap. 1.

is not only possible, but is being accomplished in selected instances. However, in most cases it involves an evolutionary procedure which might be termed "the progressive steps to automation."

Progressive Steps to Automation. The General Electric Company has devised the chart shown in Figure 5–1 to show the progressive steps to automation. Another delineation of the various stages of manufacturing and their characteristics is shown below: [3]

1. Job Shop—lowest volume, highest unit costs
   a) Individual part handling
   b) Individual processing
   c) Hand fitting of parts at assembly
2. Departmentalized—moderate volume, high unit costs
   a) Individual part handling
   b) Processing by department or function
   c) Semiautomatic machines
   d) Hand feeding and assembly
3. Progressive—medium volume, medium unit costs
   a) Individual handling of materials and product
   b) Some semiautomatic machines; some automatic
   c) Partial product straight-line processing
   d) Hand feeding and hand assembly
4. Conveyorized—high volume, moderate unit costs
   a) Conveyor handling of materials and product between machines
   b) Many automatic machines
   c) Straight-line processing by product
   d) Hand feeding and hand assembly
5. Automation—highest volume, lowest unit costs
   a) Automatic handling of materials and product
   b) Automatic line processing by product
   c) Automatic control
   d) Continuous flow
   e) Mechanized assembly

And probably the most complete delineation is Bright's [4] "levels of mechanization," shown in Figure 5–2. It can be observed from looking over the 17 levels of mechanization that most plants have a long way to go before they can be considered fully automatic. In fact, reviewing the levels, one will find that the "average" plant falls somewhere between levels 3 and 8, with most of them nearer the lower end of the range. Bright's "Mechanization Profile," in Figure 5–3, shows this to be true, even in a relatively complex and modern installation.

[3] Based on "Future of Automation," R. W. Bolz in *Automation,* Jan. 1958.
[4] Bright, *op. cit.,* p. 45.

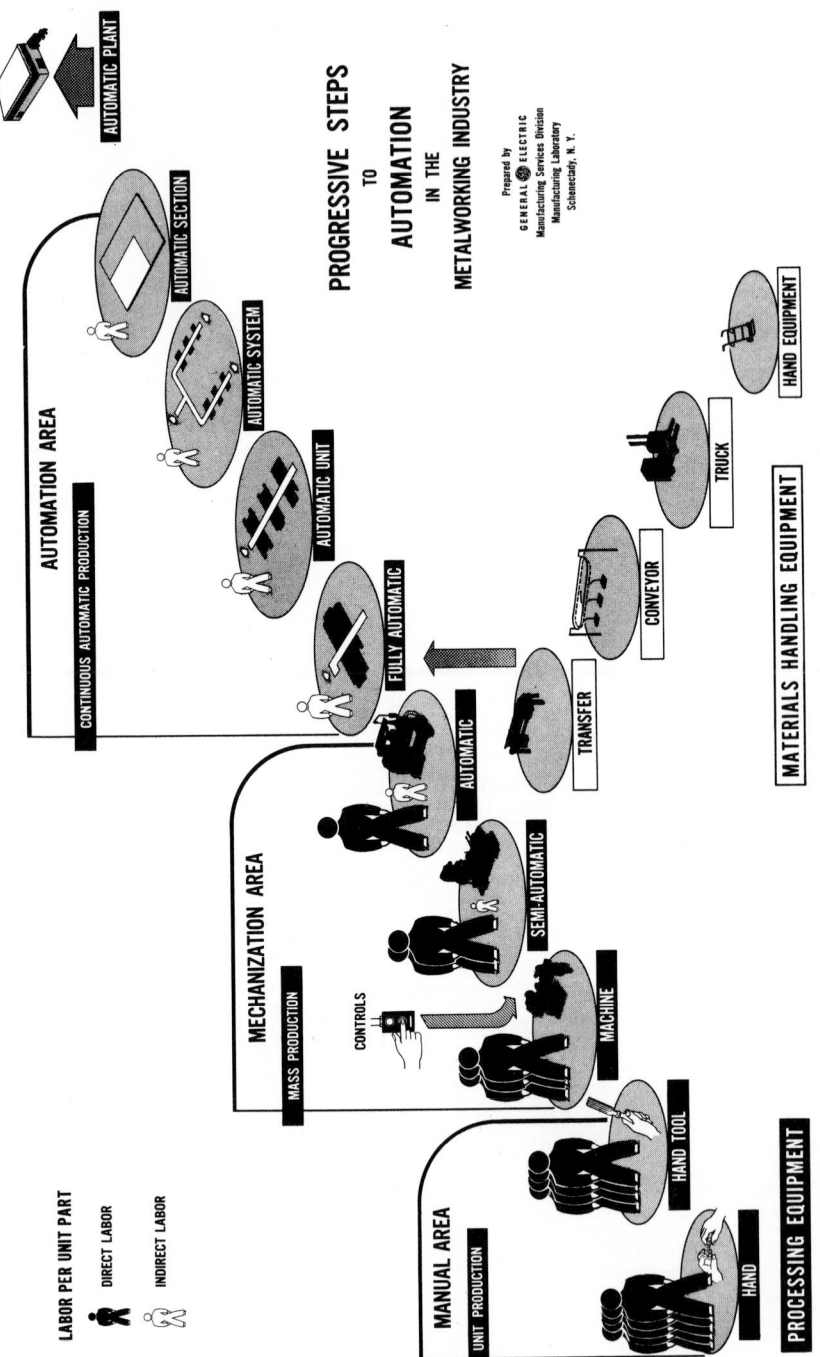

Fig. 5-1. Progressive steps to automation. (By permission of General Electric Co.)

Initiating Control Source		Type of Machine Response		Power Source	Level Number	LEVEL OF MECHANIZATION
From a variable in the environment	Responds with Action	Modifies own action over a wide range of variation		Mechanical (Nonmanual)	17	Anticipates action required and adjusts to provide it.
					16	corrects performance while operating.
					15	Corrects performance after operating.
		Selects from a limited range of possible pre-fixed actions			14	Identifies and selects appropriate set of actions.
					13	Segregates or rejects according to measurement.
					12	Changes speed, position, direction according to measurement signal.
		Responds with signal			11	Records performance.
					10	Signals pre-selected values of measurement. (Includes error detection)
					9	Measures characteristic of work
From a control mechanism that directs a pre-determined pattern of action	Variable	Fixed within the machine			8	Actuates by introduction of work piece or material.
					7	Power Tool System, Remote Controlled
					6	Power Tool, Program Control (sequence of fixed functions)
					5	Power Tool, Fixed Cycle (single function).
From man					4	Power Tool, Hand Control.
					3	Powered Hand Tool.
				Manual	2	Hand Tool.
					1	Hand

Fig. 5–2. Seventeen levels of mechanization and their relationship to power and control sources. (By permission of Harvard Business School.)

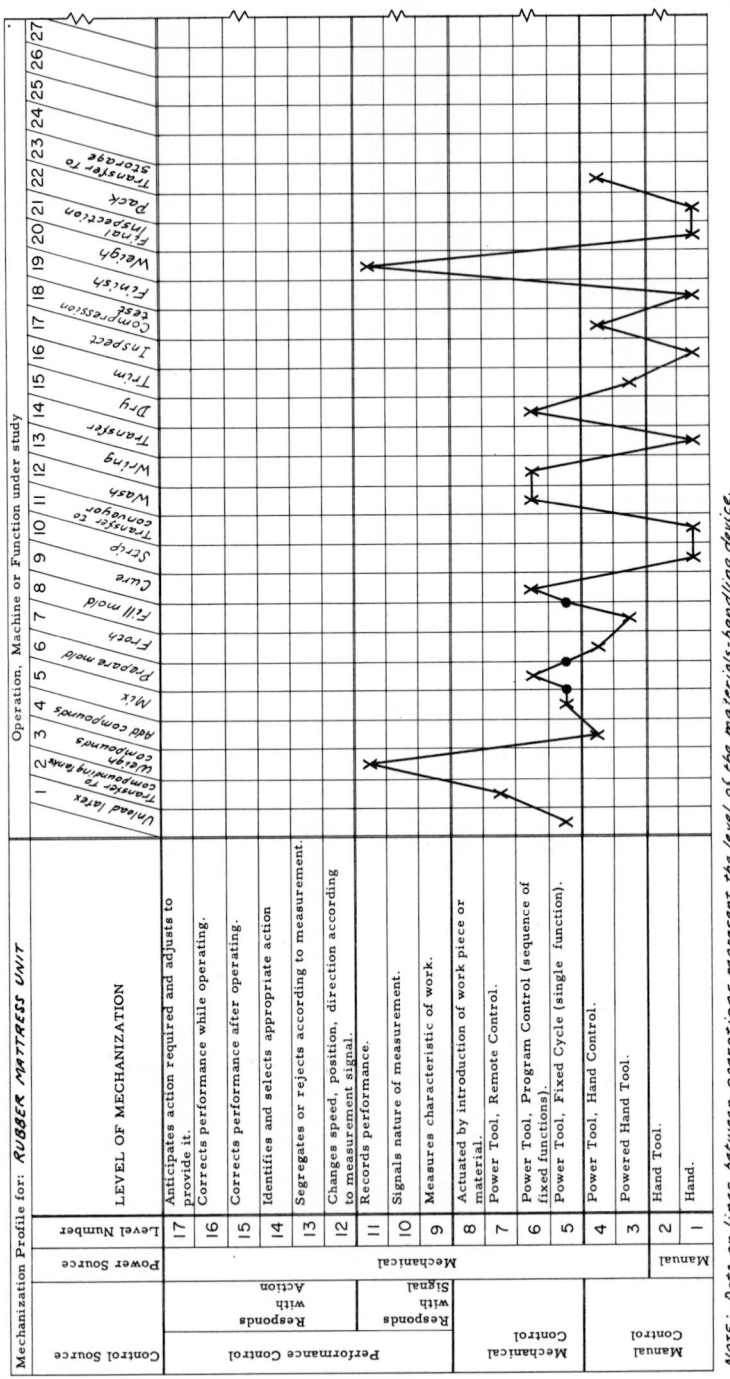

NOTE: Dots on lines between operations represent the level of the materials-handling device.

Fig. 5-3.   Mechanization profile for foam mattress manufacturing.   (By permission of Harvard Business School.)

Figure 5–4 shows an attempt to classify industries by "degree" of mechanization. This, too, bears out the observation above—that there is still a long way to go!

Pros and Cons of Automation. Dr. E. M. Grabbe has listed objectives, benefits, and disadvantages of automation as follows: [5]

1. Primary Objectives of Automation
   a) Increased capacity
   b) Reduction of direct labor cost
   c) Improved quality of product
2. Secondary Objectives of Automation
   a) Improved working conditions (safety, shorter hours, easier work, etc.)
   b) Better operations (reduced scrap, lead time, set-up time, floor space, inventory, etc.)
   c) Peripheral advantages (sales promotion, pride, morale, etc.)
3. Unexpected Benefits
   a) Higher productivity than anticipated
   b) Quality improvements not anticipated
4. Incentives to Automation
   a) Competition and survival
   b) Increasing cost of labor
   c) Pay-as-you-go financing
   d) National defense, etc.
5. Disadvantages of Automation
   a) High cost of design and construction
   b) Installation and debugging troubles
   c) Operation and maintenance problems
   d) Both volume and product may be inflexible
6. Deterrents to Automation
   a) High capital investment
   b) Management difficulties in evaluating automation proposals
   c) Management difficulties in keeping up with modern technology
   d) Management inertia
   e) Labor resistance
   f) Archaic economic thinking
   g) Reduced flexibility
   h) Risk of obsolescence
   i) Difficulties in sales forecasting

Designing for Automatic Manufacturing. Rather obviously, automation, or automatic manufacturing, is most feasible when product design is simplified and standardized, and of course, when volume is high. This concept is shown vividly in Figure 5–5, from a General Electric presentation.

[5] Grabbe, E. M. "Notes on Automation," privately circulated.

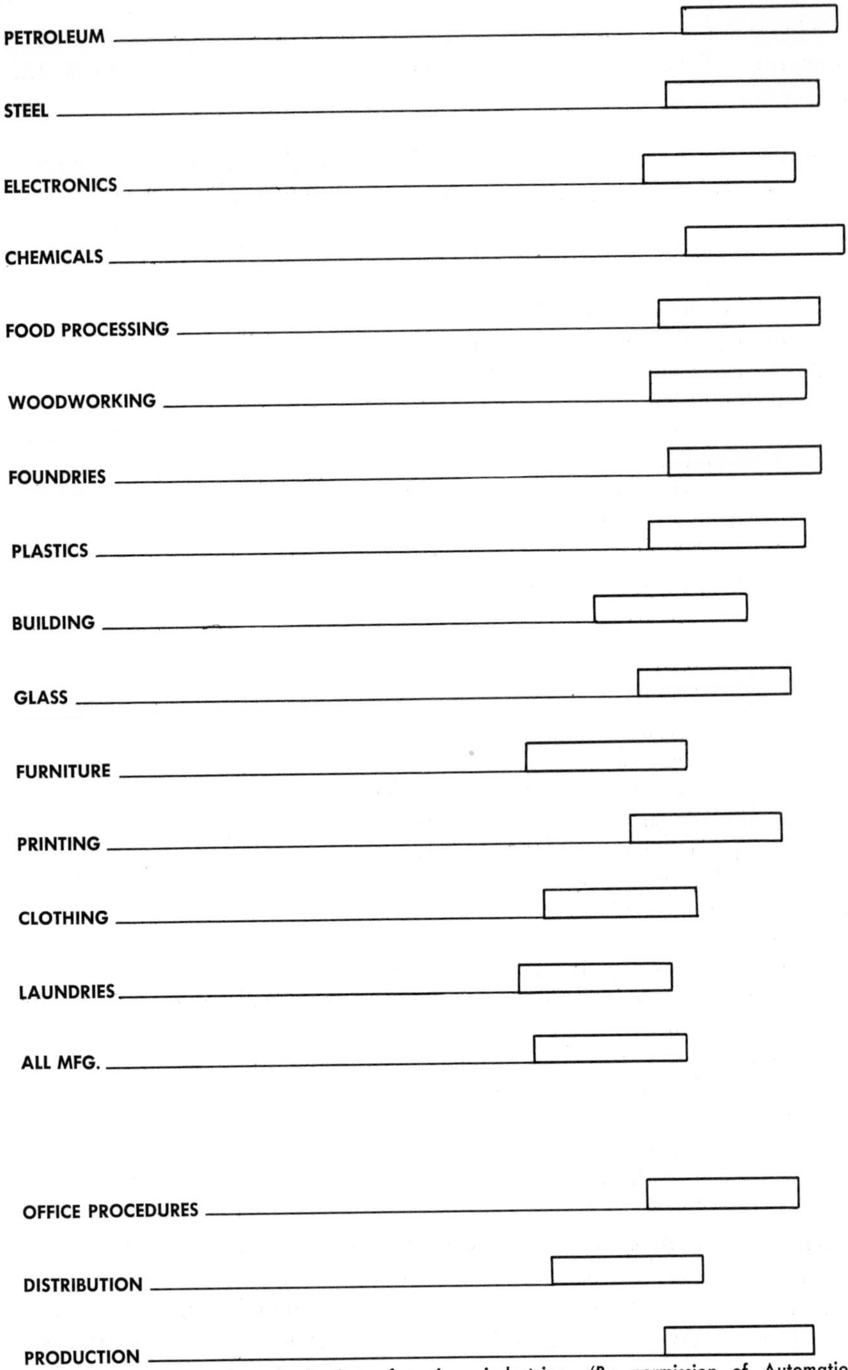

PETROLEUM

STEEL

ELECTRONICS

CHEMICALS

FOOD PROCESSING

WOODWORKING

FOUNDRIES

PLASTICS

BUILDING

GLASS

FURNITURE

PRINTING

CLOTHING

LAUNDRIES

ALL MFG.

OFFICE PROCEDURES

DISTRIBUTION

PRODUCTION

Fig. 5-4. Degree of mechanization of various industries. (By permission of Automation Magazine.)

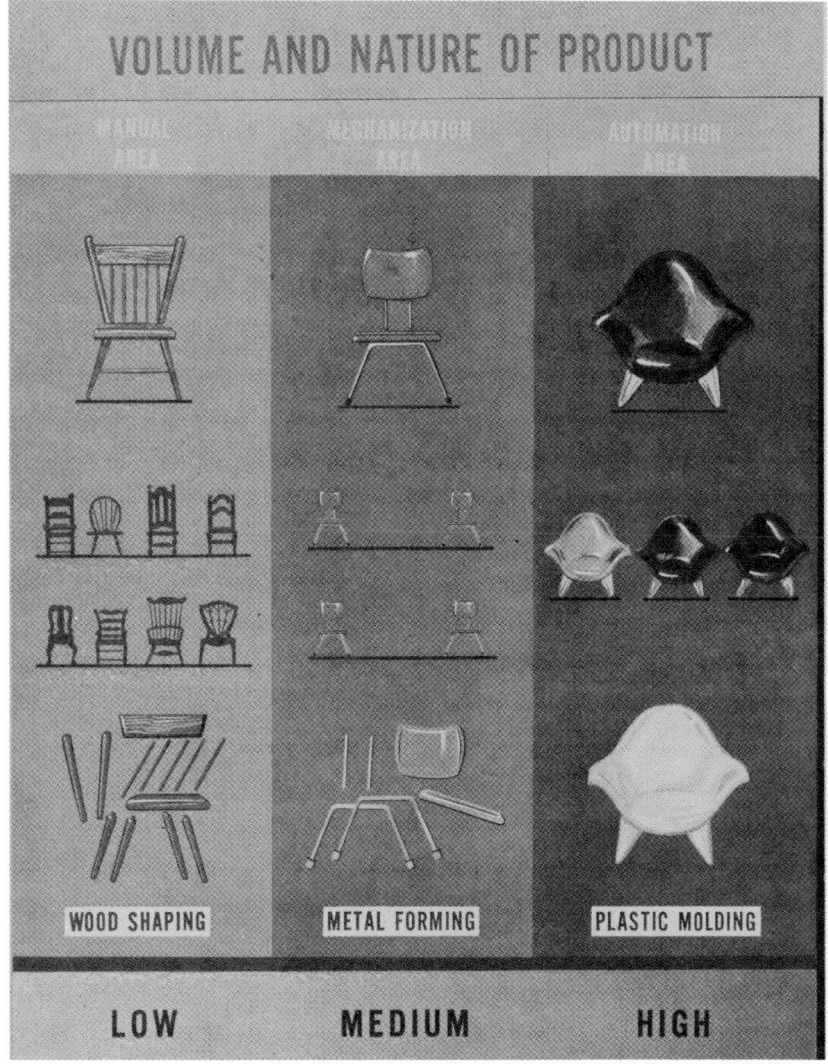

Fig. 5–5. Relationship between volume and nature of product. (By permission of General Electric Co.)

This function is the responsibility of the product engineers. They must be acutely aware of the need for simplicity of manufacture as well as the need for an absolute minimum of design changes.

Basic "Systems" of Automation. Actually, automation may be accomplished in a variety of ways—from the very simple to the extremely complex. One of the simplest possible ways to "automate," is to "con-

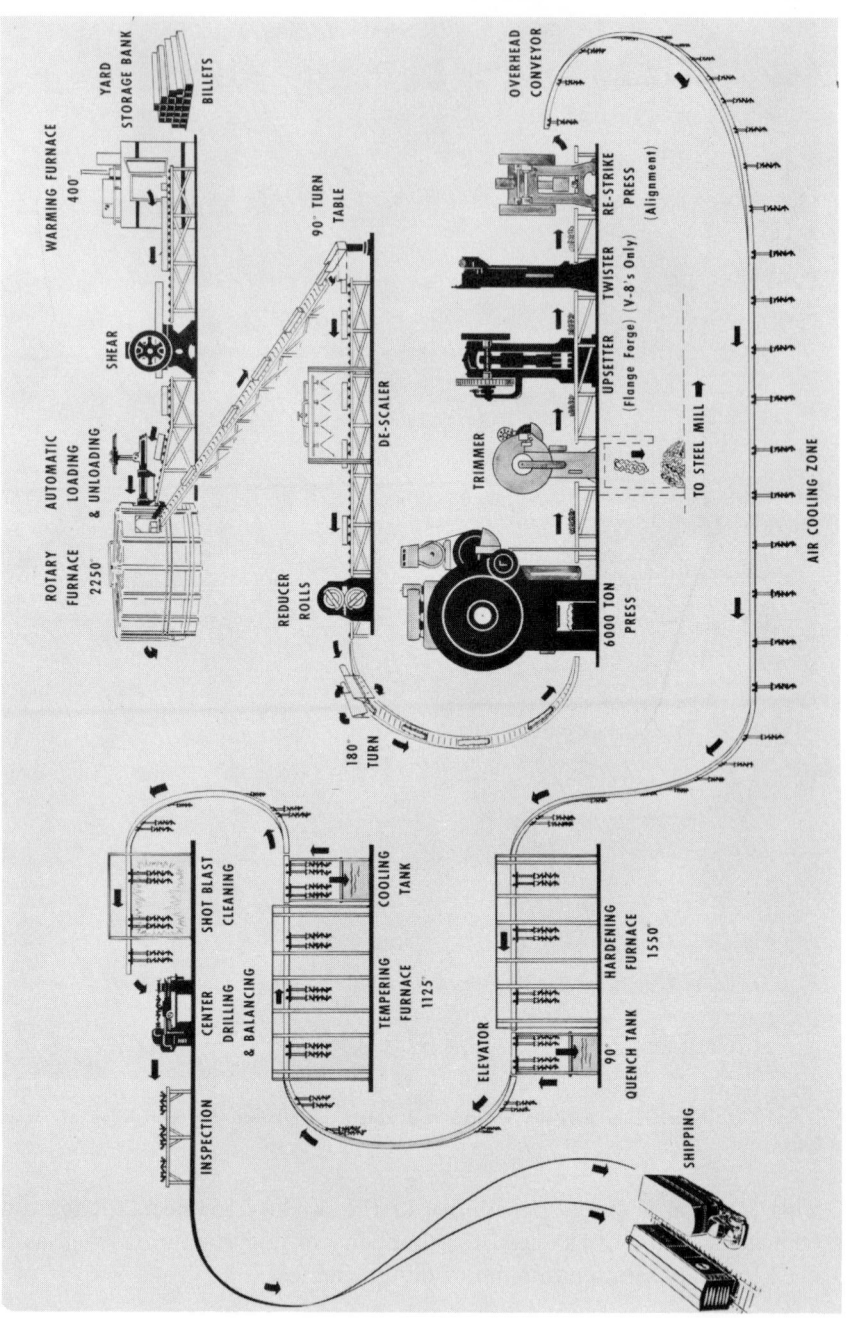

Fig. 5–6. Typical illustration of automation by "connecting" standard production equipment with standard materials handling equipment. (By permission of Chrysler Corporation.)

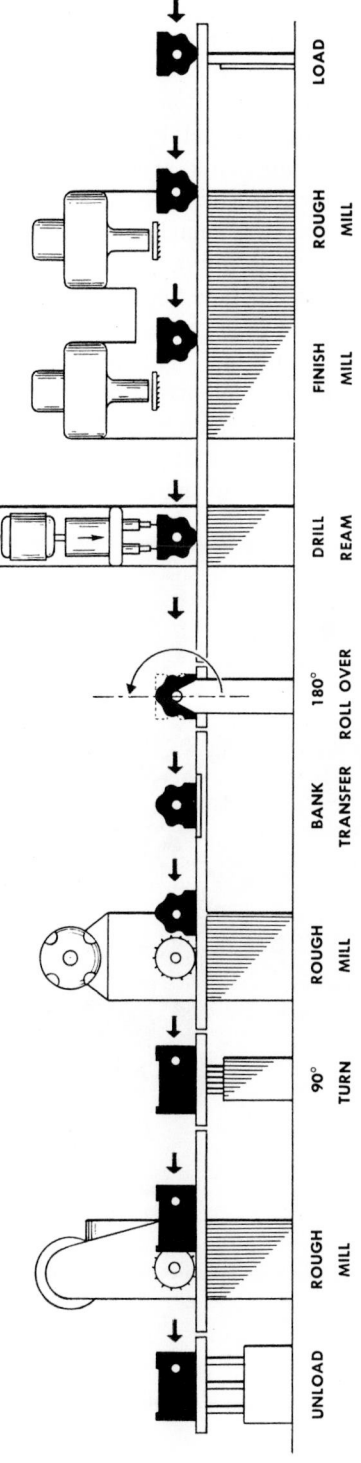

Fig. 5-7. Diagrammatic representation of a transfer machine. (By permission of Cincinnati Milling Machine Co.)

nect" existing, basic production equipment by means of materials handling or transfer devices. This technique is shown in Figure 5–6.

Probably the next step in automation was the development of the transfer machine. This is usually a specially designed grouping of relatively standard machine tool components around a transfer conveyor. This type of application is shown in Figures 5–7, 5–8, and 5–9.

Since the so-called "standard" machine tools do not lend themselves readily to "integration," the building-block system has been developed. This is basically a group of machine "heads" designed to perform specific functions, and all are mountable on a standard base—between which transfer mechanisms can be placed. This is shown in Figure 5–10.

The ultimate, and coming development, is the use of numerically controlled machines, or groups of machines. This technique begins with the conversion of a typical engineering drawing, Figure 5–11, to a coordinate diagram, Figure 5–12. The resulting mathematical equivalent of the

Fig. 5–8. Transfer machine for machining connecting rods. (By permission of Greenlee Bros.)

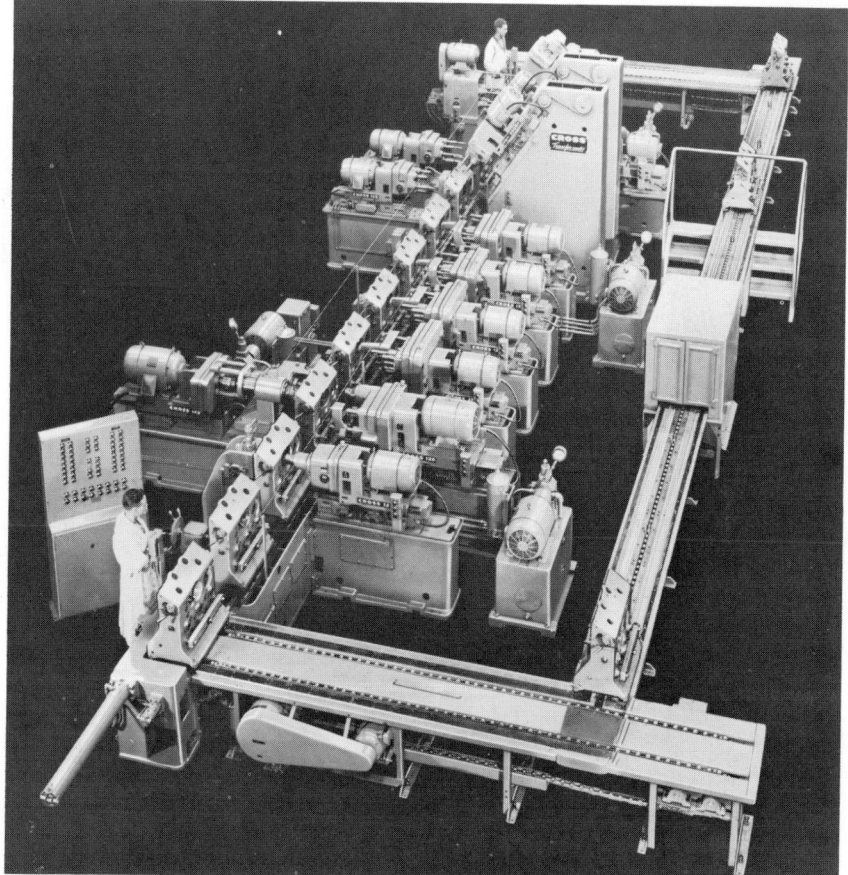

Fig. 5–9. Transfer machine showing mechanism for returning empty fixtures for re-loading. (By permission of The Cross Company.)

drawing is converted to punched or magnetic tape; the procedure progresses somewhat as shown in Figure 5–13.

Characteristics of Automation. As guides to the thinking of the plant layout-or process engineer, Mr. C. F. Hautau [6] has stated the following characteristics of automation. He says it:

1. Starts with the receipt of raw materials.
2. Never lets go of a part until it's finished.
3. Avoids inter-machine storage, mechanically transfers parts in process from one operation to the next without delay.
4. Automatically gages or inspects the part after each key operation.

[6] Hautau, C. F. "How You Can Automate," *Factory Management and Maintenance,* Aug. 1954, p. 118.

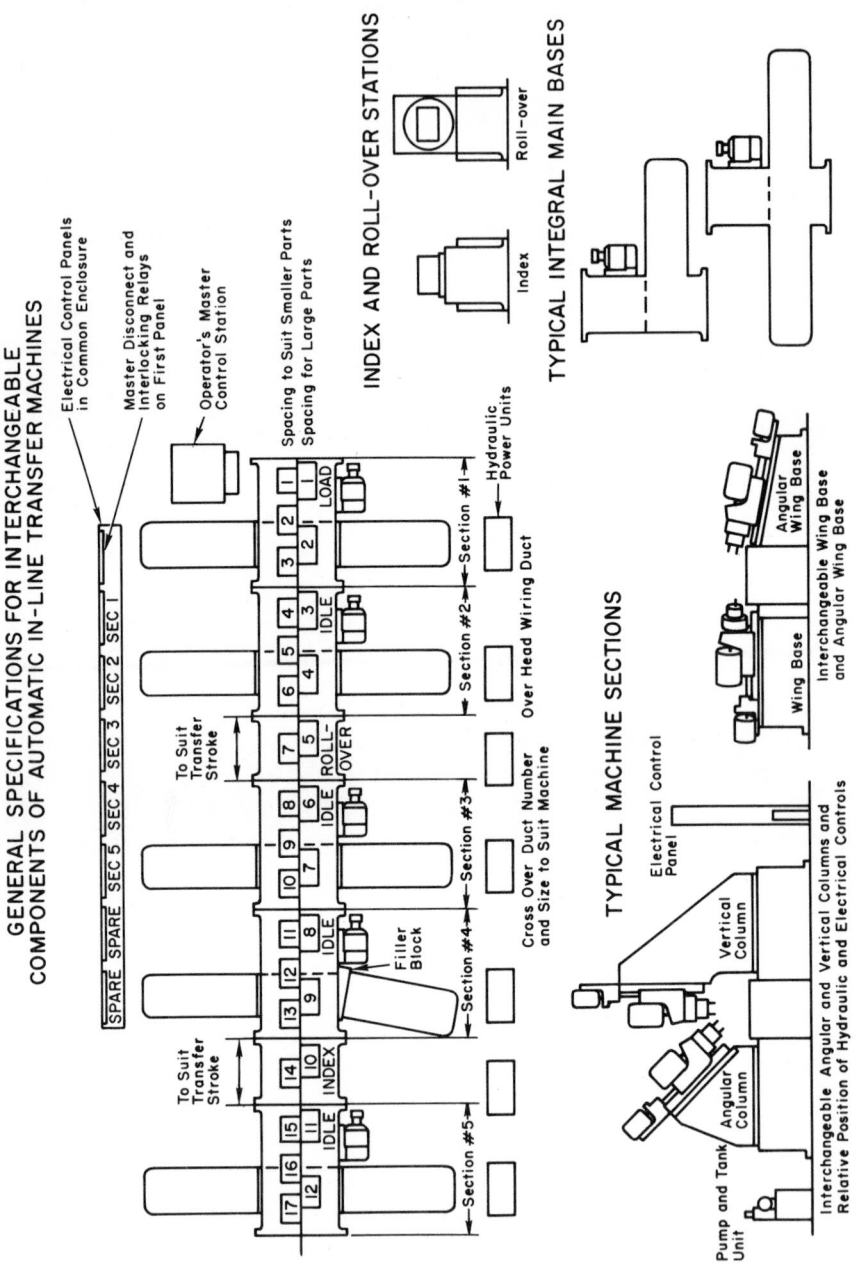

Fig. 5–10. The principle of "building block" automation. (By permission of American Machinist.)

5. Corrects machine or process activity when the parts begin to drift from quality limits.
6. Calls for controlled cycling of individual machines or processes to result in balanced lines.
7. Requires machines that combine or reduce operation to a compact and efficient line.
8. Calls for electrical control of operations. If possible, desirable, or economically feasible, a master panel should control the entire production line.
9. Integrates all assembly, finishing, and packaging operations.

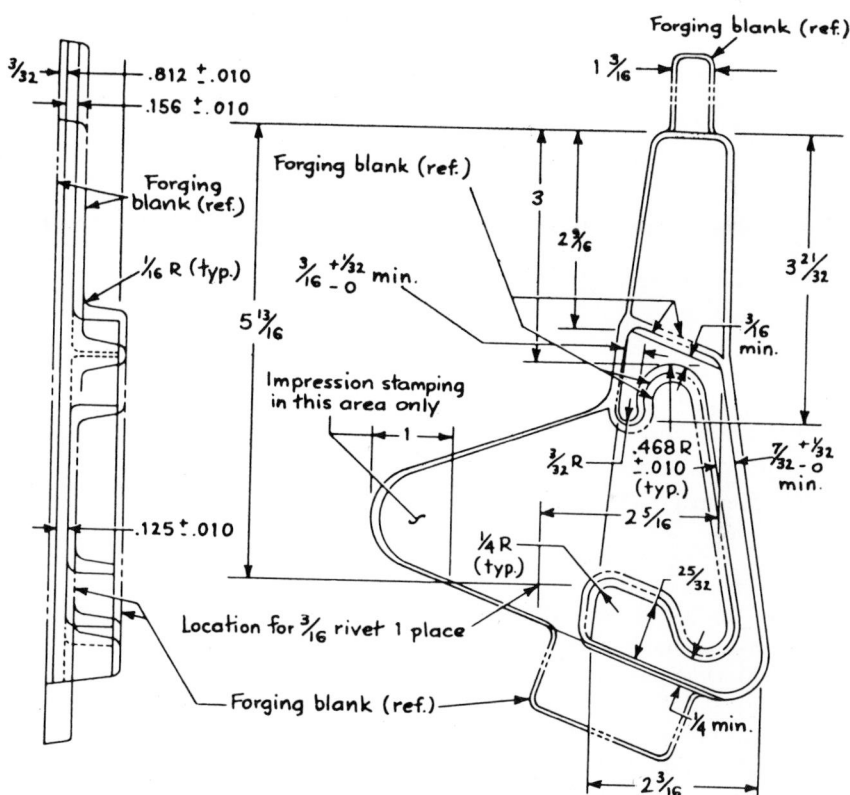

Fig. 5–11. Typical drawing for an aircraft fitting. (By permission of Automation Magazine.)

While the above may appear to be the optimum in automation, it will be recognized that many of the characteristics are rather commonplace in separate situations or applications. As a system becomes increasingly complete and complex, it embraces more and more of these characteristics. This thought will be observed in the accompanying illustrations.

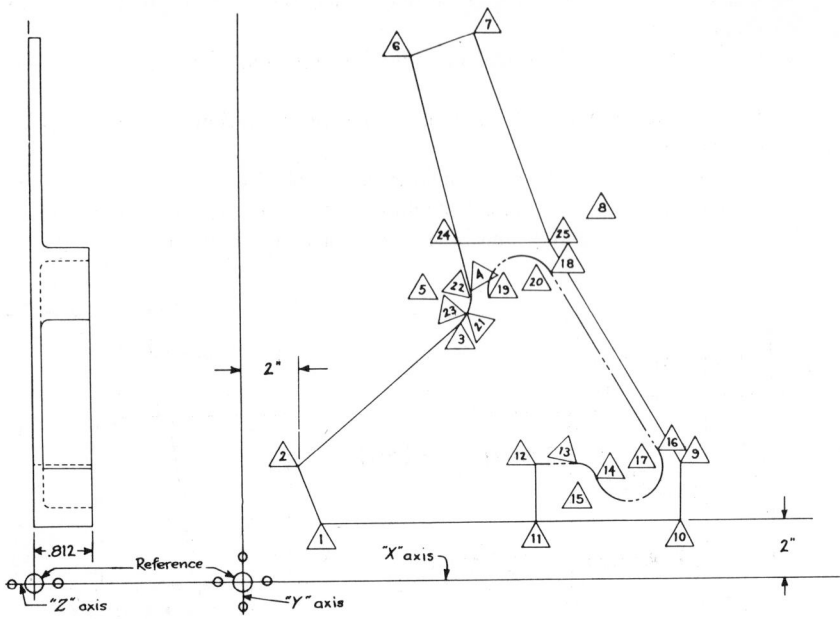

Fig. 5–12. Coordinate diagram for cutting specifications for an aircraft fitting. (By permission of Automation Magazine.)

Under the heading of "Considerations for Practical Automation," Mr. C. G. Menard [7] lists the following to supplement the above "characteristics:

1. Suitable production quantities
2. Coordinated part design
    a) Favorable machining character
    b) Orienting, locating, and transferring surfaces
    c) Stability of design
3. Adequate tool, cutter, and wheel life
4. Preinspection
5. Clean work locating surfaces
6. Safety interlocking
7. Complete foolproofing
8. Continuous chip removal
9. Cleaning chips from parts
10. After-gaging, feedback, and automatic sorting
11. Banking of work pieces
12. Centralized controls

[7] In "Evaluating Machine Tool Arrangements for Automated Production," *Automation*, Aug. 1956, p. 72.

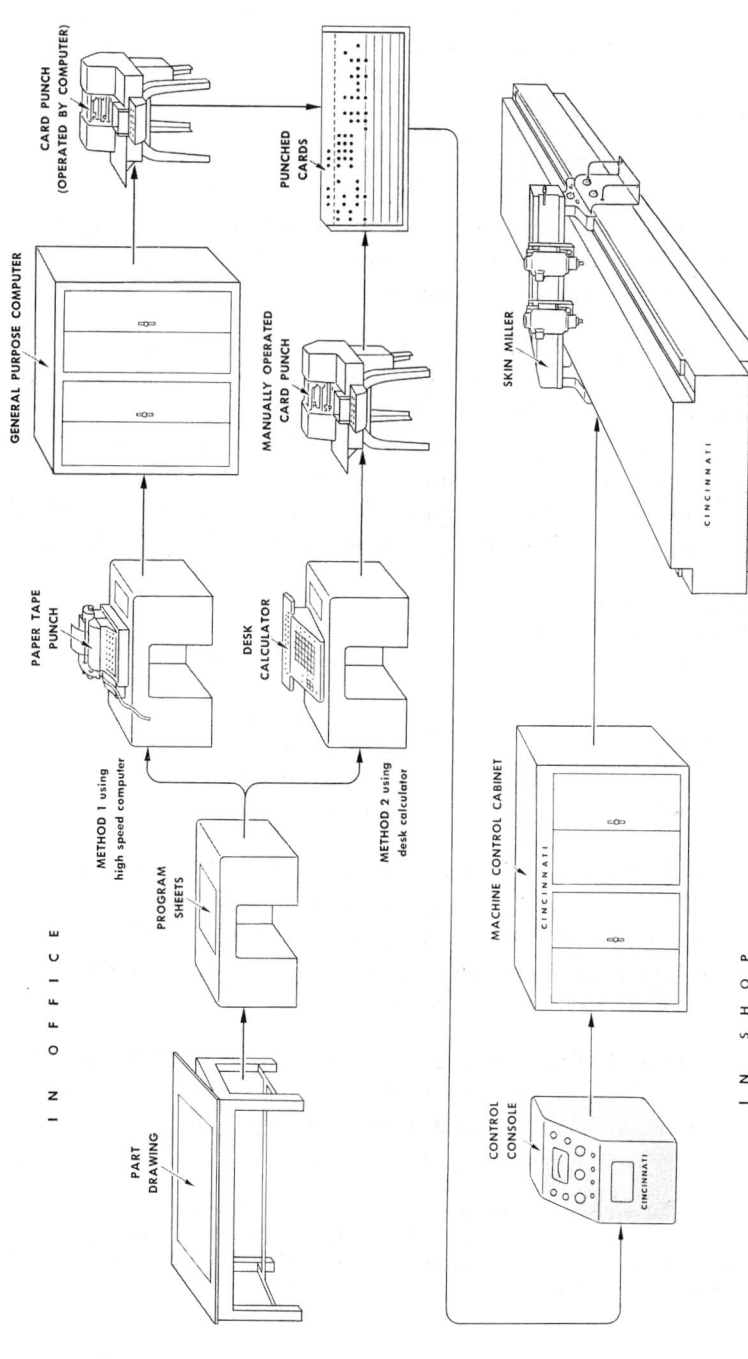

Fig. 5-13. Diagrammatic representation of a numerical control system. (By permission of Cincinnati Milling Machine Co.)

13. Auxiliary set-up controls
14. Quick tool adjustments and replacement
15. Maintenance and accessibility
16. Trouble free components
17. Centralized automatic lubrication
18. Changeover flexibility

These, too, are ideal characteristics for which to strive. They should not be considered as a group, nor as impossible hurdles. Individually or in combination they can be accomplished.

Automating Production Equipment. Automation need not be as complex or awe-inspiring as intimated in the previous section. Many "standard" machine tools can be modified so as to include some of the major aspects of automation. It is this area which is probably of most interest to the plant layout or materials handling engineer, since it pertains primarily to work feeding and removal. Some of the more common attachments, functions, or pieces of auxiliary equipment used in such adaptations are: [8]

1. Magazine feed
2. Loading arm or "hand"
3. Elevator
4. Shuttle
5. Vibratory hopper
6. Barrel hopper
7. Dial feed
8. Gravity chute
9. Transfer arm
10. Chain conveyor
11. Transfer conveyor
12. Automatic lift
13. Turnover
14. Tool slide
15. Coil handlers
16. Sheet lifters

The plant layout engineer, with the cooperation of the materials handling and methods engineers will make use of many of the above devices in implementing the materials flow patterns. The integration of one or more machines by means of these devices is a step toward automation—in even the smallest or lowest production plants.

Automation Application. See Figures 5–14 and 5–15 for two automation installations. They are not presented as ideal or complete applications, but as examples of what has been done. It is hoped that they may serve as a source of ideas in plant layout planning.

[8] For an excellent exposition of many of the above ideas, see *American Machinist,* Apr. 21, 1958; June 30, 1958; July 28, 1958; Sept. 22, 1958, under "How to Automate Production Equipment." See also *Automation,* Oct. 1956, Nov. 1956, and Dec. 1956, under "Automated Assembly."

Fig. 5–14. A transfer machine for the complete machining of automotive cylinder blocks. (By permission of The Cross Company.)

Fig. 5–15. Another automotive cylinder block transfer machine. (By permission of Cincinnati Milling Machine Co.)

CONCLUSION

As indicated at the outset, this chapter was not intended to be a complete treatise on automation. The objective has been to acquaint the reader with what is meant by automation, show what it is doing, and stimulate plant layout thinking along the lines of automation.

QUESTIONS

1. What is meant by automation?
2. How extensive is the application of automation?
3. Will it eventually "take over" and put many out of work? Why? Why not?
4. What stages might be involved in "converting" from hand or job-shop manufacturing to automation?
5. What is meant by "levels of mechanization?" Describe several.
6. What is a mechanization profile? For what could it be used?
7. What are the objectives and benefits of automation? The disadvantages?
8. Why and how is the product engineer important in automation?
9. Describe some of the basic systems of automation: step-by-step, transfer machines, building block automation. Numerical control—differentiate between them.
10. What are some of the characteristics of automation?
11. What are some of the considerations which must be given attention in planning for automation?
12. Where does the plant layout engineer fit into the automation picture?

6

Considerations in Planning Materials Flow

Importance of Planning Materials Flow. In the operation of any business enterprise involving the movement of people, material, merchandise, or other physical items, there must exist a flow pattern. This is the path, or paths, by which the items move or progress from the point at which they enter the operation, through the necessary operations, to the point at which they leave, or are delivered, shipped or stored. Whether it is a grocery store, print shop, cafeteria, or manufacturing facility, the efficient flow of materials is a key to the success of the undertaking.

A primary objective of an efficient business enterprise is to plan a flow pattern that will facilitate the movement of materials through the physical facilities in as direct a path as is practical. Therefore, this flow pattern must be carefully planned, and all factors bearing on it should be thoroughly considered.

The importance of this concept in a manufacturing plant might be stated as follows:

1. The primary requisite for economical production is an efficient plan for the flow of materials.
2. The materials flow pattern becomes the basis for an effective arrangement of physical facilities.
3. Materials handling converts the *static* flow pattern into a *dynamic* reality —by providing the means by which the materials are caused or permitted to flow.
4. Effective arrangement of facilities around the materials flow pattern should result in efficient operation of the various processes.
5. Efficient operation of the processes should result in minimum production costs.
6. And . . . minimum production costs should result in a successful enterprise.

On the basis of the above, it may be concluded that an efficient materials handling plan—flow pattern plus materials handling facilities—is the base upon which the entire manufacturing plan rests. It follows then, that the successful operation of the enterprise is dependent upon the design of an effective materials flow pattern. This can be depicted graphically as shown in Figure 6–1.

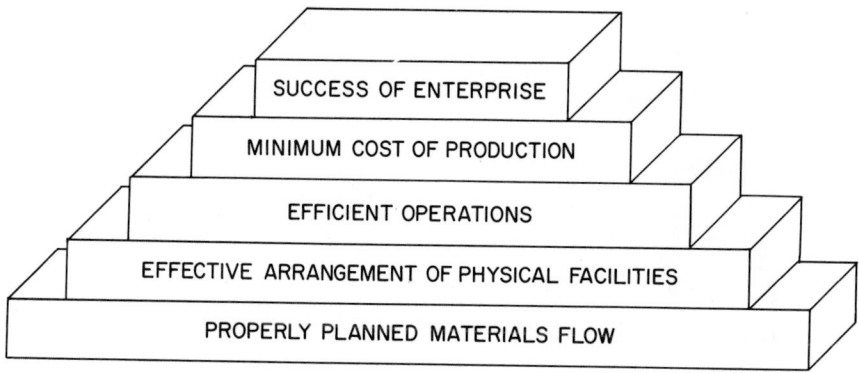

SUCCESS OF ENTERPRISE

MINIMUM COST OF PRODUCTION

EFFICIENT OPERATIONS

EFFECTIVE ARRANGEMENT OF PHYSICAL FACILITIES

PROPERLY PLANNED MATERIALS FLOW

Fig. 6–1. Importance of the materials flow pattern.

Some examples of over-all materials flow patterns are shown in Figures 6–2, 6–3, 6–4, and 6–5. A review of these illustrations will indicate what is meant by—as well as the importance of—a flow pattern.

Advantages of Planned Materials Flow. Too much emphasis cannot be placed on the importance of determining the most efficient plan for the flow of materials through the production facilities. However, it is precisely at this point that many manufacturing plans fall short. Indeed, it is not at all uncommon for a management group to "plan" a factory building, erect it, then stand back, view it with pride, and say: "Well, let's see how we can arrange the production equipment!" This, of course, is entirely the reverse of what should have been done.

As has been indicated previously, the flow pattern is an important early step in the planning of an efficient plant layout. Only by designing a master flow pattern—early in the planning process—can one be sure that all subsequent planning efforts are directed toward a worthwhile goal. However, this is not to say that a flow pattern, devised early in the planning stages, will not be subject to changes as the planning progresses toward the final plant layout.

A well-conceived and carefully planned materials flow pattern will have many advantages. In fact, a good flow pattern will go a long way toward

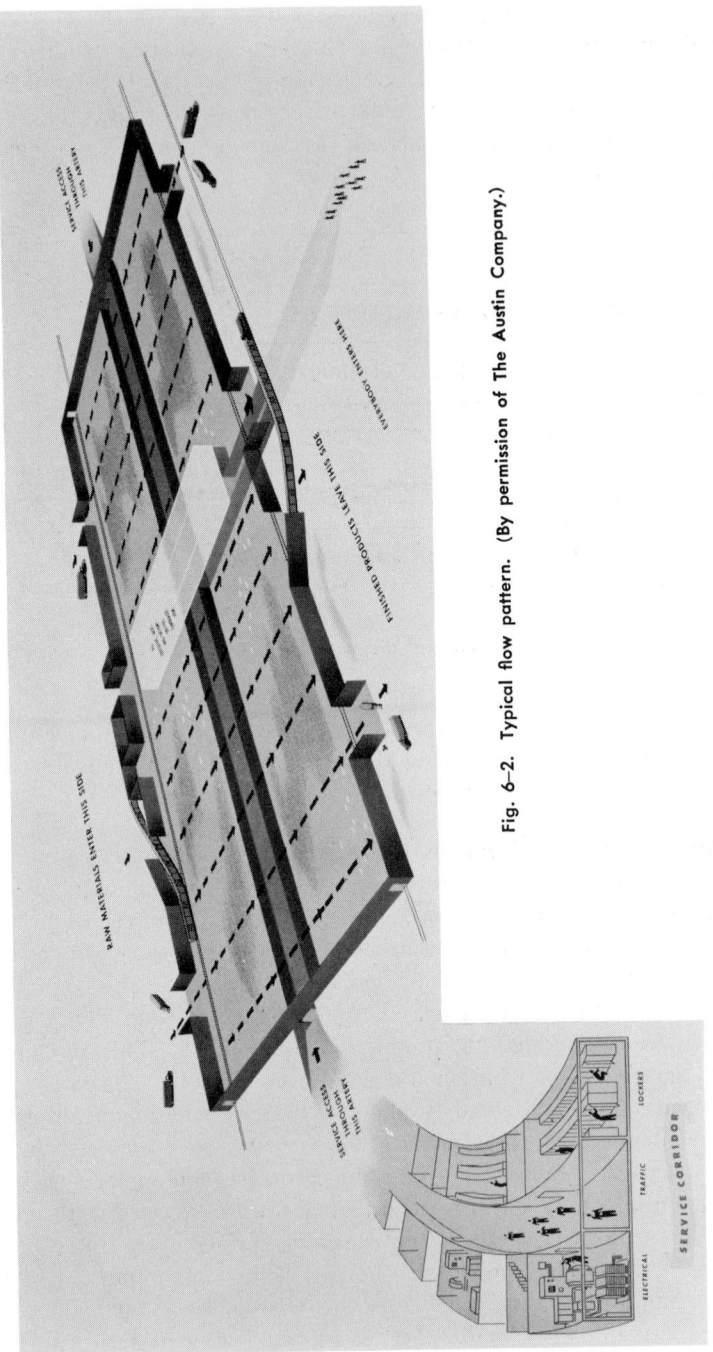

Fig. 6-2. Typical flow pattern. (By permission of The Austin Company.)

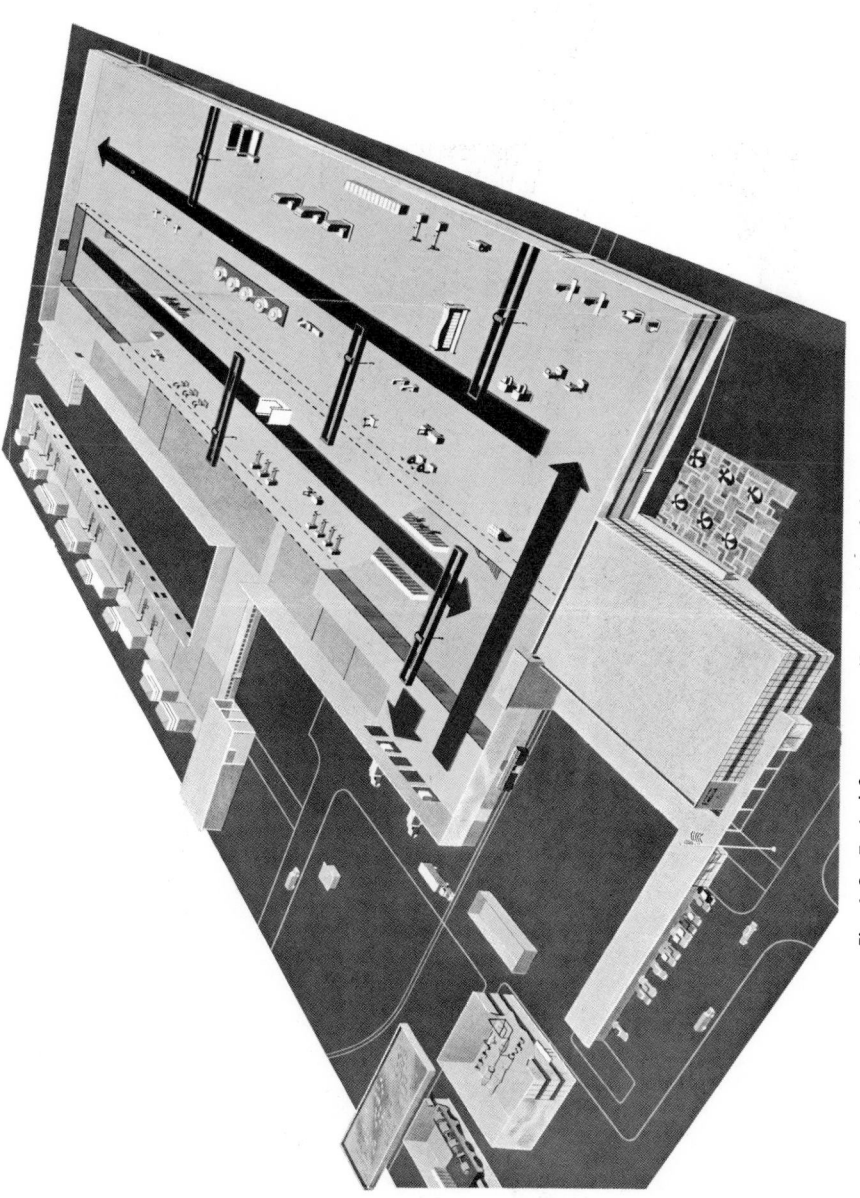

Fig. 6–3. Typical flow pattern. (By permission of The Austin Company.)

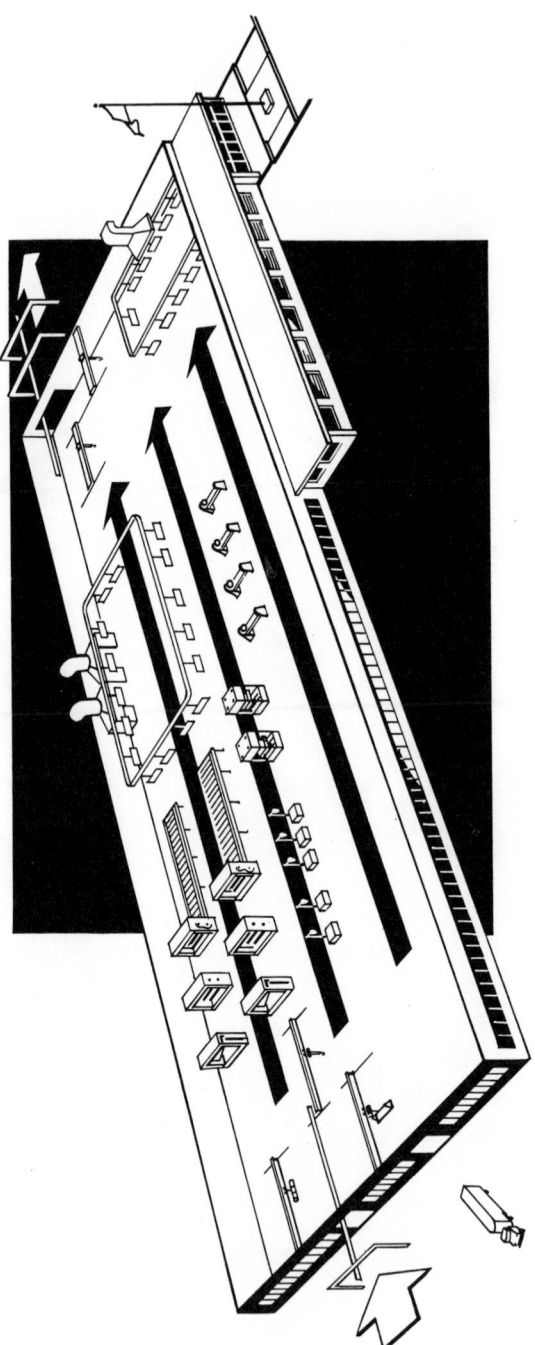

Fig. 6–4. Typical flow pattern. (By permission of The Austin Company.)

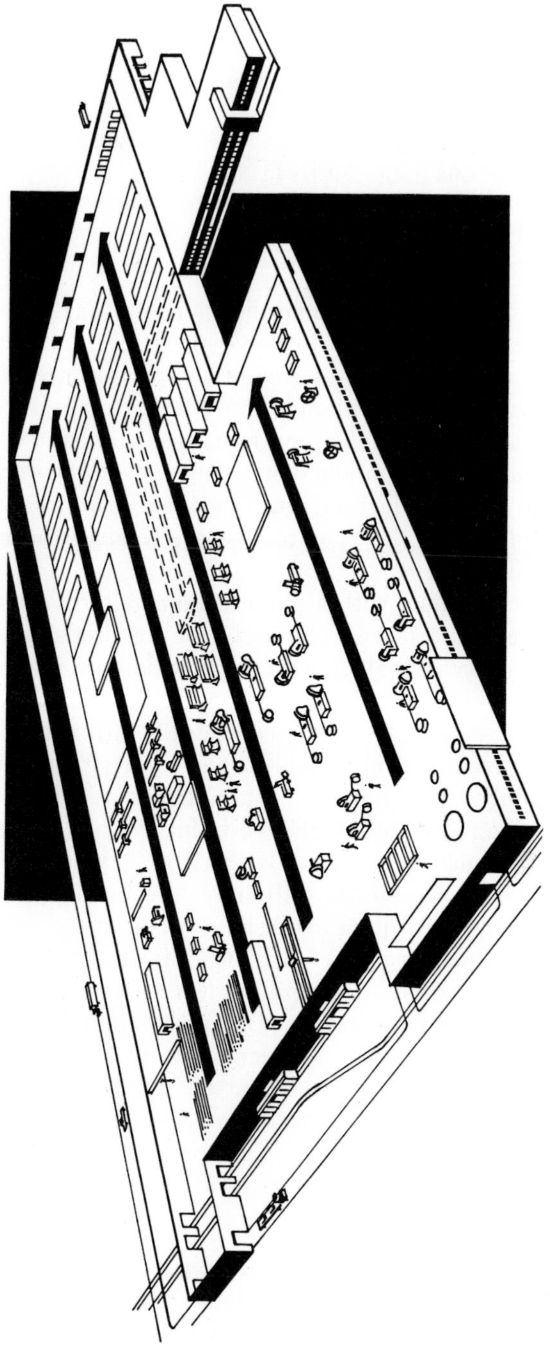

Fig. 6–5. Typical flow pattern. (By permission of The Austin Company.)

achieving several of the objectives of plant layout, as stated in Chapter 1. Some of these advantages are as follows:

1. Facilitate the manufacturing process.
2. Materials handling will be minimized.
3. More economical use can be made of operator time.
4. Overhead costs will be lowered.
5. Over-all time of manufacturing will be reduced, resulting in higher turnover of materials inventory.
6. Product cost will be lower as a result of all the savings indicated above.

A proper flow pattern will help the manufacturing process along instead of hindering it. Materials will move along in an orderly, rather than a haphazard, manner. As a matter of fact, if one were to stand on the floor of many of today's plants, it would certainly appear, upon observation, that no over-all flow pattern exists; or else it was planned to interfere with efficient production! Actually, no flow pattern is *planned* to interfere with production; but one that wasn't planned, or which is gradually allowed to degenerate, eventually gives the impression of organized confusion.

Materials handling, with a planned flow pattern, should be minimized both in extent and in cost. Because the materials handling is initially planned, or conceived, along with the flow pattern, there will be less handling, which will most likely result in a less costly handling operation.

Operator time can be more economically utilized if the flow pattern causes the productive materials to flow through the various operations more smoothly. This should result in less effort by the operator himself in the handling of materials related to his work cycle.

Because of increased materials handling efficiency, the factory overhead costs will be proportionately lower. A moving piece of material has less opportunity to acquire overhead charges.

Total manufacturing time, and therefore inventory turnover, will also be improved. The total time will be less as a result of the more efficient materials flow, and the turnover of inventory will be more frequently accomplished. In other words, materials will move through the plant more quickly.

Then, as a result of all the above, the total product cost should be appreciably lower—less handling, more economical handling, more efficient operator performance, shorter manufacturing time, and increased inventory turnover.

Need for a Master Plan. The preceding discussion has emphasized the extreme importance of carefully planning a master flow pattern for the movement of materials. It is a matter of prime concern if an effective plant layout is to be developed, whether it is for a proposed production facility or for an existing plant. In fact, it is our contention that *every* plant should have a master, or "dream," plan—toward which all planning efforts should be directed. If the plant is yet to be built, it serves as a guide at every step in the planning process. On the other hand, if the plant now exists, the development of a theoretical, or "dream," plan, will serve as goal toward which every subsequent change should be directed —until one day the actual plant becomes the "dream" plant.

PRELIMINARY CONSIDERATIONS IN FLOW PLANNING

Flow Planning Principles. As indicated previously, the over-all objective of an efficient flow pattern is to facilitate the orderly flow of materials throughout the entire manufacturing process. Such an objective cannot be achieved without some carefully guided planning efforts. An aid to such efforts might be the principles stated below. It should be emphasized that they cannot all be followed in every case, but their consideration throughout the planning process will aid in arriving at a better and more effective flow pattern. These principles are:

1. Plan for movement of materials in as direct a path as possible through the plant.
2. Minimize backtracking.
3. Use the line-production principle wherever feasible.
4. Plan for incoming materials to be delivered directly to the work areas when practicable.
5. Install materials handling equipment which will permit production employees to spend full time on production.
6. Use mechanical handling equipment to assure a constant rate of production.
7. Combine operations whenever possible to eliminate handling between them.
8. Eliminate "rehandling."
9. Combine processing with transportation whenever practicable.
10. Plan for storage of a minimum of material in the work area.
11. Minimize walking required of production operators.
12. Reduce manual handling to a minimum.
13. Plan for each operator to dispose of a part in a convenient location for the next operator to pick it up.
14. Use gravity to move materials.
15. Place related activities near each other.
16. Plan for processes involving heavy materials to be located near the receiving area.

A study of the flow patterns in Figures 6–2, 6–3, 6–4, and 6–5 will show that many of these principles *have* been considered in their development.

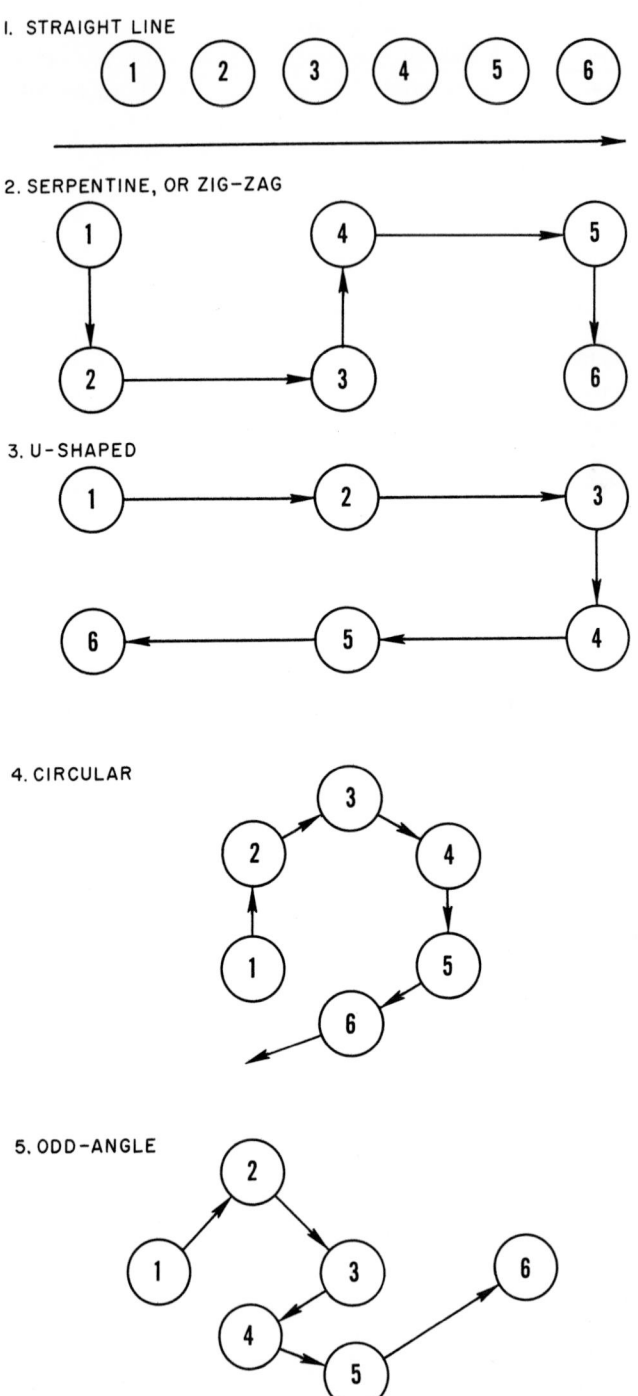

Fig. 6-6. General Flow Patterns.

Look especially for principles 1, 2, 3, 4, 9, 15, 16. It is evident that many of the principles cannot be applied in the preliminary or over-all flow patterns but should be considered as smaller areas and greater details are worked out.

General Flow Patterns. Since there have been literally thousands of flow patterns developed in various plants and industries, it is obvious that there must be some *general* flow patterns which have been found applicable, or adaptable, to other situations. Such patterns as might be considered general are shown in Figure 6–6. A few comments will aid in understanding the reasoning or application of each:

Fig. 6–6(1)—Straight line—applicable where the production process is short, relatively simple, and contains few components and/or few pieces of production equipment.

Fig. 6–6(2)—Serpentine, or zig-zag—applicable where the "line" is longer than it would be practicable to allocate space—therefore it bends back on itself to provide a longer flow line in an economical building or area shape and size.

Fig. 6–6(3)—U-shaped—applicable where it is desirable for the finished product to end the process in the same relative location as it begins —due to exterior transportation facilities, use of a common machine, etc. Also for the same reason as Figure 6–6(2).

Fig. 6–6(4)—Circular—applicable when it is desired to return a material or product to the exact place it started, such as for a foundry flask, where shipping and receiving are at the same location, or to use a machine a second time in a series of operations.

Fig. 6–6(5)—Odd-angle—no recognizable pattern but very common when the primary objective is a short flow line between a group of related areas, where handling is mechanized, when space limitations will not permit another pattern, or where permanent location of existing facilities demands such a pattern.

Various applications, adaptations, or combinations of the above are shown in Figure 6–7. The beginning and ending points of the flow are dependent, to a certain extent, on the location of external transportation facilities such as highways, railroad sidings, and docks or piers on navigable waterways. In Figures 6–7a and 6–7d, it is assumed that such facilities are available alongside the plant. If a few long production lines are necessary, work flow would be as in Figure 6–7b. If transportation were to be available at the ends of the plant, flow might be as shown in Figure 6–7b; or if available at one end and one side, as in Figure 6–7c. Figures 6–7e and 6–7f indicate methods of fitting a relatively long flow line into

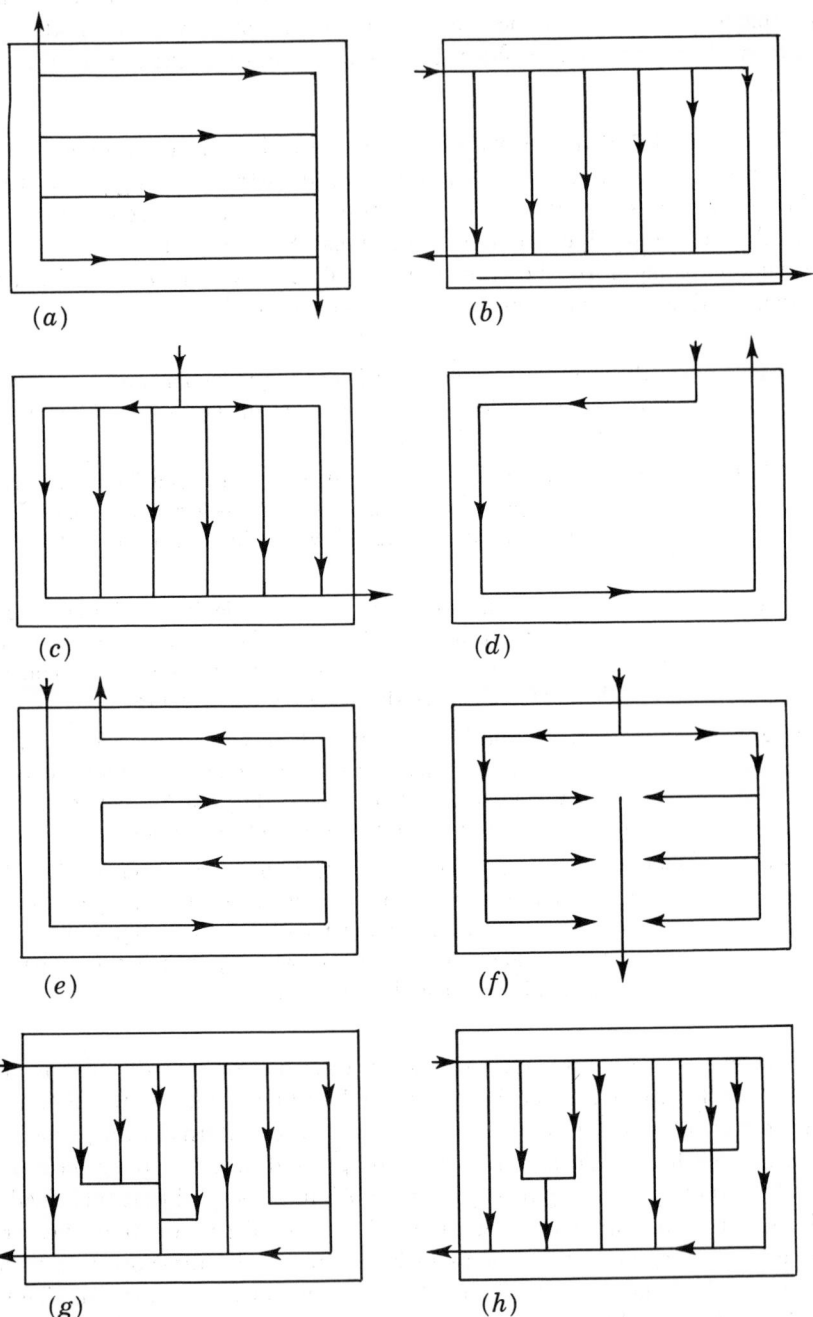

Fig. 6–7. Typical materials- or production-flow patterns.

a rectangular space. In Figures 6–7g and 6–7h are shown flow patterns involving subassembly operations.

An excellent idea of what is meant by a flow pattern, is shown in Figure 6–8. This diagram shows the general flow of power-truck parts through the Yale and Towne plant in Philadelphia. This company designed its plant around a planned materials handling system based upon an efficient production layout.

Another illustration of a flow pattern is shown in Figure 6–9. As can be seen in the illustration, sheet metal parts come in from the press and subassembly areas at the upper right. Metal finishing operations take place in the area at the upper part of the picture. Assembly begins at the left center where the outer shell is placed on the slat conveyor. At the lower left the inner shell is added. Then along the line, the refrigeration unit is added, door is hung, fixtures are placed, inspections are made, and the unit is packed.

No "prefabricated" flow pattern can be prescribed for a given situation, however. Each plant layout problem must be analyzed, and a flow pattern designed to best accomplish all the factors involved. At the same time, it must comply with as many of the objectives and principles as is possible. In the ideal situation, a planned materials flow pattern becomes the basis for an efficient plant layout. The plant layout, in turn, becomes the basis for the design of the plant building—which is in reality a functional "roof" over an efficient materials flow pattern.

Factors for Consideration in Flow Planning. Before the actual task of designing a flow pattern can be undertaken, there are many factors which must be considered. These are items which, singly or in combination, will determine some of the characteristics of the flow pattern, or its relationship to other phases of the plant layout planning project. Not all of these can be properly considered at one time, nor can they all be adequately covered in this chapter. However, let us treat each one briefly at this point as an overview—then further discuss selected factors as they become appropriate in later chapters. For convenience, the factors are classified according to the phase of the layout project with which they are most closely related. The factors are:

A. General
   1. Levels of activity
   2. Movement of personnel
   3. Working conditions
   4. Cost
B. Product
   5. Volume of production
   6. Number of parts

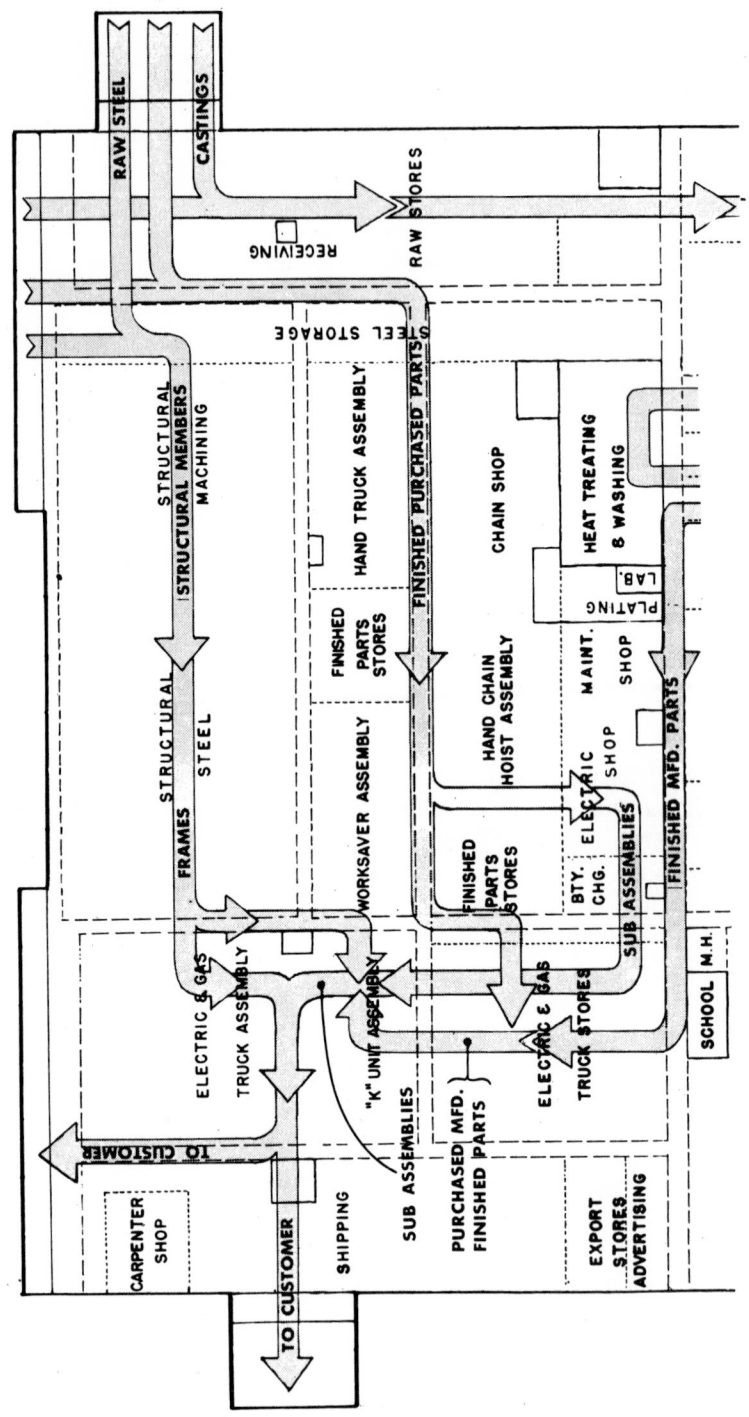

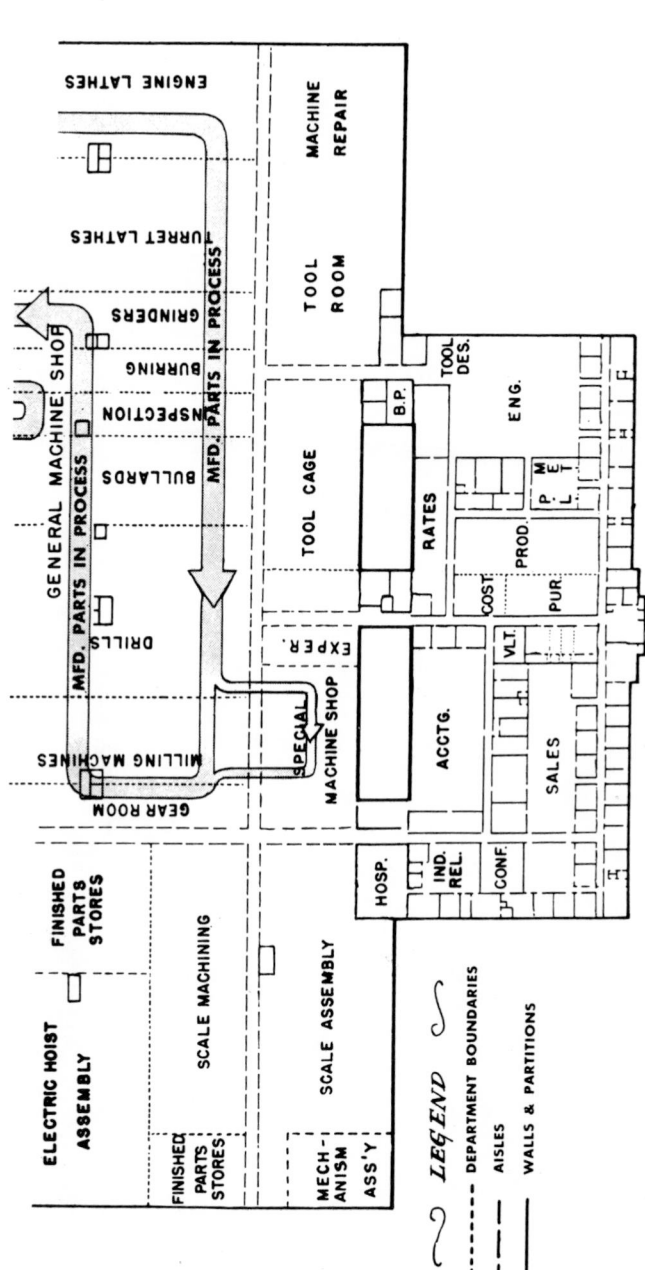

Fig. 6–8. Materials flow pattern for power truck products. (By permission of Yale and Towne Manufacturing Co.)

Fig. 6–9. Materials flow in a refrigerator plant. (By permission of Armstrong Cork Co.)

C. Process
    7. Specific requirements of activities
    8. Number of operations
    9. Sequence of operations
   10. Number of subassemblies
   11. Product vs. process layout
   12. Quantity of equipment
   13. Space requirements of equipment
D. Flow Pattern and Materials Handling
   14. Required flow between work areas
   15. Preliminary materials handling plans
   16. Location of shipping and receiving
   17. Storage requirements
   18. Aisle area
   19. Desired location of departments
   20. Desired location of service areas
   21. Supervisory requirements
   22. Production control
   23. Flexibility
   24. Expandability
E. Building and Site
   25. Building type
   26. Number of floors
   27. External transportation facilities

Discussion of factors.

1. *Levels of Activity.* Most of the thinking in the planning of a layout centers, for obvious reasons, around the activity which occurs on or at the floor level, that is, the space required by equipment, stock, aisles, columns, etc. Very seldom is sufficient attention given to the fact that plant production activity occurs at other "levels" also. These levels were first identified by H. H. Dasey as a concept suggesting the extreme value of scale models in plant layout planning. The levels are:

1. THE BASE LEVEL. The foundation, or under-the-floor area or space in a plant building. It is this space which may enclose such items as heating, ventilating, power, water, air, sewer, drain, scrap removal, and similar facilities.
2. THE FLOOR LEVEL. The actual plant floor which supports the equipment, stock, personnel, etc.
3. THE FLIGHT-OF-PRODUCT LEVEL. This is an imaginary plane—about 36 to 46 inches above the floor and represents the line of product flow throughout the plant at work-height level.
4. CLEAR-SPACE LEVEL. The area above the mean operating "ceiling" (i.e., above the tops of the machines, etc.) and below the bottom chord of the trusses supporting the roof. This space usually contains conveyors, ovens, elevated stock rooms, storage, etc.

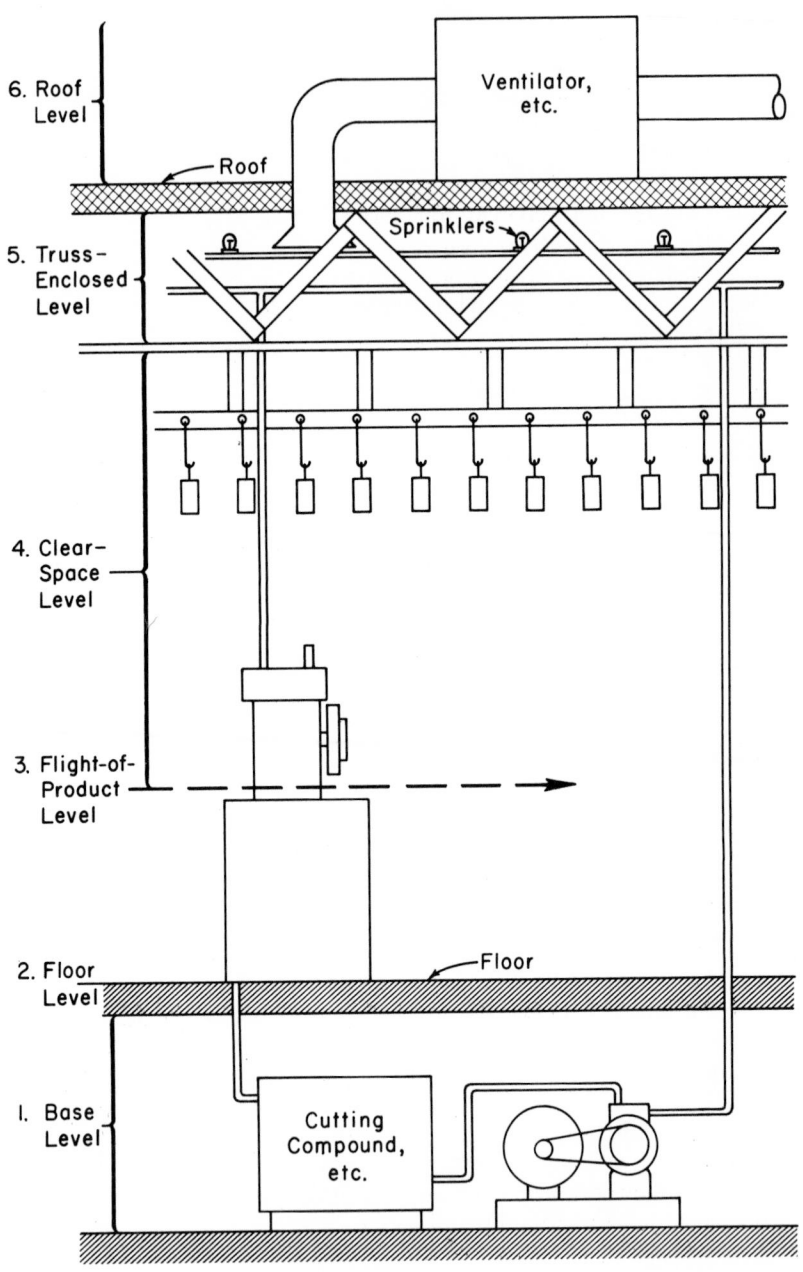

Fig. 6–10. Levels of activity in an industrial plant.

5. Truss-Enclosed Level. The area above the bottom truss chord and below the roof or ceiling. This area commonly encloses sprinkler lines, other utility lines, heating and ventilating equipment, etc.
6. Roof Level. The space available, outside the plant, on the roof. This space may be used for ovens, cooling towers, water tanks, elevator shaft access, ventilators, etc.

This concept is shown graphically in Figure 6–10. It is evident that all six levels must be kept in mind during the planning process. This will assure that the proper item will be allocated to the level in which it properly belongs and where it can make most economical use of the plant space. It should never be forgotten that a factory consists of *cubic* feet to be efficiently utilized—not merely square feet, on the floor. It is the *cube* which must be properly utilized.

2. *Movement of Personnel.* In our attention to the importance of materials handling, it should not be forgotten that personnel must also move through the plant. Since all "man time" can be reduced to dollars per minute, it is obvious that excess time spent in walking costs an excess amount of dollars. Consideration must be given to necessary and frequently traveled paths. For example, one large company, in the planning phase, tried to economize on plumbing by installing only one lavatory. It was calculated that this would save $4,000 in construction costs. However, subsequent investigation showed it would cost $6,300 *per year* in extra walking time of persons using the lavatory. Personnel not only must move about the plant, but they occupy space in so doing. This fact not only removes space which might be better utilized, but it also creates a safety hazard—both to those who are walking about and to those who may be distracted by them. For these reasons, planners frequently turn to overhead walkways or to underground corridors. These are illustrated in Figures 6–11 and 6–12.

3. *Working Conditions.* The major factors to be taken into consideration in connection with working conditions are listed and commented on below.

1. Illumination. (See Appendix IV C.)
   a) Lighting should be adequate and suited to the job.
   b) Use should be made of natural lighting when practicable.
   c) Artificial lighting should be immediately available for every work space because of possible dark days, night work, and the need for a high intensity of illumination on close work.
2. Ventilation.
   a) Must be adequately provided for in all areas.
   b) Special precautions should be taken in locating painting, plating, heat treating, etc., so that fumes may be removed because of the discomfort they cause, and to eliminate fire hazards.

Fig. 6–11. Overhead walkway for servicing and inspecting facilities. (By permission of The Austin Company.)

Fig. 6–12. Underground corridor for service areas and employee facilities. (By permission of Albert Kahn Associated Architects and Engineers.)

  c) Lavatories, locker rooms, showers, smoking rooms, etc., should be located for convenient access and provided with good ventilation.
3. Heating.
  a) Adequate heat must be provided for every work area.
  b) Building construction should be planned so that the layout of the heating systems provides for convenience in maintenance, additions, and alterations.
4. Noise and Vibration.
  These are two of the chief causes of unpleasantness, annoyance, and letdown in production efficiency in industrial plants. They can be overcome to a certain extent by:
  a) Proper location or isolation of such equipment.
  b) Proper installation of equipment, both in fastening to the floor and in an enclosure if necessary.
  c) Proper selection of purchased equipment.
  d) Proper design of any equipment made in the plant.
5. Employee Facilities.
  In planning the layout, special consideration must be given to providing facilities for rest, recreation, etc. This subject is covered in Chapter 8.
6. Safety.
  The problem of safe working conditions is one of the most critical facing industrial management. Safety records are, in the long run, constantly improving due to the increased emphasis that is being placed on this phase of activity. Factors to be considered in plant layout, from a safety point of view, are:
  a) Aisle location and aisle widths.
  b) Machine location in relation to surroundings.
  c) Machine and conveyor guards.
  d) Type of flooring.
  e) Floor load limits.
  f) Provision for fire protection—extinguishers, sprinkler systems, exits, etc.
  g) First aid facilities.
  h) Light and ventilation.

4. *Cost.* Although it will not be considered in detail here, it is obvious that no phase of the layout planning process can escape the close scrutiny of cost justification. Every decision made will cost more or less than some other alternative. The least costly practical alternative should be chosen in all cases.

5. *Volume of Production.* The desired sales and production volume was discussed in Chapter 4 under Sales Department and Top Management contributions to the planning process. No single factor is of greater importance to layout planning than the quantity to be manufactured.

6. *Number of Parts.* Of great importance is the number of parts making up the product. Think for a moment of the differences in complexity of the flow pattern for such varying products as:

1. Yo-yo	5. Radio
2. Foot stool	6. Typewriter
3. Bicycle	7. Automobile
4. Refrigerator	8. Aircraft

Note how the greater the number of components, the more complex must be the flow pattern and, likewise, the more detailed and accurate must be the plans for the production facilities.

7. *Specific Requirement of Activities.* Because of their unusual characteristics, some activities require special treatment in their relationships to the rest of the plant operations. Some examples are:

Type of Process or Material	Special Requirements
Heat treating	Ventilation, fire protection
Painting	Ventilation, fire protection, heating
Plating	Ventilation, protection against acid and fumes, electrical insulation
Forging	Ventilation, heat removal, noise, and vibration dampening
Foundry	Heat removal, ventilation, fire protection
Power house	Heat and dirt removal, noise dampening
Heavy parts	Facilities for materials handling
Final assembly	Nearness to shipping or stock room
Inspection	Air conditioning, central location
Precision assembly	Air conditioning
Inflammable materials	Ventilation, fire protection

8. *Number of Operations.* As was indicated in Number 6 above (Number of Parts), the number of operations on each part is a major factor in planning the flow pattern. For instance, a part requiring only an operation or two will probably require only a machine or two and, consequently, little space and few people to perform the work. Contrast this with the example on page 37 where a single part required 39 machines, 194 tools, and 157 gages. This factor will be explored later when Operation Process Charts are presented as a means of analyzing part and operation interrelationships.

9. *Sequence of Operations.* As pointed out in Chapter 4, the production routing lists the operations which must be performed on each component of a product and the order in which they are to be performed. Frequently this sequence of operations becomes the physical order in which the equipment is arranged for their performance. This topic will be discussed in greater detail in subsequent chapters.

10. *Number of Subassemblies.* A subassembly is the assembly of parts into a unit of the final assembly such as a refrigerator door, an automobile instrument panel, a clock motor, a desk drawer, etc. Subassemblies are made for specific reasons, for example:

1. To facilitate the handling of smaller or larger parts at the assembly point
2. To shorten the general assembly line, where the subassembly requires much space
3. To reduce final assembly time if a subassembly requires a greater amount of time than can conveniently be fitted into the operations planned for the line
4. To separate from the line any equipment, the nature of which would interfere with the line
5. To reduce complications on the line when a part must be machined after it is assembled, and the processing equipment could not well be fitted into the line
6. When the subassembled unit requires testing before becoming a part of the final assembly
7. When the subassembled part may become a part of any one of several different products

Each subassembly is, in a sense, an interruption in the over-all assembly process and must be carefully worked into the flow pattern to cause as little disruption of the over-all flow as is possible.

11. *Process vs. Product Layout.* There are two basic and common methods of arranging equipment—the process method and the product method.

In the *process method* machines of the same or a similar kind for the performance of a particular type of operation are grouped in one area, such as all the drill presses in one area or department, all the lathes in another, etc. A part being worked on then travels from area to area according to the established sequence of operations, where the proper machines are located for each operation.

When the product is not, or cannot be standardized, or where the quantity of similar parts or products in process at any one time is low, then the process-type layout is more desirable because of its flexibility.

In the *product method,* individual machines and other manufacturing equipment are arranged in the order of the processes called for on the Production Routing. Each part travels from one machine, for instance, a drill press, to the succeeding machine, say a lathe, for the next operation, and so on through the entire cycle of operations required to complete it. The path for each part is in effect a straight line.

If the product is standardized and is made in large quantities, the product method of layout is desirable.

This latter type of layout is used in modern mass production plants, such as those found in the automobile, electrical appliance, and similar large-scale manufacturing enterprises.

Usually all the equipment necessary to produce a part is located in one area. On a piston, for instance, a machine is provided for each operation, from the first turning operation to the last inspection; and the machines are arranged in sequence so that the part can be literally passed from one operator to the next.

Each of the methods is illustrated in Figure 6–13.

The advantages of each method may be summarized as follows: [1]

ADVANTAGES OF PROCESS LAYOUT

A. Lower investment in machines because of less duplication. Only enough machines of each kind are necessary to handle normal maximum load instead of one in each product line. Overtime hours usually will take care of overloads.

B. Machines can be kept busy most of the time because the number of machines of each kind usually is held to the number needed for normal production.

C. Wide flexibility in getting work done. Possible to assign jobs to any machine in the same class available at the time.

D. Workers are more skilled because they must know how to run any machine —small or large—in the group, and how to set up work, perform special operations, gage the work, and qualify as mechanics instead of operatives.

E. Foremen and supervisors become skilled and efficient in the operation of their respective kinds of equipment and are able to direct the set-up and performance of all jobs done on this equipment.

F. Manufacturing costs can be held down. Labor costs may be higher per unit under peak loads, but will be less under low production, than on a product line. Unit overhead costs will be lower under moderate production. Hence, total costs may be lower when the plant is not near peak capacity.

G. Failures of equipment do not hold up a succession of operations. Work is merely transferred to another machine, if available, or a slight change in scheduling is made if the job is "rush" and no machines are idle at the time.

ADVANTAGES OF PRODUCT LAYOUT

A. Flow of work is over direct mechanical routes, which cuts down delays in manufacturing.

B. Less material handling because of shorter travel of work over a succession of adjacent machines or work stations.

C. Close coordination of manufacturing because of the definite sequence of operations over adjacent machines. Less likelihood of loss of materials or delays in operations.

D. Less total time for production. Delays between machines avoided.

E. Smaller quantities of work in progress. Little banking of materials at individual operations and in transit between operations.

F. Smaller floor areas occupied per unit of product because of concentration of manufacturing.

G. Limited amount of inspection, perhaps only one before product goes on line, one after it comes off of line, and small amount of patrolling inspection in between.

H. Production control greatly simplified. Visual control replaces much of the paper work. Fewer forms and records used. Work checked on and off the production line. Fewer work orders, inspection tickets, time tickets, move orders, etc. Less accounting and lower clerical costs.

I. It is easy to break in workers on any operation in the production line.

[1] Alford, L. P. and J. R. Bangs, *Production Handbook* (New York: The Ronald Press Co., 1947), pp. 757–761.

OPERATION SEQUENCE

Part	Oper. 1	Oper. 2	Oper. 3
A	lathe	drill	lathe
B	drill	mill	
C	lathe	mill	drill

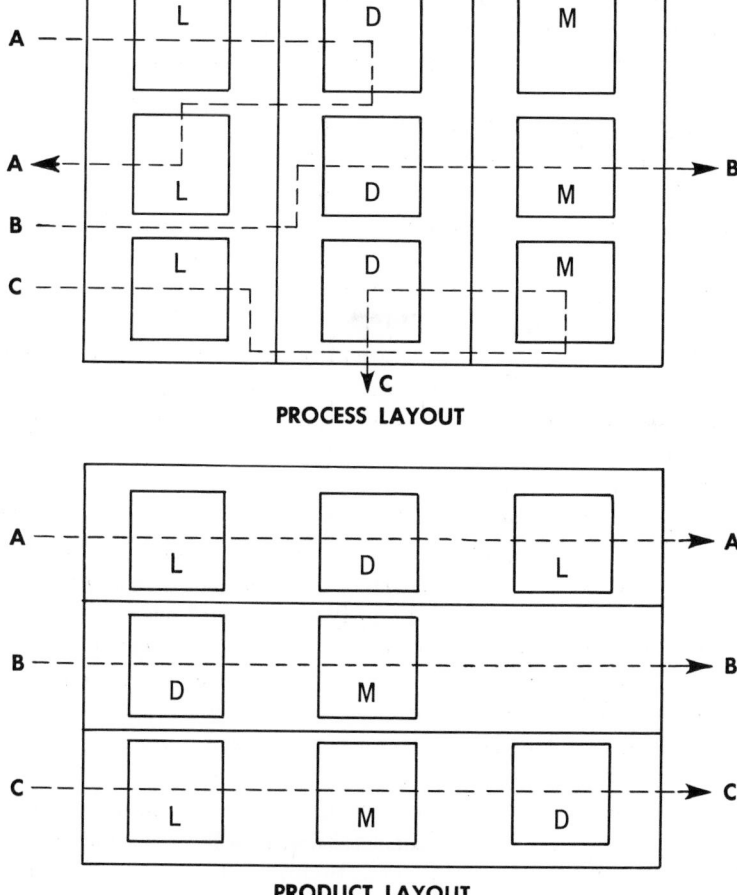

Fig. 6–13. Process and product methods of machine arrangement.

12. *Quantity of Equipment.* Not only the sequence of operations (as indicated in 11, above) but the number of machines and/or pieces of equipment will determine the flow pattern. If several work stations are required to perform one operation—because of its relatively slow rate of production—then the preceding machine, or machines, must "split" their output to feed it to the several succeeding machines and vice versa. This not only indicates what the flow pattern must be but also complicates the materials handling, as will be seen in later chapters.

13. *Space Requirements of Equipment.* It must always be remembered in layout work that space must be allowed not only for a machine, but also for the operator; the material to be worked on; the work completed; auxiliary equipment such as benches, chutes, slides, gondolas, inspection devices, tool and blueprint racks, etc.; access to the machine for repairs, and access to any safety devices for emergency use.

In addition, space must be left for moving equipment in or out in case of changes in layout. This is particularly a problem when columns, walls, nearness to elevator shafts, etc., are involved.

14. *Required Flow Between Work Areas.* As indicated many times previously, the work in the plant usually flows from one workplace to the next. This, of course, will be an important factor in determining the flow pattern. Further complications may arise if the part must go to another general area in the course of its processing. This will also be true if it must backtrack to make use of a machine a second time because it is not economical to provide two identical machines.

15. *Preliminary Materials Handling Plans.* As discussed in a previous chapter, the materials handling plans and/or equipment may have been decided upon in a general way prior to the establishment of the over-all flow pattern. If this is true, it will be an important factor in determining the flow pattern.

16. *Location of Shipping and Receiving.* The existing and/or proposed location of the shipping and receiving area will establish the beginning and ending points of the flow pattern. This was shown in Figure 6–7.

17. *Storage Requirements.* In nearly every plant area, there will be a need for the storage of work awaiting processing, or awaiting movement to another area after processing. The amount—size and volume—of storage space required must be planned and will depend on a number of factors.

18. *Aisle Area.* The aisle area in a plant is intended fundamentally for traffic and transportation but is often used for many other purposes. In order to insure adequate space throughout the production areas, there is a tendency, in planning new construction, to allow too much aisle area. In existing plants, on the other hand, there is a tendency to cut down on the aisles by using part of the allotted area for stock, additional equipment, etc.

Considerable planning should go into the decision as to aisle width. Aisles are non-productive areas and each square foot used for aisles is lost to production. Production "pays" for its floor area; aisles do not. Aisles are discussed further in a later chapter.

19. *Desired Location of Departments.* In addition to some of the factors discussed above, the location of production areas might well be based on the proper combination of:

1. Number of pieces to be handled per time unit
2. Rough weight of each piece
3. Weight of stock removed from each piece at each operation
4. Distance in number of feet, over which rough piece, semifinished piece, or scrap must be moved

There will then be a tendency for departments working on heavy parts to be located near the receiving department. As the manufacturing progresses, the parts should be kept moving in the general direction of the assembly line or shipping department.

20. *Desired Location of Service Areas.* Service areas can be divided into two broad classes:

1. Serving production
2. Serving personnel

A partial list of service areas which must be included in most plants might be as follows:

SERVING PRODUCTION	SERVING PERSONNEL
1. Inspection	1. Cafeteria
2. Machine repair	2. Hospital
3. Maintenance	3. Lavatories and showers
4. Materials handling equipment storage	4. Locker rooms
5. Power house or electrical distribution centers	5. Offices
6. Receiving	6. Parking lot
7. Shipping	7. Recreation area
8. Elevators	8. Stairways
9. Storage space	9. Time clock stations
10. Tool room and tool crib	10. Fire escapes
11. Offices	
12. Heating and ventilating equipment	

When planning the location of the areas providing these facilities, the following factors should be considered:

1. Number of persons using service
2. Frequency of use
3. Equipment and floor space required
4. Physical factors (heat, danger, height)

21. *Supervisory Requirements.* As was indicated in Chapter 1, effective supervision is an objective of good plant layout. Only if the work supervised by one person is relatively centrally located can he oversee it effectively. The layout should be constructed in such a way that each supervisor can conveniently "cover" his area in a reasonable amount of time.

22. *Production Control.* Plant design and layout have a great effect on the facility of controlling production. Factors in design and layout affecting production control are:

1. Number of floors
2. Shape of building
3. Lines of flow of work
4. Size of departments
5. Shape of departments

An ideal situation might be to have a long narrow, one-story building housing a continuous process, or an assembly line, with feeder lines at right angles. As we deviate from this situation to multistory, or odd-shaped buildings and departments, the problem of keeping track of production becomes increasingly difficult.

23. *Flexibility.* Flexibility is one of the most important characteristics of a good plant layout. In nearly every instance, the layout under consideration at the moment will be subject to change in the future. Therefore, one must always keep in mind that the space may someday be occupied by activity of a greatly different nature. For example, an area might be planned for use as a light assembly department requiring a relatively low overhead clearance of 12 feet. Future plans might develop for the use of this area as a machine shop or even a storage area—both of which would be much more efficient with a higher overhead clearance of 14 to 20 feet. Similar consideration should be given to floor construction and load limits, utility feeders, column spacing, etc.

24. *Expandability.* In much the same line of thinking as above, an area may, at a later date, require expansion. Any flow pattern or building should be planned to permit easy expansion. This is accomplished in three general ways: (1) locate the structure on the site to permit expansion on two or three sides; (2) construct these two or three walls for ease of dismantling, if necessary; and (3) locate equipment and facilities to permit this expansion to take place with a minimum of disruption to present activities. This factor will be discussed in more detail in subsequent chapters.

25. *Building Type.* The building itself, either existing or as proposed, will often have a bearing on the layout. If the building exists, the layout may have to be fitted into it without major building alterations. If a new building is being considered, it can be planned around the layout.

26. *Number of Floors.* In new buildings, single stories are more common than multiple floors. However, many situations call for multiple floors and, of course, many older buildings have more than one story. The number of floors has a considerable influence on the flow pattern.

27. *External Transportation Facilities.* It goes without saying that the external facilities available for transportation will affect the flow pattern. As indicated under number 16, above, the receiving and shipping areas are the beginning and end of the flow pattern; and the external transportation facilities may dictate these locations. The facilities may be highway, rail, water, or even air; but their relative proximity to the building site will be a major factor in determining the starting point for the flow pattern.

CONCLUSION

As indicated at the start of this section, the factors discussed above must be considered during the process of planning any flow pattern or layout. Admittedly there are many, but all are important. The good plant layout engineer has bumped into or stumbled over them so many times that he has them memorized to be sure they won't be overlooked. It would be well for the beginner to memorize them also to avoid the possibility of overlooking an important factor.

QUESTIONS

1. What is meant by "flow pattern"?
2. What is the over-all objective of a flow pattern?
3. Why is it necessary to *plan* a flow pattern?
4. What are the advantages of planning a flow pattern?
5. What is meant by a "master plan"?
6. Of what value is a master plan to an already existing plant?
7. Name and discuss some of the flow planning principles.
8. Name and indicate the types of general flow patterns and the reasons or uses of each.
9. What is meant by the "levels of activity" in a plant?
10. Differentiate between process and product layout. Give several advantages or uses of each.
11. Why are shipping and receiving considered key activities in planning a flow pattern?
12. How can a flow pattern affect supervisory duties in a plant?
13. Why are flexibility and expandability of importance in flow planning?

7

Receiving, Storage, Warehousing and Shipping Activities

Introduction. Having discussed briefly the many factors involved in planning the flow pattern, it is now necessary to consider in some detail a few of the more important factors. This chapter will cover the items noted in the title. Chapter **8** will deal with the more important service functions serving both production and personnel.

The major activity areas concerned with the "non-productive" movement and handling of materials are classified as:

Receiving—getting the materials, etc., into the plant
Storage—safekeeping and issuing of materials, etc., before and during the production operations
Warehousing—safekeeping of finished goods
Shipping—issuing and distributing the finished goods to customers, etc.

Since these functions are closely interrelated, they are brought together in this chapter. Each will be discussed separately, with one exception. It will be found that many factors which must be considered in planning for one are either similar to or exactly the same as for others. Examples of these are docks, bay size, and doors.

In most cases, these will be discussed only once—when they first appear as major factors. However, they must be considered as important factors in all four of the activity areas. It might be well to study this entire chapter before attempting to plan any of the activities covered. This will assure consideration of the many overlapping aspects of the functions involved.

RECEIVING

Definition and Scope. Receiving is that activity which is concerned with the orderly receipt of *all* materials coming into the plant and their proper disposition to the various functions requiring the items received. It includes such responsibilities as:

100

1. Unloading materials from carriers
2. Unpacking from shipping containers
3. Identifying and sorting materials
4. Checking receipts against packing slips
5. Recording evidence of receipt on receiving slip
6. Noting shortages, damage, defects, etc.
7. Maintenance of adequate records
8. Disposition of materials to areas of use

A function closely related to Receiving, but usually not under its jurisdiction, is Receiving Inspection. Receiving Inspection normally reports to the Quality Control, or Inspection Department, and is responsible for the careful inspection of all incoming production and supply items. From a plant layout point of view, this means that the Receiving Inspection area should most logically be located adjacent to the Receiving area. The Receiving Inspection function will normally require space for:

1. Orderly temporary storage of materials awaiting inspection
2. Adequate space for the storage, handling, and work areas necessary for carrying out inspection operations
3. Area for temporary storage of inspected items, awaiting delivery to their respective points of use or storage

Development of Receiving Requirements. The planning of the receiving area requires consideration of:

1. Characteristics of receipts
2. Determination of the work load
3. Handling methods
4. Space requirements

The actual or expected receipts should be analyzed in order to determine the various types of material to be received; the package, unit, or container each will arrive in; and the destination (within the plant) of each type of item. For each type, there should also be made an analysis or estimate of:

1. Item sizes—for storage space
2. Item weights—for storage and handling methods
3. Volume of receipts—for total "work space" required

The actual or expected work load should be established by a study of:

1. Number of receipts per unit of time
2. Pieces per shipment received
3. Weight per shipment received
4. Number of trucks arriving per period of time
5. Volume by truck
6. Number of rail cars per time period
7. Volume by rail

All the above data should be worked out to arrive at an approximation of the amount of space required for the various Receiving Department activities.

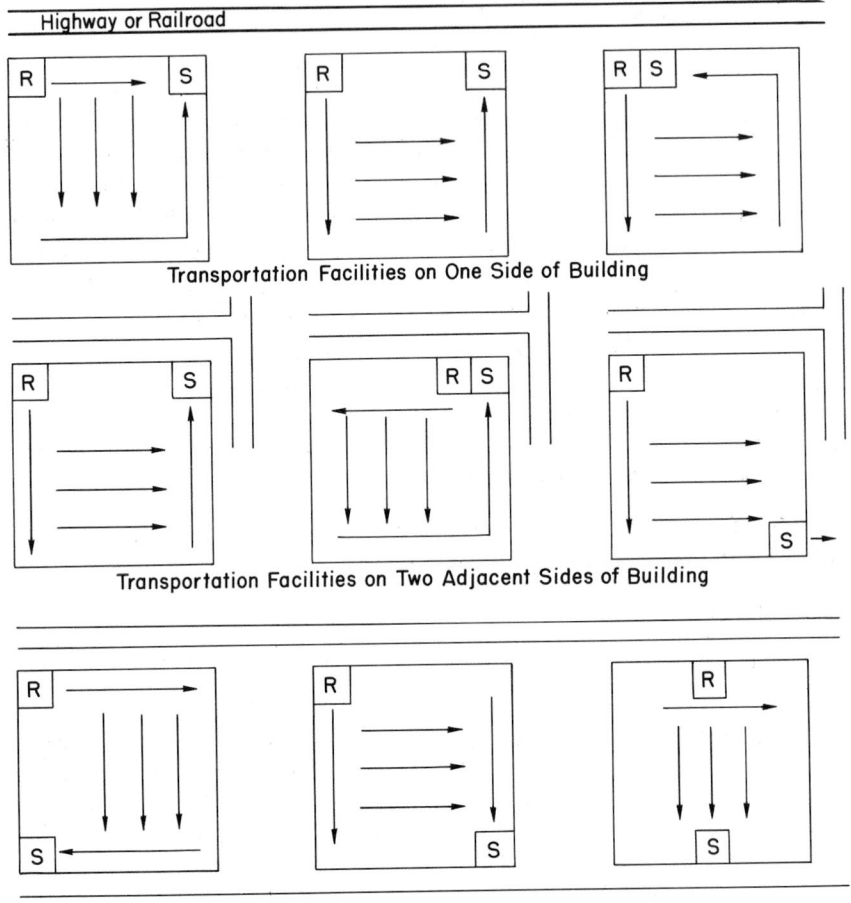

Fig. 7–1. Possible arrangements of shipping and receiving areas.

Handling methods can be accurately determined only after having considered the physical characteristics of all the types of items received. In most plants, the minimum equipment would consist of a two-wheeled hand truck and a fork lift truck for unloading, handling, and storage; a conveyor for movement of certain items to or through receiving inspection; and space or storage equipment for holding receipts pending disposition.

Planning Receiving Space Requirements. In addition to the determination of the space requirements for the various activity areas mentioned above, there are several general factors concerning the physical facilities which must be considered. Among them are:

1. *Location of Receiving Area.* As has been mentioned previously, the Receiving Department is the beginning of the entire materials flow pattern. Of necessity, it must be located conveniently to the external transportation facilities—highways, railroad tracks, or waterways. In the case of a new plant facility then, the location of these transportation facilities may dictate the location of the Receiving function. In other cases, the road or rails can be brought to the desired plant location. Considering the two alternatives, (1) locating Receiving near transportation facilities and (2) extending transportation facilities to the desired location of the Receiving area, Figure 7–1 illustrates several possible arrangements.

Where the manufacturing activity is large enough to warrant it, the local government unit and the railroad will frequently go out of their way to provide desired transportation facilities. When activity is small, it is more common to adjust the plant facilities to the existing transportation facilities.

It should be noted that frequently the Shipping area will be located adjacent to the Receiving activity. There are two major reasons for this: existing location of transportation facilities and efficient use of personnel in the smaller plant.

2. *Docks.* Both truck and rail docks may be required and will be considered here—whether for Receiving or Shipping. Since truck docks are more universally used, their requirements are presented in greater detail. Factors for consideration and related facts are as follows (based on *Modern Methods of Dock Design,* Kelley Co., Inc., Milwaukee, Wis.)

    a) Approach—for 8-feet wide vehicles operating in two directions, minimum width 20 feet

    b) Right-angle intersections and curves—minimum turning radius of 35 feet; 50 feet desirable

    c) Apron (space required for maneuvering and spotting truck)

Over-all Length of Tractor-Trailer	Width of Berth	Apron Space
	10′	46′
35′	12′	43′
	14′	39′
	10′	48′
40′	12′	44′
	14′	42′
	10′	57′
45′	12′	49′
	14′	48′

d) Width of berth—10 to 14 feet

e) Overhead clearance—14 feet

f) Dock height—46 to 54 inches (48 inches common)

g) Platform depth—15 feet

h) Platform width—12 feet per truck × maximum number of trucks at peak period

i) Column spacing—24 feet

j) Doors—overhead type, 9 feet by 9 feet minimum

k) Lighting—10 foot-candles minimum

l) Ramps—maximum recommended grades

Type of Equipment	Max. Grade
Power operated hand trucks	3%
Powered platform trucks	7%
Low-lift pallet trucks	10%
Electric fork trucks	10%
Gasoline fork trucks	15%

m) Dock "boards," etc. (for bridging gap between truck and dock)

(1) Portable

(2) Built-in to dock, mechanical or hydraulic

(3) Truck leveling devices, built into truck well or pit

(4) Wedges—on pit floor, for backing truck up on, to match dock height

For similar information regarding railroad track and building relationships, refer to Figure 7–2.

3. *Office.* Depending on the amount of Receiving activity, an office might consist of anything from a "stand-up" desk to a full-fledged office.

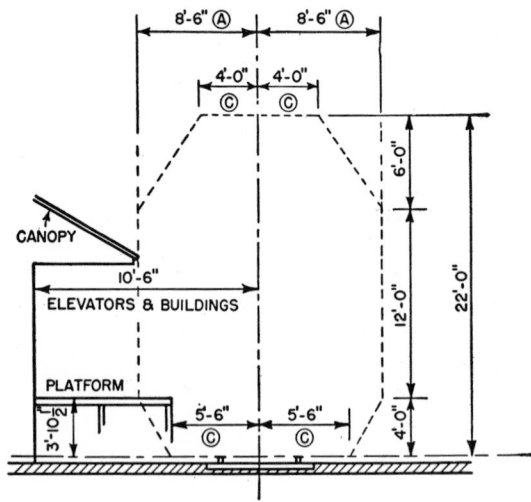

Fig. 7–2. Necessary clearances for a railroad siding. (By permission of Materials Handling Engineering.)

The actual space will have to be determined by the number of persons required to handle the record keeping and other paper work. For estimating purposes, an area of approximately 100 square feet per person could be allowed.

Receiving Area Requirements and Location. With the above information on the requirements of the Receiving activity, the plant layout engineer should "rough out" the over-all area to be allocated.

For the necessary procedures for planning, the space requirements, refer back to the section on Development of Receiving Requirements and analyze the receipts. If desired, a rough estimate of over-all space can be made at this time, and the detailed planning completed later.

It will also be necessary to determine the Receiving location before going much farther with the planning of the materials flow pattern.

STORAGE

Definition and Scope. Storage is that activity which is concerned with the orderly safekeeping of *all* materials in the plant prior to their use— between production operations and in certain situations (excepting the warehousing of finished goods) while awaiting final disposition of the materials. It includes such responsibilities as:

1. Storage of raw materials awaiting manufacturing operations
2. Storage of purchased parts (finished items) awaiting use in manufacturing
3. Storage of supplies and other items used in the plant (tools, manufacturing supplies, maintenance supplies, office supplies, packaging supplies, etc.)
4. Storage of manufactured materials between operations and while awaiting assembly
5. Storage of scrap, rejects, and salvage items awaiting disposition
6. Storage of unused manufacturing equipment, auxiliary equipment, office equipment, materials handling equipment, containers, etc.
7. Issuing items as required
8. Maintaining proper records of receipts and issues
9. Taking inventory of materials in storage

It will be noted that the above excludes the warehousing of the finished product, since that activity is usually a separate function and is accomplished in a separate location. Those factors concerned with warehousing (that differ from storage) will be discussed later in this chapter.

The general objectives of good storage methods are:

1. Maximum use of building cube
2. Effective use of time, labor, and equipment
3. Ready accessibility of all items
4. Rapid, easy movement of materials

5. Positive item identification
6. Maximum protection of materials
7. Neat and orderly appearance

Consideration of the various items discussed below will aid materially in the achievement of these objectives.

Development of Storage Requirements. Before it is possible to determine actual storage space requirements, it is necessary to consider a number of factors bearing on the eventual space needed. It will be necessary to make many decisions in light of these factors, as the planning process develops.

It should be noted here that much of the following discussion pertains also to finished goods warehousing, and much of the warehouse planning procedure is nearly identical.

The factors for consideration in the development of storage requirements are as follows:

1. Storage activities
   a) Receiving of materials from the Receiving Department
   b) Sorting of the materials
   c) Storage of the materials
   d) Handling methods
   e) Issuing of materials as required
   f) Keeping necessary records
2. Materials to be stored
   a) Types of items
       (1) Raw materials
       (2) Purchased finished items
       (3) Supplies (manufacturing, maintenance, office, packaging, etc.)
   b) Physical characteristics of items
       (1) Size
       (2) Weight
       (3) Bulk
       (4) Shape
       (5) Quantity
       (6) Nature (hazardous, perishable, expensive, etc.)
   c) Relative activity of items (volume of movement per time period)
   d) Storage location of items
       (1) In "storage" area, stock room, etc.
       (2) In manufacturing area) general area or
       (3) At assembly   ) at point of use
       (4) Out of doors (see later discussion)
3. Storage methods
   a) Bulk (large lots of material)
   b) Rack

  c) Unit load
  d) Shelf
  e) Bin
  f) Special (bulk materials, bars, etc.)
  g) Issuing or dispatching procedures
  h) Space arrangement
  i) Storage aids
  j) "Storage" conveyors
4. Handling methods
  a) Into storage area
  b) At storage area
  c) Out of storage area
5. Physical characteristics of space
  a) Floors
  b) Doors
  c) Aisles
  d) Docks
  e) Clear height
  f) Elevators
  g) Lights
  h) Column spacing

All of the above will have an important bearing on the actual storage space requirements. This text cannot possibly cover the ramifications of all these factors, but excellent detailed information can be found in the references in the bibliography.

Planning Storage Space Requirements. Having given consideration to the factors listed and discussed above, the plant layout engineer must reduce the basic storage data to the actual space required for materials storage. It must be remembered that the various materials may be stored in at least three locations:

1. Stock room (awaiting issue)
  a) Large items
  b) Large quantities (bulk of item)
  c) Items used in several places
  d) "Rough" stores, raw materials
2. In departments where used
  a) All items, if practicable
  b) Amount used in relatively short period
  c) Items not used elsewhere
  d) Materials in-process
3. At point-of-use (work area or station)
  a) Quantity for immediate use
  b) Small items (total quantity)
  c) Materials in-process

It should be noted that to keep overhead costs at a minimum, materials handling must be also kept to a minimum. This means the ideal situation would be to unload an item from a carrier and deliver it directly to the point-of-use. Except for the necessary operation of receiving inspection, this should be an over-all objective in layout planning. However, it is not always practicable. Figure 7–3 shows an example of point-of-use storage where the *entire* inventory of all items used in an assembly are stored as near the actual work place as is physically possible. The material above normal reach height is all "reserve" storage. Figure 7–4 shows the portable work bench removed for restocking the reserve supply by fork lift truck. Notice the air and electrical connections hanging down for connection to the portable work bench.

Fig. 7–3. Point-of-use storage. (By permission of Clarke Floor Machine Co.)

Fig. 7–4. Re-stocking point-of-use materials supply. (By permission of Clarke Floor Machine Co.)

In any case, it will be necessary to make an analysis of all material or material types to be received and stored. Basic data required on each item will include:

1. Annual usage
2. Normal inventory amount
3. Normal purchasing quantity
4. Physical volume of amount to be stored in each area
5. Type and size of container in which received [1] and/or stored
6. Desired storage location(s)
7. And others, as found on Figure 7–5

[1] Whenever possible, vendors should be required to pack materials in containers which can be stored "as is" and used as dispensers at the point of use.

These factors can be reduced to storage space required with the aid of a Storage Analysis Sheet, as shown in Figure 7–5. In many cases, a few simple calculations will suffice to make an approximation of the storage space required at any one location.

Assume that production requirements call for the storage of 2 weeks' supply of a certain casting. Production is at the rate of 50 units per hour, or 4,000 units for two 40-hour weeks. If one casting is approximately 6 × 6 × 6 inches, then eight castings will require 1 cubic foot. A 3′ × 5′ × 2½′ container will hold:

$$3' \times 5' \times 2\frac{1}{2}' \times 8 \text{ per cu. ft.} = 300 \text{ units}$$

then 4,000 can be contained in:

$$\frac{4,000}{300} = 13\frac{1}{3}, \text{ or 14 containers.}$$

If containers can be stacked only 3 high, because of floor-load or ceiling-height limitation, then:

$$\frac{14}{3} = 4\frac{2}{3} \text{ or 5 stacks will be required.}$$

As each stack requires 15 square feet of floor space, then 75 square feet of floor space will be required to store a 2-week supply of the castings.

Similar calculations should be made for all parts of considerable size, whether they are raw materials, parts in process, or finished parts.

By means of the Storage Analysis Sheet and/or such calculations as shown above, it can be determined how many square (or cubic) feet of storage space will be required for rough materials (stores), in-process materials, or finished parts (stock). Figure 7–6 shows how a similar form was used for tabulating the data for the area shown in Figure 7–3.

Location of General Storage Area. The *general* storage area, or stockroom, must obviously be located as conveniently as possible between receiving and production. This will minimize the materials handling activity.

Outdoor Storage. In many cases, materials can be stored out of doors. The primary reasons for this are:

1. Lower or no construction cost.
2. Protective coatings and covers provide adequate covering.
3. Many materials need no protection from weather.
4. Availability of improved vehicles for outdoor use.

Regardless of the type of materials stored outside, much the same planning must be done as for indoor storage. Different factors for consideration are the yard surface, access roadways, location, and amount of pro-

Analyzed By: A.M.J.   Date: Mar. 17

COMPANY __Powrarm__

☐ Finished Parts
☐ Finished Product

PRODUCT __Model 1__

ANNUAL PROD'N. __100,000__

STORAGE ANALYSIS SHEET

| ITEM OR PART | | | Size in inches | | | | QUANTITY | | | RECEIPT | | HANDLING UNIT | | | | | | | SPACE REQUIREMENTS | | | | | | STOR. LOC. |
No.	Description	No. per assy.	L	W	Ht	Wt	Max. Inv.	Mo. Reqt.	Norm. Rec't.	Freq.	Carr. Type	Type	L	W	Ht	Wt	Items/ Hdlg. Unit	Hdlg. Units For Max. Invent.	Bulk or Pallet — no. hdlg. units high	no. base units	sq.ft. per base unit	sq.ft. for max. no.hdlg. units	cu.ft. for max. no.hdlg. units	Shelf bin	
1	Base	1	6"	6"	6"	10#	4000	8000	2000	1/wk	truck	pallet box	5'	3'	2½'	8000#	300	14	3	5	15	75	526	- -	Rec.

Fig. 7–5. Storage Analysis Sheet—receiving.

STORAGE ANALYSIS SHEET FOR 610 – 620

QUARTERLY SALES 610-355 620-200

PRODUCTION LOT SIZE 610-120 620-56

CODE NO.	Qty	ITEM DESCRIPTION	PURCH.	QT. LOT	L	W	H	TYPE	SIZE	NO. PCS.	PER PALL.	L	W	H
213804	1	Grommet	5000	555	5/8	5/8	1/2	Carton						
627802	1	Sheet CR/SL	300	555	33-1/2	27	3/16				1000	36	36	62
627804	1	Sheet DC/SL	300	555	25-3/8	22-1/4	3/16				1000	36	36	62
628603	1	Tank-10 Gal-6100	355	120	16-7/8	16-7/8	20	Carton	17x17x21	1	12	39	39	55
690204	1	Adapter-Tk.-63	900	555	5-3/4	2-1/2	1-3/4	Carton	17x17x18	250				
690206	1	Adapter-Bag	660	555	16-3/8	16-3/8	1-1/2	Carton	17x17x18	20	130	36	36	36
690208	1	Adapter-Blower-6-3	350	555	3-3/4	2-1/2	1-3/4	Carton	17x17x18	250				
690602	1	Filter-Bag	800	555	13	11	1/2	Carton	17x17x18	150				
690804	2	Bracket-Hole 63	1110	370	2-5/8	7/8	1	Carton	17x17x18	1000				
690806	1	Bracket 60	555	185	2-1/4	2-1/4	2	"	17x17x18	500				
690808	1	Bracket-CSTR-63	555	185	6	3-3/4	4	Carton			300	36	36	36
631103	4	Bushing	3000	2220	9/16	9/16	7/16	Carton	12x12x12	500				
631106	1	Bushing Valve Cup	1000	185	1-1/2	1-1/2	1/4	Carton	12x12x12	1000				
617002	1	Carton	555	185	59-1/2	50-3/4	5/8				150	59-1/2	50-3/4	75
632002	4	Clamp – 63	2220	740	2	2	5/8	Carton	17x17x16	2500				
632004	2	Clamp – 63	1110	370	3-1/2	2	1-1/4	Carton	17x17x18	400				
632006	1	Clamp-Motor	600	555	15-1/2	15-1/2	3	Carton	16x16x24	22	440	41	41	87
632008	1	Clamp Valve Tube	1000	555	3-1/4	3-1/4	1/16	Carton	10x10x6	1000				
632102	4	Retainer Clip	2500	2220	1/4	1/4	1/16	Carton						
632502	1	Cover-Lid	700	555	16-1/8	16-1/8	2-3/4	"			60	36	36	36
632504	2	Cover-Motor	700	555	8-1/4	8-1/4	4	"			200	36	36	36
632402	1	Valve Cup	600	555	2	2	1-3/8	Carton	17x17x18	800				
632404	1	Cage	1000	555	10-1/2	10-1/2	10-1/2	Carton	28x24x36	25	200	56	48	72
632410	1	Can Valve	700	555	6	6	6-1/8	Carton			180	36	36	36
632712	1	Tank-Deflector	555	185	4-1/2	3-3/8	2	Carton	17x17x14	400				
633402	1	Gasket	555	185	2-3/4	2-3/4	1/16	"	9x9x6	500				
633404	2	Gasket-Motor	1000 1110	370	8	8	3/4	"	36x36x36	700	36	36	36	

Fig. 7–6. Storage analysis chart. (By permission of Clarke Floor Machine Co.)

tection required. The requirements of various degrees of protection are shown in Figure 7–7.

An idea of the costs of various types of storage space is shown in Figure 7–8.

An interesting development in "outdoor" storage is the inflatable structure shown in Figure 7–9. This structure is held up by low air pressure from a blower. The bottom is held in place by sand in a tubular segment of the structure.

How Material Protection Requirements Affect Yard Storage							
Material Protection Required	**Elements Required in System**						
	Land Area	Surfacing	Location or Identification	Protective Cover or Packaging	Fencing	Lighting	Watchman	Material Handling Equipment
None	R	N	R	N	N	N	N	R
Weather and Atmosphere	R	N	R	R	N	N	N	R
Theft	R	N	R	D	R	D	D	R
Weather, Atmosphere and Theft	R	N	R	R	R	R	D	R

R – Required　　　　　　　　　N – Not required

D – Depends on value and ease with which it can be carried off

Fig. 7–7. Requirements for storage protection. (By permission of Modern Materials Handling.)

WAREHOUSING

Definition and Scope. Warehousing is that activity which is concerned with the orderly storage and issuing of finished goods or products. It includes such responsibilities as:

1. Receiving of finished goods from production
2. Orderly and safe storage of goods
3. Order picking, to meet shipping requirements

4. Packing of items for shipment
5. Maintaining proper records

It is obvious at this point that many of the factors involved in warehouse planning have been covered under receiving and storage. Several factors, peculiar to warehousing, will be detailed in this section.

STORAGE FACILITY COSTS

Storage Facility Type	Land Cost per Sq. Ft. Dollars	Building or Surface Cost per Sq. Ft. Dollars	10,000 Sq. Ft. of Storage Initial Cost, Dollars (Less Land)
Building — One story on slab with heat, light, offices and employee facilities	1.00	8.00— 15.00	80,000— 150,000
Building — Roof and lighting without sidewalls, heat, office space or employee facilities	1.00	4.00— 8.00	40,000— 80,000
Building — Rental with above facilities	—	2.00 yr.	—
Yard — Concrete surface	0.75	0.60	6,000
Yard — Black-top surface	0.75	0.15	1,500
Yard — Crushed stone surface	0.75	0.11	1,100
Yard — Undeveloped	0.75	—	—

Fig. 7–8. Storage facility cost. (By permission of Modern Materials Handling.)

Development of Warehousing Requirements. In general, the warehousing of finished goods or products will not involve as many different items as will the storage of raw materials or component parts. This is because many parts have been assembled into each finished product. Also, the finished products are more likely to be packaged into units lending themselves to easier handling and storage—such as cartons, boxes, crates, etc.

As with receiving and storage, the starting point for warehousing analysis is the physical characteristics of the items to be warehoused. Each item must be known, and certain facts about an item and its activity must be determined. The Warehouse Analysis Sheet, Figure 7–10, will serve as a guide in accumulating this data. The form may be used as follows:

A. Fill in columns 1 through 6.
B. Select pallet size and type. The more common pallet sizes are:

Rectangular	Area
24″ × 32″	5.33 sq. ft.
32″ × 40″	8.89
36″ × 42″	10.50
32″ × 48″	10.67
36″ × 48″	12.00
40″ × 48″	13.33
48″ × 60″	20.00
48″ × 72″	24.00
Square	
36″ × 36″	9.00
42″ × 42″	12.25
48″ × 48″	16.00

Fig. 7–9. Inflatable warehouse sustained by low pressure air from blower. (By permission of C.I.D. Air Structures Co.)

☐ Incoming Stock
☐ In-Process Materials
☐ Finished Parts
☒ Finished Product

STORAGE ANALYSIS SHEET

Analyzed By: A.M.J.
Date: Mar. 17

COMPANY Perfection Mfg. Co. PRODUCT Model 600 ANNUAL PROD'N. 4,800

ITEM OR PART							QUANTITY			RECEIPT		HANDLING UNIT							SPACE REQUIREMENTS							STOR. LOC.
			Size in inches																Bulk or Pallet					Shelf	bin	
No.	Description	No. per assy.	L	W	Ht	Wt	Max. Inv.	Mo. Reqt.	Norm. Rec't.	Freq.	Carr. Type	Type	L	W	Ht	Wt	Items/ Hdlg. Unit	Hdlg. Units For Max. Invent.	no. hdlg. units high	no. base units	sq.ft. per base unit	sq.ft. for max. no.hdlg. units	cu.ft. for max. no.hdlg. units			
1	Model 600	—	15	15	41	35	400	—	—	—	truck	pal-let	4'	4'	$7\frac{1}{2}$'	530#	18	23	3	8	16	128	2760	—	—	ship.

Fig. 7–10. Storage analysis sheet—finished product.

C. Pallet size will depend, to some extent, on:
1. Package, or item size.
2. Column spacing.
3. Carrier type and size.
4. Handling methods and/or equipment.

The above sizes have been designated as standard by the American Standards Association in cooperation with the technical societies and pallet users.

Determine size(s) to be used and fill in columns 7 and 8.

D. Select equipment (see Chapter 13).
1. Vehicle.
   a) Two-wheel hand truck (individual items).
   b) Stacker—with forward extending "outriggers" to balance load.
   c) Lift truck—counterbalanced.
   d) Tractor-trailer train.
2. Conveyors.
   a) Roller, wheel, belt.
   b) Tow line—overhead or under floor.
3. Racks.
   a) Permanent.
   b) Adjustable.
4. Pallet loader.
5. Storage aids.

The type(s) of equipment selected will have an important bearing on the method of warehousing, aisle width, space requirements, etc.

E. Determine arrangement(s)[2] of items on pallets and number of items per pallet. Fill in column 9.

F. Determine unit load height and fill in column 10.

G. Determine number of pallets required $\left(\dfrac{\text{col. 3}}{\text{col. 9}}\right)$ and fill in column 11.

H. Determine height to which pallets can be stacked and calculate number of pallets that can be stacked up. Enter this in column 12
$$\left(\frac{\text{clear ht.} - \text{sprinkler clearance}}{\text{col. 10}}\right).$$

I. Determine number of "base" pallets (on the floor) and enter in column 13
$$\left(\frac{\text{col. 11}}{\text{col. 12}}\right).$$

J. Determine space required.
1. Square feet (col. 8 × col. 13) and enter in column 14.
2. Cubic feet (col. 14 × col. 10 × col. 12) and enter in column 15.
3. Rack spaces (same as column 11, or calculate if more than one pallet per opening, as on bottom or top level. [See Figure 7–4.]) Enter in column 16.

[2] See *The Palletizer*, by Modern Materials Handling, for details of selecting pallet pattern.

At this point the figures in column 14 can be totaled. To this total must be added allowances for:

1. Aisles—for 1,000 lb. stacker, add 33 per cent.

      —for 1,000 lb. lift truck, add 36 per cent.
      —for 2,000 lb. lift truck, add 38 per cent.
      —for 3,000 lb. lift truck, add 47 per cent.

2. Columns (estimate 1 square foot per column).
3. Elevators and ramps (determine and add).
4. Office space (add square feet as required).
5. Marshalling area for receiving and issuing items (use 5 per cent of storage space).

The sum of the above figures will provide a satisfactory estimate for layout planning purposes. For more detailed information on warehouse planning, consult the references in the bibliography.

Columns 17 to 21 are used for calculating future warehousing allowances and are determined as follows:

Columns 17—expected per cent increase in volume
         18—per cent in col. 17 × col. 13
         19—per cent in col. 17 × col. 14
         20—per cent in col. 17 × col. 15
         21—per cent in col. 17 × col. 16

Automation in Warehousing. A recent development which should not be overlooked is the so-called "automatic" warehouse. Many periodicals have described such installations that are used primarily for the warehousing of large volumes of case items such as drugs, bottled goods, and food. Basically, the "automatic" warehouse is an installation of conveyors on which the goods are loaded, with the system controlled by push buttons, punched cards, or magnetic tape. An example is shown in Figure 7–11.

Warehouse Location. In general, the finished goods warehousing activity is located within the plant building, or at least on the plant property. It should be conveniently accessible from the end of the assembly "line" and/or packing area. It should be remembered that warehousing and shipping are closely related, if not one and the same general area, in many cases. Again, the finished goods warehousing might be advantageously located adjacent to the receiving and stock room—especially in the small plant where a small crew might handle both functions. Also, as discussed in Chapter 6, the location of external transportation facilities could be the governing factor in the location of the warehousing function and the related shipping activities.

Fig. 7–11. Automatic warehouse showing storage racks and console. (By permission of Mathews Conveyer Co.)

SHIPPING

Definition and Scope. Shipping is that activity which is concerned with the selection of stock to fill orders, the packing of items for shipment, and their loading onto the carrier for delivery.

As has been pointed out previously, the shipping function is frequently carried out in conjunction with the receiving and/or warehousing activity. Due to the close interrelationship between receiving, warehousing and shipping, they must be considered together in the layout planning project. This has been evident in the foregoing sections of this chapter—since many of the factors involved in planning the shipping activity have already been considered under receiving and warehousing.

Planning Shipping Space Requirements. Since the space and work load determining factors and problems for the shipping activity are so nearly identical to those alreday covered, they will not be detailed again. Instead, the reader may want to refer back to selected topics and adapt his thinking and planning to the shipping activity. Factors to be reconsidered here are:

1. Physical characteristics of items handled
2. Determination of work load
   a) Number of shipments per unit of time
   b) Pieces per shipment

RECEIVING AND SHIPPING AREA PLANNING SHEET

Company _Ajax Mfg Co._ _____ Analyzed by _AMJ._ Date _Apr. 14_

	RECEIVING	SHIPPING	
Units	**Estimated Weekly Activity**		**Units**
81	Number of Items		4
60	Number of Shipments		5
10,000 lbs	Total Weight		9,000 lbs
1,000 ft³	Total Physical Volume		2000 ft³
20	Total Man Hours		½

RECEIVING	Areas in Square Feet		SHIPPING
Unloading platform (In) (Max. area required to maneuver largest item received)	400	600	Accumulation (In) (Awaiting packing)
Unpacking and sorting	200	100	Packing and labelling
Storage at receiving	400	200	Storage at shipping
Receiving inspection	100	300	Marshalling (Out) (awaiting pick-up)
Marshalling (Out) (awaiting delivery to production or storage)	100	200	Loading platform
Truck well (14' x 40' per truck & trailer)	560	560	Truck well
Siding (R.R.)	—	—	Siding (R.R.)
Ramp	—	—	Ramp
Aisles, etc.(add 50% of Storage)	200	100	Aisles,etc.(add 50% of storage)
Handling equipment storage	80	(same)	Handling equipment storage
Office	100	(same)	Office
TOTALS	2140	2060	**TOTALS**

Fig. 7–12. Receiving and Shipping Area Planning Sheet.

    c) Number of carriers arriving and time schedule
    d) Volume by truck and rail
  3. Design of docks and related equipment
  4. Office space for record keeping
  5. Handling methods and equipment
  6. Location of shipping area

A brief review of the above topics in previous sections should enable the plant layout engineer to develop space requirements for the shipping activity.

Of most importance in space planning are (1) the "hold" area in which items are placed awaiting packing and/or shipping, (2) the packing area itself, and (3) the additional truck or rail space—over and above that required for receiving. A recap of normal and peak shipping loads, using the techniques discussed earlier, should permit the development of square foot requirements adequate for planning purposes. The form shown in Figure 7–12 will be found helpful in estimating space requirements for receiving and shipping.

Interrelationship of Receiving, Storage, Warehousing, and Shipping. In review, the plant layout engineer should remember that the four activities discussed in this chapter are very closely interrelated. If a "theoretical" arrangement could be devised, it would place these activities in an arrangement somewhat similar to one of those shown in Figure 7–13. In an actual situation, all factors must, of course, be taken into consideration —especially the location of external transportation facilities. Another very important factor is future expansion. The activities should not be so located in the proposed building that expansion possibilities are blocked by "permanent" structures such as roads, railroad tracks, truck wells, etc. —which would be costly or even impossible to move.

Vendor and Customer Relationships in Shipping and Receiving. One last, but very important, factor remains for consideration by the plant layout engineer—the close cooperation with both vendors and customers. Nothing can so disrupt the receiving and storage functions as to receive a shipment of castings in an old 55 gallon drum, when both handling and storage facilities are geared to the use of fork trucks, standard unit load containers, and pallet racks. Or for another example—to receive a large quantity of bearings or electric motors in individual boxes or cartons. So, it is only good business for both Purchasing and Sales Departments to work closely with the vendors and customers on the use of packaging methods and containers acceptable to both parties. Much time, effort, handling, and money can be saved by both parties if goods are both received and shipped in containers suitable for use in subsequent handling operations.

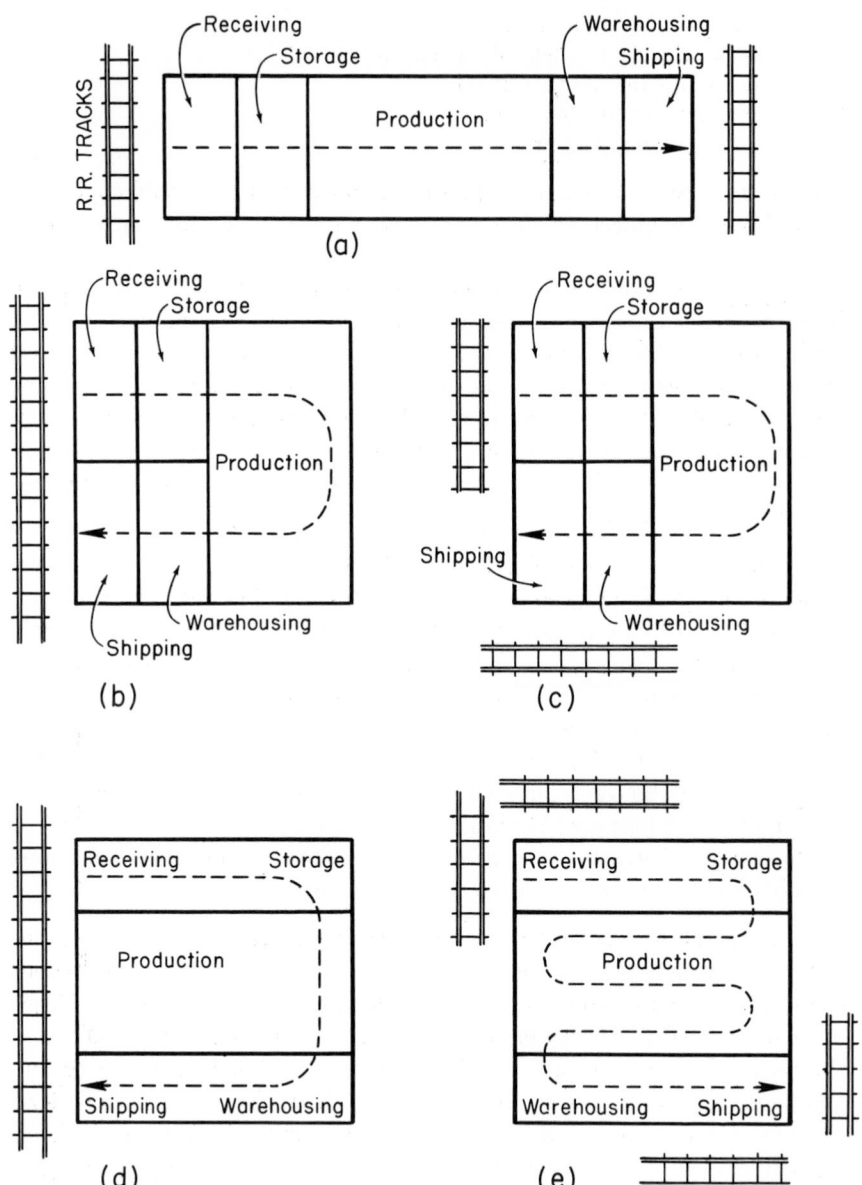

Fig. 7–13. Theoretical space relationships.

CONCLUSION

Receiving, storage, warehousing, and shipping are key activities in the planning of preliminary materials flow patterns. If the plant layout engineer will carry out the suggestions and procedures in this chapter, he will have accumulated sufficient data on space requirements to proceed with the materials flow planning.

The next chapter will deal with one last subject for consideration before returning to the actual flow planning—plant service areas.

QUESTIONS

1. Distinguish between receiving, receiving inspection, storage, warehousing, and shipping.
2. Why must these functions be considered *before* proceeding with the planning of the over-all flow pattern?
3. What are some of the more important items to be considered in developing receiving requirements?
4. Discuss the problem of locating the receiving activity.
5. How are receiving and shipping functions sometimes interrelated?
6. What are some objectives of good storage methods?
7. What major items must be considered in developing storage requirements?
8. What are the three general areas in which materials may be stored?
9. How does the container in which materials are received affect storage and handling activities? Give examples—good and bad. How can the problem be minimized?
10. What are some advantages of outdoor storage?
11. What factors would help determine the size of pallet to use in warehousing?
12. Explain how and why receiving, storage, warehousing, and shipping are interrelated and must be planned together.

8

Offices and Plant Services

Definition and Scope. Up to this point, we have dealt primarily with the space and flow problems of the production function. Of equal importance in plant layout planning are the multitude of plant service activities, varying from such obvious items as office space to the easily overlooked factors such as drinking fountains, scrap storage, and vending machines.

Every plant requires an office space for carrying out the business functions of the organization. This may vary from a very small area (100–200 square feet) in a smaller plant up to many thousands of square feet in a large organization. Other service functions, primarily related to the production activities, will also require space planning and allocation in the layout planning project.

The service areas may be divided into four categories:

1. General—those functions that serve the entire plant, consisting mostly of the "general" office areas and related activities.
2. Production—those functions that primarily serve the production organization.
3. Personnel—those services that are operated primarily for serving or handling the needs of people.
4. Physical Plant—those services that are primarily concerned with the needs of the physical facilities—building, equipment, utilities, etc.

A fairly complete list of these services is given in Figure 8–1. There are nearly 60 of these services or areas requiring the allocation of space in the final plant layuot. Although the size of the plant, i.e., the number of employees, will determine the relative importance of many of these functions, even the smallest plant *must* provide—in some way—for most of them. For example, a large plant may have 40–50 or more persons in an Accounting, Product Engineering, Production Control, or Maintenance Department—while in a small plant, any one of the more than 60 functions might be handled by only a part of one employee's time. Nevertheless, each function must be accounted for in the development of total space requirements.

Details on Selected Plant Services. It would be impractical to go into detail in this book on all of the plant services indicated in Figure 8–1. However, a number of them are sufficiently general in nature to warrant coverage here. Those to be considered are:

> Offices
> Health and medical facilities
> Food service
> Lavatory, wash rooms, etc.
> Tool room and tool crib
> Parking areas

Receiving, storage, warehousing, and shipping were considered in the previous chapter; and certain others are given some attention in other chapters.

Offices. As can be seen in Figure 8–1, office space is required for many persons and purposes. In the smaller plant, all offices are commonly combined into one area for convenience of communication between individuals. The area is frequently in the front of the building, for the convenience of visitors. In the larger plant, the general or administrative offices may be in the front of the building, while offices for services to production and personnel may be located within the production area for the convenience of factory personnel. In many large plants, the general offices may be located in a separate building to maintain closer coordination between various functions and to provide a better work environment for tasks not closely connected with production.

In the layout of any office area, an analysis of the work done, or to be done, should be made in much the same way as for the manufacturing processes, to find out what kinds of work are to be performed and to plan for the special requirements of certain groups. Such an analysis makes it possible to plan proper physical relationships between groups of employees who must work in close cooperation with one another. At this point, an examination of the company organization chart is helpful to indicate or suggest logical groupings of related functions. Many of the techniques presented in Chapter 9 will be found helpful in the planning of "non-productive" space relationships. Especially useful are the Activity Relationship Chart and the From–To Chart.

Some suggestions on office layout are listed here as general guides in planning the effective arrangement of office facilities.[1]

1. In laying out the departments, sections, working units, etc., remember that a straight line is the shortest distance between two points; and then,

[1] Adapted from *Office Standards and Planning Book,* Art Metal Construction Co. (Jamestown, N.Y., 1958), pp. 19–23.

General

1. President
2. General Manager
3. Sales and Advertising
4. Accounting
   a. general
   b. cost
   c. payroll
   d. credit
5. Product Engineering
   a. research
   b. development
   c. design
   d. drafting
   e. testing and experimental
6. Purchasing
7. Personnel
   a. general
   b. employment
   c. training
   d. credit union
   e. safety
8. Product Service
9. File Room
10. Conference Room
11. Vault
12. Reception Room
13. Switchboard
14.
15.

Production

16. Industrial Engineering
    a. plant layout
    b. materials handling
    c. methods
    d. standards
    e. packaging
    f. process engineering
    g. tool design
17. Production Control
    a. planning
    b. routing
    c. scheduling
    d. dispatching
    e. traffic
    f. follow-up
18. Quality Control
    a. receiving
    b. in-process (floor)
    c.
19. Plant Engineering
    a. general
    b. maintenance
20. Receiving
21. Stock Room (Storage)
22. Warehousing
23. Shipping
24. Tool Room
25. Tool Crib
26. Materials Handling Equipment Storage
27. Supervision
28.
29.
30.

Fig. 8–1. Plant

Personnel

31. Health and Medical Facilities
32. Food Service
    a. kitchen
    b. dining
    c. vending machines
33. Lavatory
    a. showers
    b. locker room
    c. toilets
34. Smoking Area
35. Lounge Area
36. Recreation Area
37. Parking
38. Time Clock
    a. bulletin boards
39. Fire Escapes
40. Drinking Fountains
41. Telephones (booths, etc.)
42.
43.
44.
45.

Physical Plant

46. Heating Facilities
47. Ventilating Equipment
48. Air Conditioning Equipment
49. Power Generating Equipment
50. Telephone Equipment Room
51. Maintenance Shops
52. Air Compressors
53. Scrap Collection Area
54. Vehicle Storage
55. Fire Protection
    a. extinguishers
    b. hoses
    c. equipment
    d. sprinkler valves
56. Stairways
57. Elevators
58. Plant Protection
59.
60.

service areas.

as nearly as is practical, have the flow of the work conform to this principle.

2. In planning the general layout, consider any electrical or structural need which must be conformed to in connection with mechanical equipment which is to be used.

3. Remember that office space must be conserved, but not, of course, at the expense of appearance, production, or comfort.

4. Place related departments near each other.

5. Aisles should be at least 3 feet wide.

6. In assigning working space, provide for the peak load rather than for bare minimum requirements.

7. Use the past annual increase in the volume of work handled as a basis for planning space requirements for future expansion.

8. Group minor activities around major ones so that when more space is needed the major functions will be taken care of first.

9. The type of work to be done is the basis for departmentalizing the office work.

10. Each employee, including his desk, chair space, and his share of the aisle, requires 50 to 75 square feet of working space.

11. In any given department, all employees should face in one direction with the natural light coming over the left shoulder or from the back. Where employees must be placed back to back, it is well to leave at least 4 feet between chairs.

Private Offices.

1. The tendency is distinctly away from private offices except where privacy is absolutely necessary.

2. Never construct a private office so that it cuts off the natural light and ventilation from those who work in the adjacent outer office.

3. Those who do work which requires much concentration are entitled to privacy. Suggested office space requirements as follows:

Senior executives	300–400 sq. ft.
Department heads	150–300 sq. ft.
Supervisors	100–200 sq. ft.
Staff personnel	75–125 sq. ft.

4. By providing a general conference room where confidential meetings may be held, the need for private offices is often minimized.

5. In making private offices, transparent or translucent glass can be used in the upper portion of 66 to 72-inch high partial partitions.

The General Office.

1. One large office is a more efficient operating unit than the same number of square feet split up into smaller rooms because (a) supervision and control are more easily maintained, (b) communication between individual employees is more direct, (c) better light and ventilation are possible. Centralization, however, has the disadvantages of the general noises, con-

versations, etc., that characterize large groups of people. There are also disturbances from aisle traffic.

2. Standard widths for main circulation aisles vary from 5 to 8 feet. Less important aisles vary from 3 to 5 feet.
3. Desks in general offices for clerical workers should not be less than 4 feet apart at chair spaces, with a minimum of 18 inches at the sides of the desks.
4. Passages between rows of desks or between desks and solid or window walls may be from 24 inches to 3 feet wide.
5. Rooms facing directly south or west are in general the least desirable.

Noise. Insofar as possible, segregate in one place all noisy equipment and appliances, such as typewriters, duplicating machines, etc., thus reducing distracting influences.

An example of office layout is shown in Figure 8–2.

Health and Medical Facilities. Some space must be provided in every plant, no matter how small, for medical services of one kind or another. The simplest solution for the smaller plant is merely a room with a bed or cot, a chair or two, and first-aid equipment. These are the minimum requirements in case of an accident or sickness. Some of the largest plants are equipped with complete hospitals, including operating rooms, X-ray facilities, and dental clinics. Most plants, however, will require facilities somewhere between these two extremes. Two examples of health facilities are shown in the layouts [2] in Figures 8–3 and 8–4. The layout in Figure 8–3 is designed for a plant of about 1,500 employees. The layout in Figure 8–4 is planned for a smaller plant employing less than 500 persons.

Food Service. Most modern plants provide an area in which employees may eat meals in pleasant surroundings, away from their work. Some of the advantages of such an arrangement are:

1. Takes worker away from his workplace, thereby providing a break in routine.
2. Keeps food and related waste out of the plant proper.
3. Offers healthful, sanitary, and pleasant surrounding for meals.
4. Makes possible the preparation of complete or partial meals for employees to replace or supplement the cold lunches usually carired.

However, separate eating areas are not a necessity. Various common types of eating facilities are: [3]

1. *Snack Bar.* Some firms that do not have central lunchrooms, serve coffee, tea, milk, rolls, etc., a nominal cost. In fact, some offer such service

[2] *Plan for an Industrial Medical Department,* American Mutual Liability Insurance Co. (Boston, Mass.), pp. 1 and 4.

[3] Adapted from *Lunchrooms for Employees,* Policyholders Service Bureau, Metropolitan Life Ins. Co. (New York), p. 4.

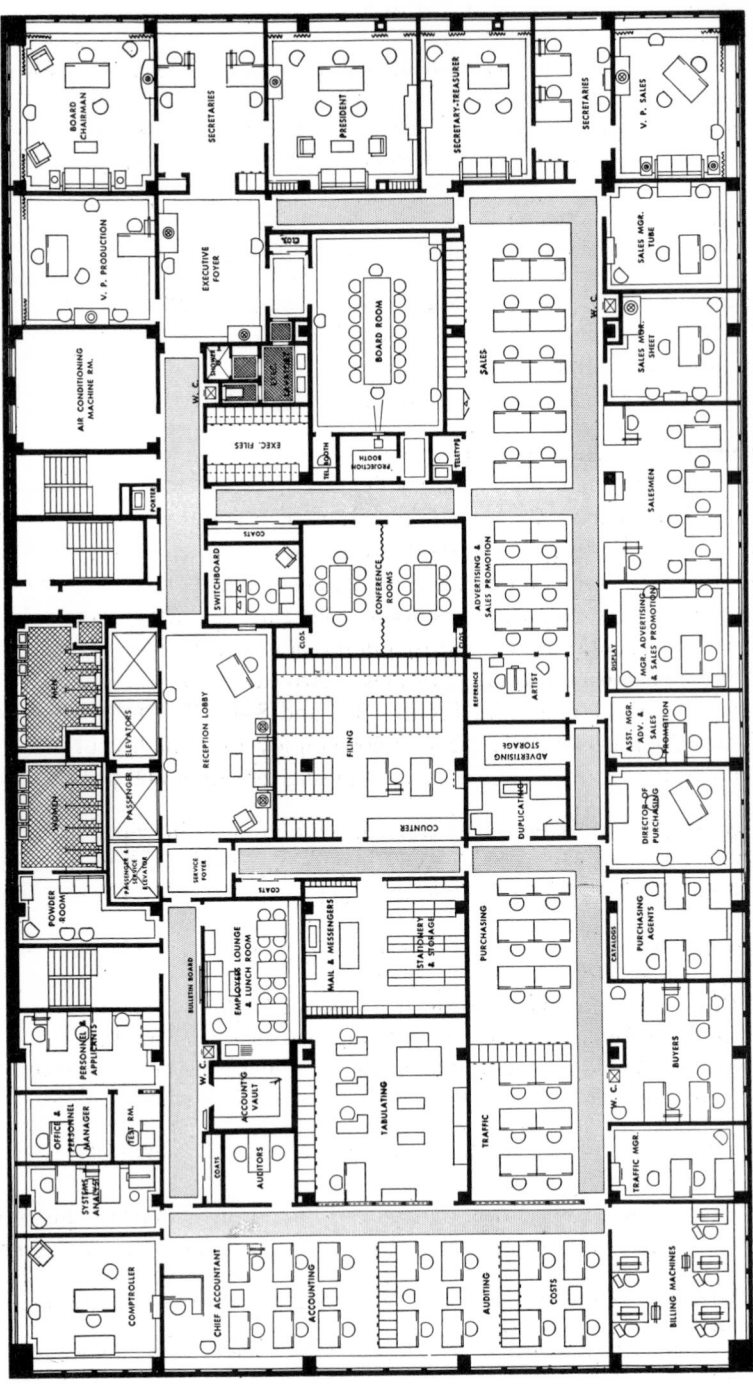

Fig. 8–2. Typical office layout. (By permission of Rodgers Associates.)

free- of charge. The installation of a snack bar requires but a small amount of space and equipment (counter, sink, coffee-brewing equipment, tableware, refrigerator, and storage cabinet). A small part of an employee's time is all that is required in its operation. The snack bar is usually open only during lunch periods and coffee breaks. The service is often extended to include the dispensing of cold drinks. In addition to

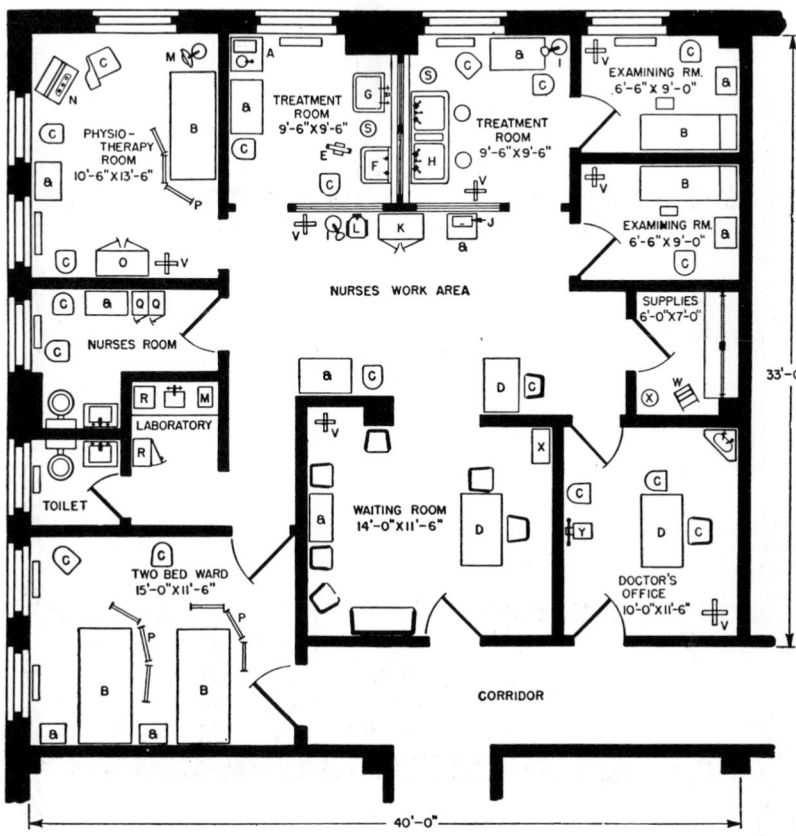

Fig. 8–3. Layout of a typical industrial medical department. (By permission of American Mutual Liability Insurance Co.)

drinks, other items sold may include ice cream, pastry, candy, and cigarettes. The snack bar often is a part of, or an adjunct to, a recreation room, where employees may go to smoke, relax, read, play games, or eat the lunches they bring with them.

2. *The Rolling Cafeteria.* The traveling lunch truck is used in plants and yards where conditions are such as to render a central kitchen or

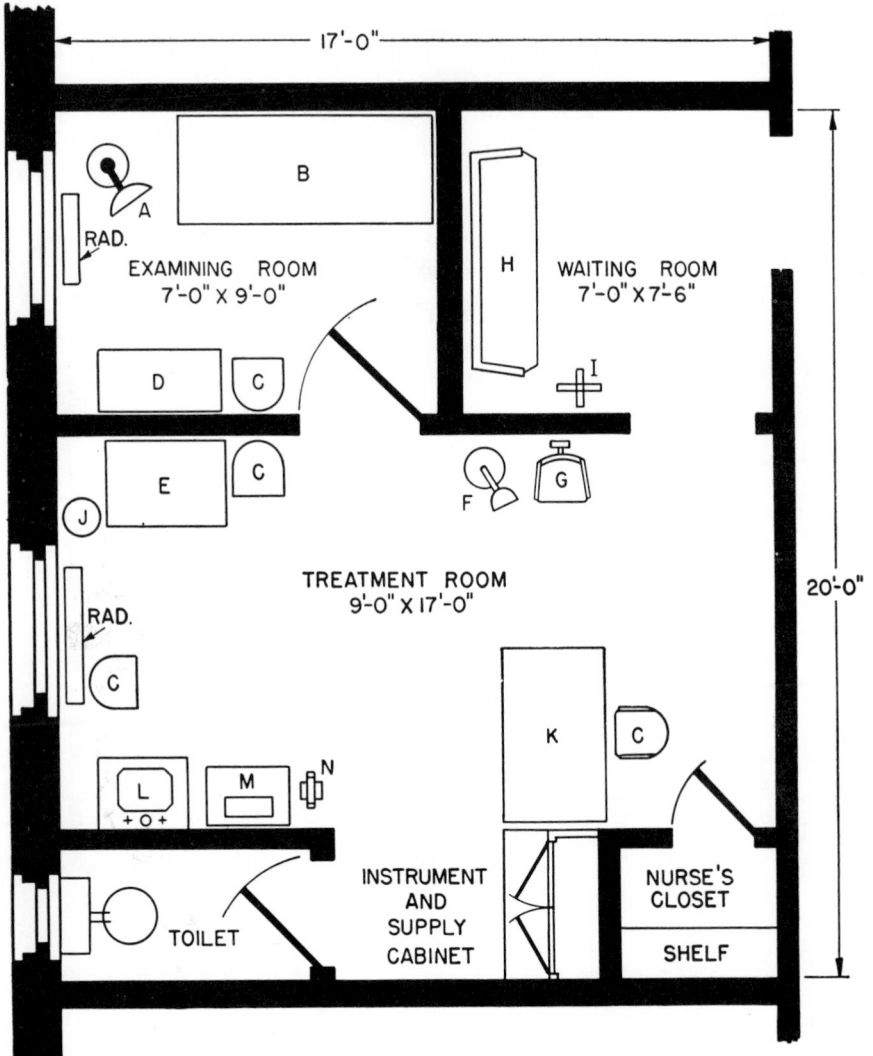

Fig. 8–4. Layout for a small plant dispensary. (By permission of American Mutual Liability Insurance Co.)

eating area impractical. In fact, the kitchen may be off the premises and the services supplied by catering companies. Such a service is advisable for employees who should not leave the processes on which they are working for a sufficient length of time to go to a central lunchroom.

An advantage in the rolling cafeteria plan is that it can be expanded and contracted to meet changing needs more easily than a fixed form of lunchroom. On the other hand, rolling cafeterias do not meet all needs.

Fig. 8–5. Typical snack bar. (By permission of International Paper Co.)

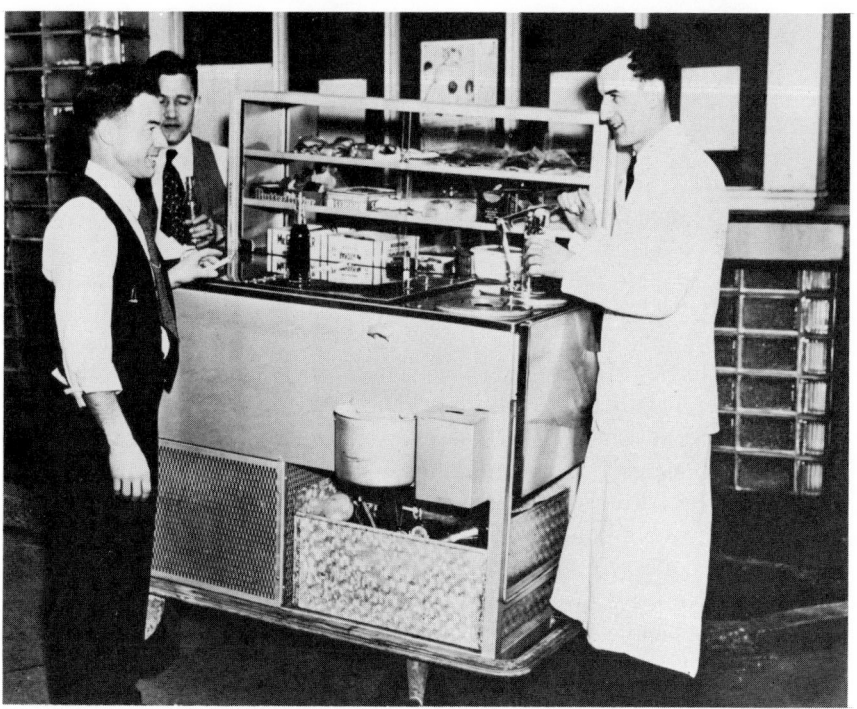

Fig. 8–6. Rolling "cafeteria" for dispensing food throughout the plant. (By permission of United Service Equipment Co.)

Close supervision is required so that time will not be wasted by employees meeting the trucks. Unless adequate provision is made for replacing the items carried on the trucks, employees may be tempted to go to the truck instead of waiting until it comes to them.

3. *Vending Machines.* There is a growing trend toward the use of vending machines for the entire food service. Modern vending machines handle literally everything "from soup to nuts." Both hot and cold foods may be served, including soups, entrees, sandwiches, rolls, desserts, ice cream, hot and cold drinks, and fresh fruit.

Fig. 8–7. Vending machines serving as a "cafeteria." (By permission of Vendo Company.)

4. *The Diner.* The use of the neighborhood diner is encouraged by many firms. This is an institution which serves people at odd hours, but in order to be successful it needs steady patronage. As most employees will buy but one meal a day, the diner relies for a part of its business on outside sources. Free use of the ground on which the diner stands is sometimes offered as an inducement to attract the right type of diner management. The manufacturers of dining cars provide a very effective service program which helps assure good food and cleanliness. Although a single diner cannot handle large numbers of people at one time, it can provide a supplementary eating facility that is comfortable and convenient. Neighborhood restaurants fill a similar need. Some of these, however, may be too expensive or too far away for many of the employees to patronize regularly.

5. *The Cafeteria.* Where large numbers of people are to be fed quickly, dining rooms served from a central kitchen are most satisfactory. Here full meals as well as lunches are obtainable. Such rooms are provided with an adequate number of tables and chairs so that the employees may enjoy eating with their associates. In many plants, cafeterias are used for recreation purposes, and in some cases for holding meetings and other company functions.

Fig. 8–8. Typical plant cafeteria. (By permission of Albert Pick Co.)

The main cafeteria kitchen can serve all the eating facilities of a company—separate dining rooms, rolling cafeterias, and outlying plants. The amount of kitchen equipment will depend on the number of people to be served and the type of service.

Lunchrooms should be centrally located, if possible, to provide easy access for all. If the plant has several floors, however, the eating facilities may be located on the top floor to provide adequate ventilation and prevent cooking odors from permeating the plant or offices.

The space requirements for a cafeteria will probably include:

1. Eating space
2. Kitchen
3. Dishwashing space
4. Storage areas
5. Serving counter
6. Other facilities

Some suggestions on layout are given here adapted from "Lunchrooms for Employees." [4]

1. Dining Room and Serving Counters—adequate to accommodate one sitting. Normally there are three sittings per feeding period. Where the dining room is used for both factory and office people, it is customary to serve the factory people first and the office afterwards.

2. Dining Room Area:
   a) 8 to 14 square feet per person (exclusive of serving counters).
   b) 17 square feet per person (including serving counters and dishwashing units).

3. Space in or adjacent to the dining room is essential for people waiting to be served. A covered way between the work space and the lunchroom is necessary during inclement weather.

4. Table sizes in inches—30″ × 30″, 30″ × 48″, 30″ × 72″, 30″ × 96″.

5. Kitchen and Kitchen Facilities—sufficient to provide food for only those working on the major shift—arranged for normal flow of production.

6. Economical Kitchens—rectangular in shape (length not more than twice the width). A long, narrow, or irregular shaped kitchen is costly to equip, difficult to operate, and requires more floor space.

7. Kitchen Features:
   a) Manager's office and storage room located for the control of food and supplies.
   b) Separate refrigerated space for meats, vegetables, fruit, dairy products, frozen foods, and fish. Walk-in type for large installations. The temperatures needed to keep the different types of food vary; certain kinds of food flavor others unless proper segregation is provided.
   c) Separate equipment for the preparation of salads or cold dishes.
   d) Provision for the refrigeration of garbage and disposal of refuse.
   e) Dishwashing space convenient to the dining room.

8. Kitchen Area:
   a) 22–35 per cent of total space available (exclusive of storerooms, office, washroom, and locker rooms).
   b) Based on the number of meals served during a lunch period:

Number of Meals	Sq. Ft. per Meal
100– 200	5.00
200– 400	4.00
400– 800	3.50
800–1,300	3.00
1,300–2,000	2.50
2,000–3,000	2.00
3,000–5,000	1.85
5,000–8,000	1.70

[4] *Ibid.*, p. 9.

Illustrations of typical food service facilities are shown in Figures 8–5 to 8–9.

A survey by a leading periodical [5] shows plant food service facilities used by various size plants as follows:

Facility	Number of Employees				
	Under 250	250–499	500–999	Over 1,000	Ave. Per Cent
Vending machines	87.5%	84.2%	81.0%	81.6%	83.5%
Cafeteria	26.8	42.9	66.9	83.4	55.0
Snack bar	14.3	16.4	14.1	22.2	16.8
Food carts	23.2	28.2	26.4	32.4	27.6
Other	7.1	4.5	3.1	0.3	4.5

This same survey shows that vending machines are commonly located as follows:

Location	No. of Plants
Working areas	311
Halls or corridors	282
Stations of two or more machines	145
Special rooms with chairs and tables	56
Recreation rooms	47
Cafeterias	34
Other	7

Lavatories and Wash Rooms. In the small plant, these facilities are usually in the same locations because of the problem involved in plumbing. In larger plants, toilet facilities are necessary in several locations to be conveniently accessible as workers come to or leave the plant. Frequently they are close to the employee entrance of the plant, with the time clocks placed in the path between the entrance and the locker room, but not so close that they cause a traffic problem at starting and quitting time.

Locker rooms should be placed so that they do not interfere with production. For this reason, and also to provide good ventilation, they are frequently located along an outside wall. In multistory buildings, such facilities are located one above the other to reduce plumbing costs, although it has been said that you can "run" pipe, but you can only "walk" a man. In some one-story plants, locker rooms and toilets are placed on mezzanine levels. The point to be emphasized is that the locker rooms and wash rooms should be located as conveniently as possible for access by the employees. One authority has calculated that a toilet 150 feet out of the way, in a plant of 500 employees, would cost $5,250 per year in time lost in walking.

[5] *Factory Management and Maintenance,* "The Trend Is to Vend," Jan. 1956, p. 92.

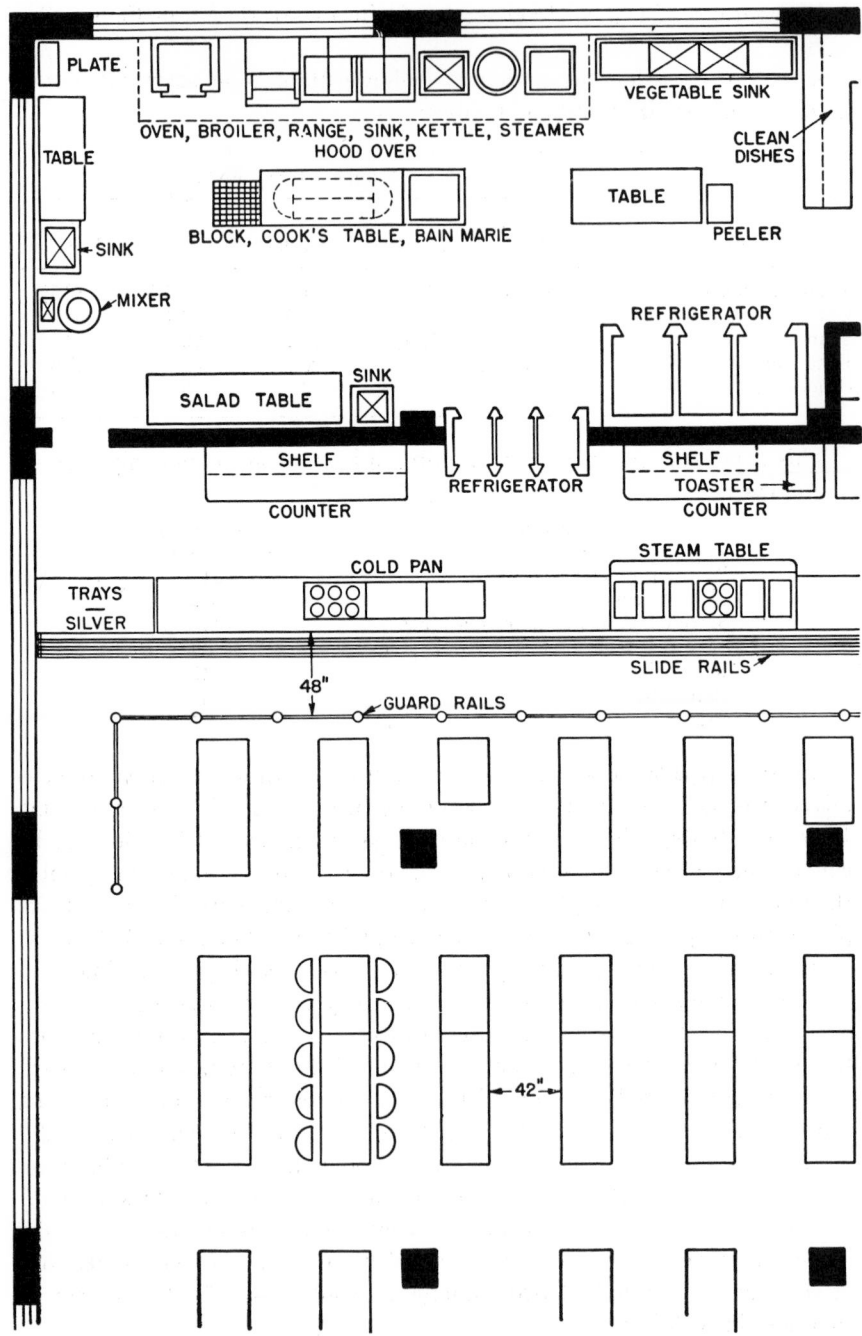

Fig. 8–9. Single-service counter cafeteria layout.

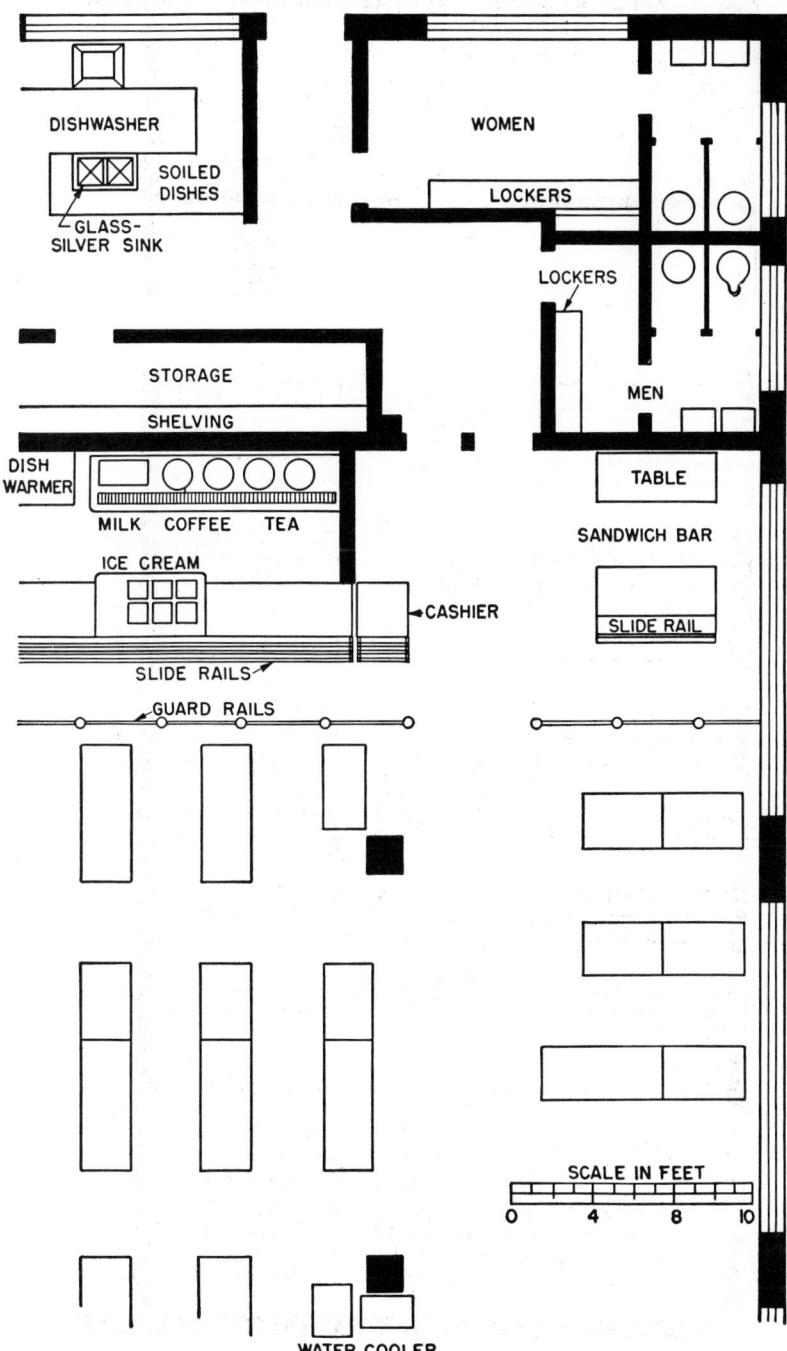

DISHWASHER

SOILED
DISHES

GLASS-
SILVER SINK

WOMEN

LOCKERS

LOCKERS

MEN

STORAGE

SHELVING

DISH
WARMER

MILK   COFFEE   TEA

TABLE

SANDWICH BAR

ICE CREAM

CASHIER

SLIDE RAIL

SLIDE RAILS

GUARD RAILS

SCALE IN FEET

0   4   8   10

WATER COOLER

(By permission of Metropolitan Life Insurance Co.)

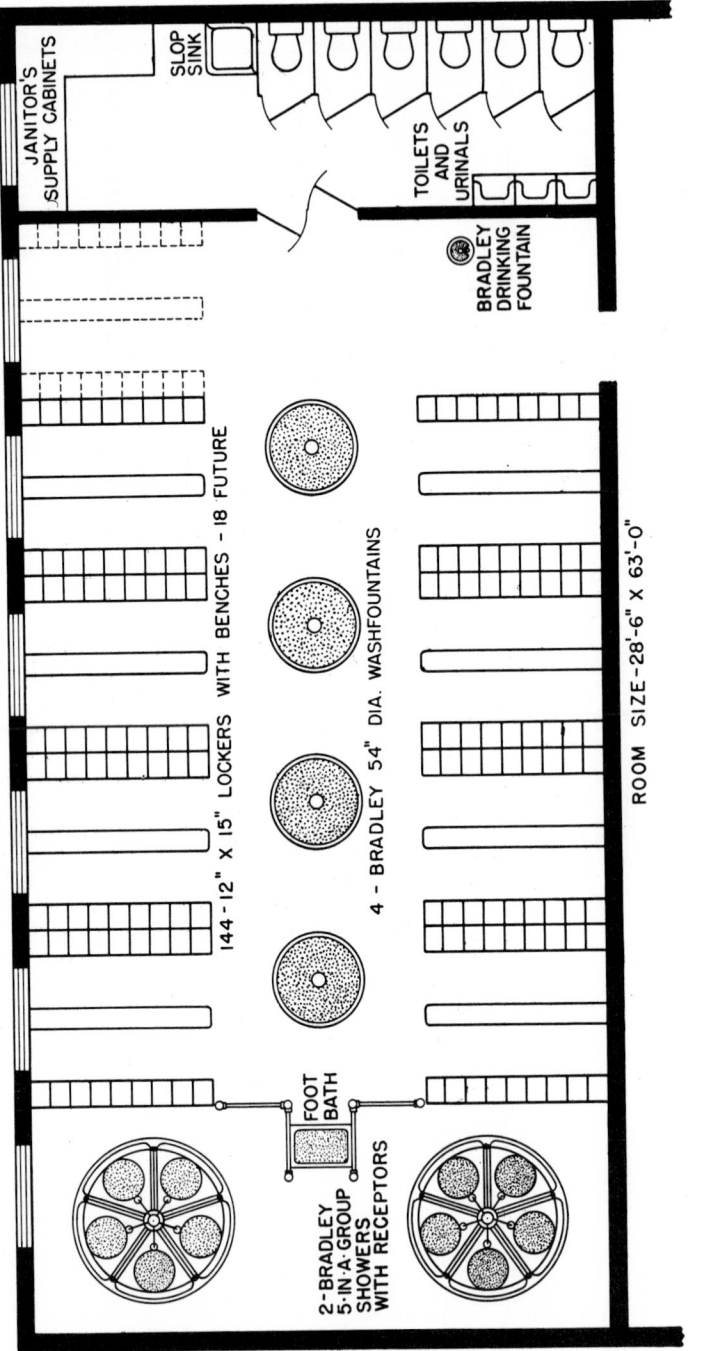

Fig. 8–10. Washroom and locker room layout for 120–160 men. (By permission of Bradley Washfountain Co.)

Many plants combine locker room, washroom, and toilet facilities. The major equipment items include:

1. Lockers
2. Benches
3. Lavatories or washfountains
4. Toilet facilities
5. Showers
6. Drinking fountain

The arrangement of facilities involves problems little different from the plant layout itself. Some of the problems are:

1. Adequate space for the number of persons to be accommodated
2. Spacing of equipment
3. Provisions to handle peak loads of personnel at beginning and end of shift
4. Effective utilization of space

Sample layouts of typical washrooms, locker rooms, and toilet combinations are shown in Figures 8–10, 8–11, and 8–12.

Toolroom, Tool Crib, and Stockrooms. Probably the first problem to be considered in the discussion of toolroom, tool crib, and stores areas is that of centralization versus decentralization. The centralization of all such facilities into one area has the following advantages: [6]

1. Ease of control
2. Ease of supervision
3. Lower operating cost
4. Faster and better service

Centralization is common in smaller plants where one such area can conveniently serve all personnel. In larger plants, however, it may not be practicable to utilize one central location because of the distances some persons might have to travel, for instance from floor to floor, or building to building. The following factors indicate the desirability of decentralized areas: [7]

1. Multistory building
2. Multibuilding plants
3. Large plants where personnel would lose time in walking excessive distances
4. Points of use of various materials are scattered about the manufacturing area
5. Bulk materials are handled in considerable quantities

[6] Bethel, etc., *Industrial Organization and Management* (New York: McGraw-Hill Book Co., Inc., 1945), p. 267.
[7] *Ibid.*, p. 267.

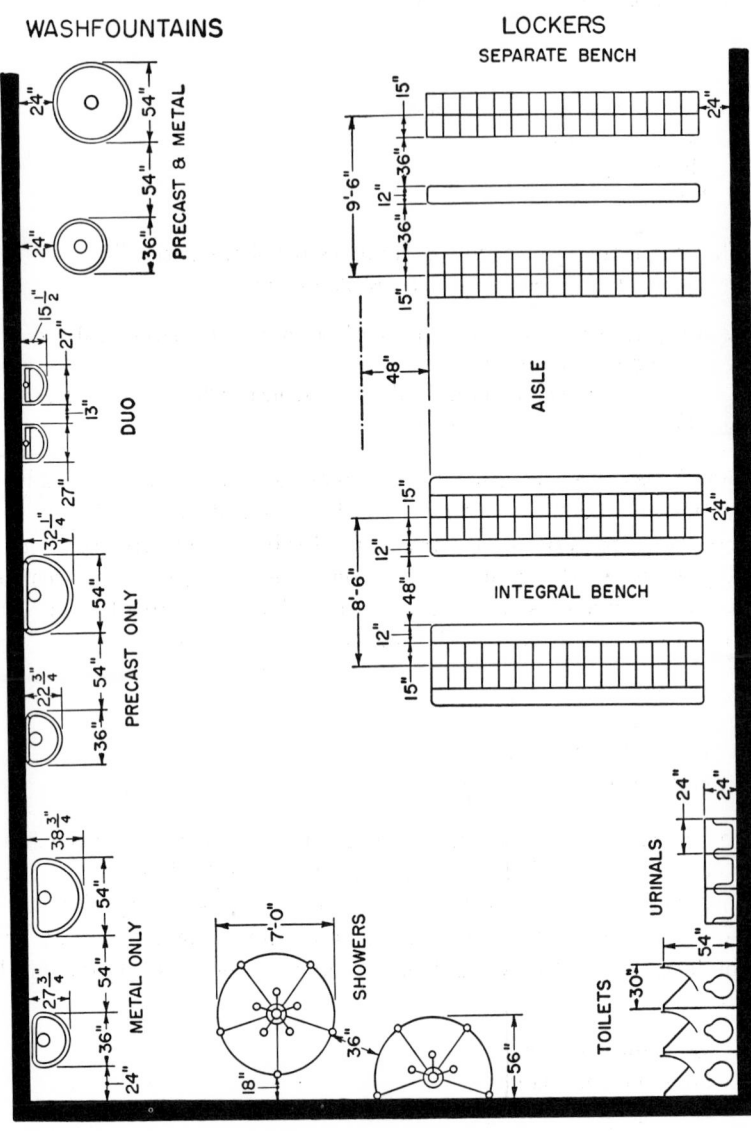

Fig. 8–11. Recommended spacing for washroom and locker room equipment. (By permission of Bradley Washfountain Co.)

Location of these areas is another important consideration. In general, the toolroom is centrally located and tool cribs are located where needed to issue tools to employees. Storage area location was discussed previously in Chapter 7. The stockroom referred to here is that in which supplies and non-productive materials are stored and issued. The problems in locating such an area are very similar to those for the tool cribs.

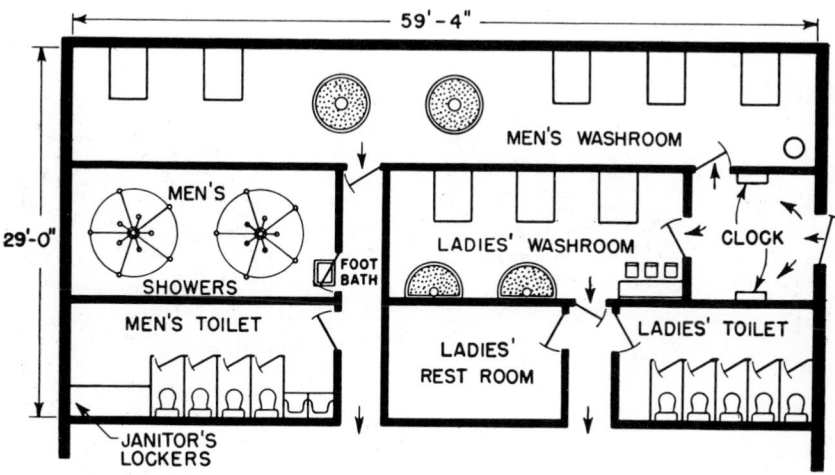

Fig. 8–12. Typical layout for men's and ladies' washrooms for a smaller plant. (By permission of Bradley Washfountain Co.)

Major considerations in the layout of tool cribs and non-productive materials stockrooms are as follows: [8]

1. Allow for easy, quick, and sure receipt, storage, and disbursement.
   a) Generally speaking, do not store tools over 6 feet high.
   b) Leave space for all sizes of tools of a given type.
   c) Provide ample aisle space between rows of bins for passage of personnel.
   d) Make shelf space adaptable to accommodate the items to be stored and so that the shelving can be readily altered for other items.
   e) Maintain flexibility in arrangement to permit expansion or contraction of space.
   f) Provide uniform storage equipment to permit expansion of bins, racks, boxes, etc.
2. Provide space and storage equipment adequate both as to size and load-bearing capacity for material to be stored.
3. Provide for protection against damage or deterioration.
4. Provide means for identifying and readily locating contents.
5. Provide for selection of oldest materials first.

[8] *Ibid.*, Adapted from p. 269.

Storage equipment is usually of steel construction, capable of indefinite expansion, and made up of units of such a nature that they can readily be disassembled and reassembled into a variety of sizes and arrangements. Typical examples are shown in Figures 8–13, 14, 15, 16. A typical storeroom layout is shown in Figure 8–17. Areas in which pallets are to be stored present problems of a different sort. Here space must be used economically and yet allow room for truck movement and the handling of the loaded pallets.

Fig. 8–13. Stockroom showing commercial steel shelving and Rotabin units. (By permission of Frick-Gallagher Co.)

Toolrooms should contain a variety of modern machines sufficient in number to provide for the proper manufacture and maintenance of tools, jigs, fixtures, and the many special production tools needed for reducing the time and cost of production operations. In smaller plants, the toolroom may be combined with the maintenance shop.

Parking Areas. An increasing problem for today's plant is the provision of adequate parking space for employees' automobiles. This problem has become more acute in recent years with the trend toward suburban plant locations, suburban living, and the accompanying trend toward "two-car" families. It has been suggested that one parking space must be provided for each five employees. This, of course, will vary with the plant location and the availability of public transportation.

Fig. 8–14. Typical stockroom shelving (note bin identifications). (By permission of Lyon Metal Products Co.)

Fig. 8–15. Typical pallet rack installation. (By permission of Unistrut Corporation.)

Fig. 8–16. Tool crib showing small tool storage racks and check-out window. (By permission of Lyon Metal Products Co.)

The following suggestions will prove helpful in the layout of a parking area: [9]

1. The width of the parking area determines the angle of the parking stall.

	90° Parking	60° Parking	45° Parking
1 row of cars	43 ft. lot	39 ft. lot	33 ft. lot
2 rows of cars	62 ft.	60 ft.	50 ft.
3 rows of cars	105 ft.	99 ft.	79 ft.
4 rows of cars	124 ft.	120 ft.	99 ft.

(See Figure 8–18 for details of stall size.)

2. As the angle of the stall increases, the number of feet of aisle space increases.

[9] Based on "How To Lay Out a Parking Lot," Western Industries, Inc. (Chicago 32, Ill.).

3. The wider the stall, the sooner the driver can start turning, thus reducing the aisle width.

4. A greater number of cars can be parked on 90° than 60° using the same stall width.

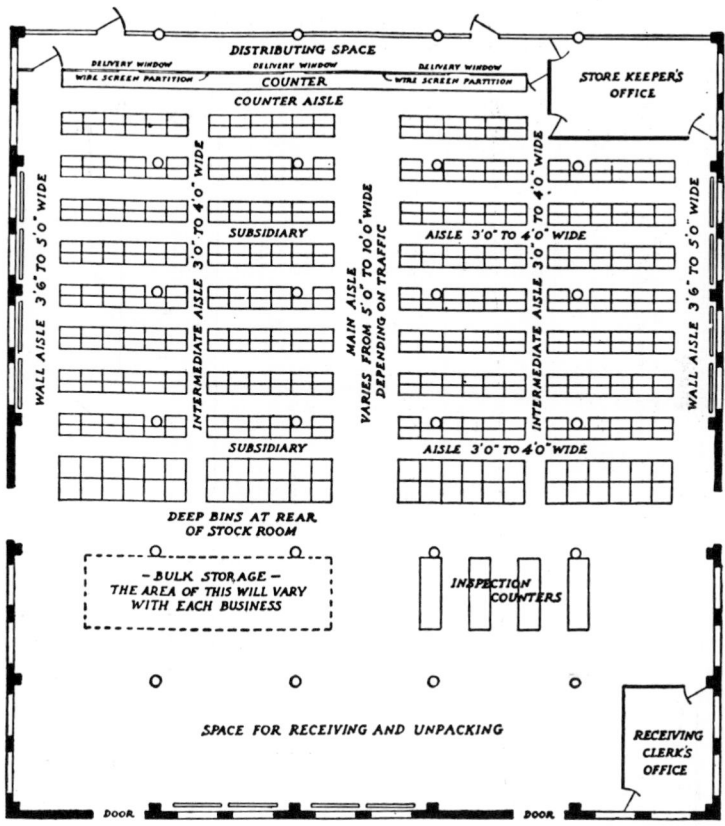

Fig. 8–17. Floor plan of a large stockroom indicating principles of stockroom layout. (By permission of Remington Rand Co.)

Figures 8–19 and 8–20 show typical parking area layouts.

Developing Service Area Space Requirements. Before proceeding to the next step (Chapter 9—Planning the detailed materials flow), it will be necessary to at least *estimate* space requirements for the various office and plant service areas. For the major areas, such as those discussed in this and the previous chapters, preliminary calculations will suffice for the next planning steps. Estimates must be made for other areas. The details of each area will be worked out as the layout planning continues—with the details settled in the final layout planning (Chapter 15).

PARKING LOT DIMENSIONS TABLE

Angle of Parking	Stall Width (A)	Curb Length Per Car (C)	Stall Depth (D)	Driveway Width (E)
0°	8'0"	23'0"	8'0"	12'0"
	8'6"	23'0"	8'6"	12'0"
	9'0"	23'0"	9'0"	12'0"
	9'6"	23'0"	9'6"	12'0"
	10'0"	23'0"	10'0"	12'0"
20°	8'0"	23'5"	14'6"	11'0"
	8'6"	24'11"	14'6"	11'0"
	9'0"	26'4"	15'0"	11'0"
	9'6"	27'10"	15'6"	11'0"
	10'0"	29'3"	15'11"	11'0"
30°	8'0"	16'0"	16'6"	11'0"
	8'6"	17'0"	16'11"	11'0"
	9'0"	18'0"	17'4"	11'0"
	9'6"	19'0"	17'10"	11'0"
	10'0"	20'0"	18'3"	11'0"
40°	8'0"	12'5"	18'4"	13'0"
	8'6"	13'3"	18'9"	12'0"
	9'0"	14'0"	19'2"	12'0"
	9'6"	14'10"	19'6"	12'0"
	10'0"	15'8"	19'11"	12'0"
45°	8'0"	11'4"	19'2"	14'0"
	8'6"	12'0"	19'5"	13'6"
	9'0"	12'9"	19'10"	13'0"
	9'6"	13'5"	20'2"	13'0"
	10'0"	14'2"	20'6"	13'0"
50°	8'0"	10'6"	19'9"	14'0"
	8'6"	11'2"	20'0"	12'6"
	9'0"	11'9"	20'5"	12'0"
	9'6"	12'5"	20'9"	12'0"
	10'0"	13'2"	21'0"	12'0"
60°	8'0"	9'3"	20'5"	19'0"
	8'6"	9'10"	20'9"	18'6"
	9'0"	10'5"	21'0"	18'0"
	9'6"	11'0"	21'3"	18'0"
	10'0"	11'6"	21'6"	18'0"
70°	8'0"	8'6"	20'8"	20'9"
	8'6"	9'0"	20'10"	19'6"
	9'0"	9'8"	21'0"	19'0"
	9'6"	10'2"	21'3"	18'6"
	10'0"	10'8"		18'0"
80°	8'0"	8'2"	20'2"	25'0"
	8'6"	8'8"	20'3"	24'0"
	9'0"	9'2"	20'4"	24'0"
	9'6"	9'8"	20'5"	24'0"
	10'0"	10'3"	20'6"	24'0"
90°	8'0"	8'0"	19'0"	26'0"
	8'6"	8'6"	19'0"	25'0"
	9'0"	9'0"	19'0"	24'0"
	9'6"	9'6"	19'0"	24'0"
	10'0"	10'0"	19'0"	24'0"
90° Back In	8'0"	8'0"	18'6"	22'0"
	8'6"	8'6"	18'6"	21'0"
	9'0"	9'0"	18'6"	20'0"

All lot layout prints, to which this chart refers, have been drawn using a stall 19' in length with 9' width. All dimensions are expressed in feet and inches, on all charts, prints and copy.

Fig. 8–18. Parking lot dimensions table. (By permission of Western Industries, Inc.)

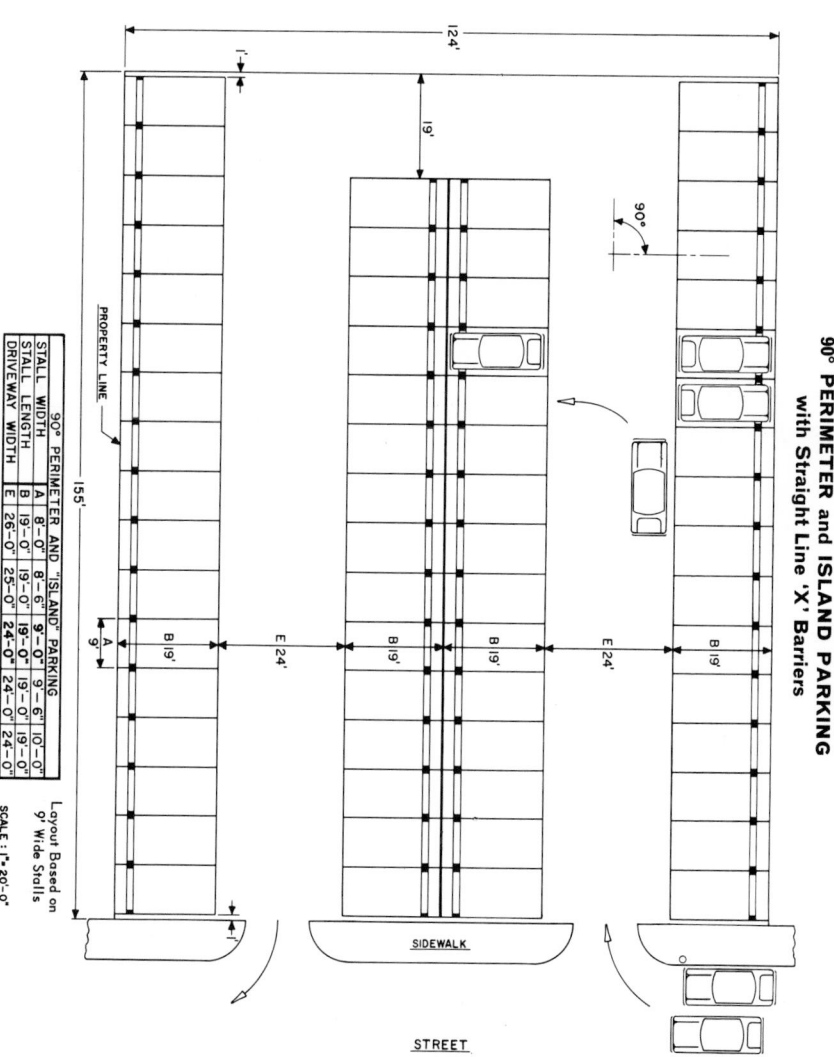

Fig. 8–19. 90° perimeter and island parking. (By permission of Western Industries, Inc.)

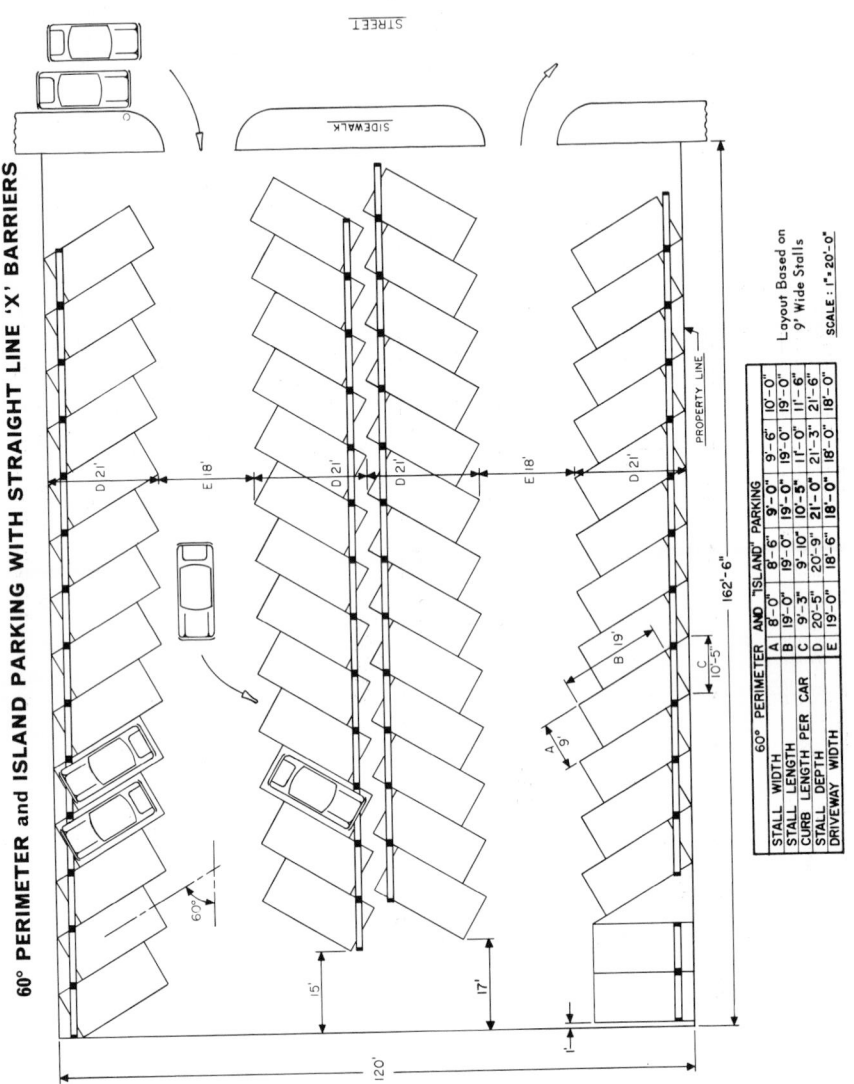

Fig. 8–20. 60° perimeter and island parking. (By permission of Western Industries, Inc.)

To aid in planning service area requirements, the "Plant Service Area Planning Sheet" (Figure 8–21, pages 152 and 153) will be found helpful. Enter the estimates in the columns provided, subtotal if desired, and total each column as indicated. For over-all space planning (i.e., total square feet), the four columns can be totaled and added to the production area estimate for a grand total estimate.

CONCLUSION

Plant service areas are an important and integral part of the complete plant layout. Their planning must be done as carefully and accurately as for the production areas. The layout planner should not progress to the next step without having studied and planned at least the preliminary requirements of the service areas considered in these last two chapters.

With preliminary flow planning having been considered in Chapters 4 and 6, and related areas discussed in Chapters 7 and 8, attention must now be given to the detailed planning of the materials flow pattern. The steps and techniques for this will be developed in the following chapter.

QUESTIONS

1. What are the major categories of plant service functions for which space must be planned and allocated?
2. What are some of the factors that would determine whether all office activities should be located in one central area—or placed in various locations about the plant?
3. What are the advantages of centralized service areas? Decentralized service areas?
4. What are some of the general considerations to be followed in planning office space?
5. What would be the minimum medical requirements in a plant too small to hire even a part-time doctor or nurse?
6. What are the advantages of providing a separate eating place for employees?
7. If you were building a new plant, what kind of eating facilities would you provide, and why?
8. If you were an employee, what kind of eating facilities would you prefer? Why?
9. What are some of the general locations in which a locker room might be placed? What would be the advantages of each?
10. What are some of the major considerations in the layout of a tool crib?
11. Why has parking become more of a problem in recent years?

PLANT SERVICE AREA

Plant (or Area) _____ Powrarm _____

General	Est. sq. ft.	Production Services	Est. sq. ft.
. 1. President		16. Industrial Engineering	
		a. plant layout	
2. General Manager	400	b. materials handling	
		c. methods	
3. Sales and Advertising		d. standards	
		e. packaging	
4. Accounting		f. process engineering	
a. general		g. tool design	
b. cost			
c. payroll		17. Production Control	
d. credit		a. planning	
		b. scheduling & dispatching	
5. Product Engineering		c. traffic	
a. research		d. follow-up	
b. development			
c. design		18. Quality Control	
d. drafting	400	a. receiving	
e. testing and experimental		b. in-process (floor)	
		c. final	
6. Purchasing			
		19. Plant Engineering	
7. Personnel		a. general office	
a. general		b. maintenance shops	
b. employment			
c. training		20. Receiving	
d. credit union			
e. safety		21. Stock Room	1400
8. Product Service		22. Warehousing	800
9. File Room		23. Shipping	
10. Conference Room		24. Materials Handling Equipment	500
		Storage	
11. Vault			
		25. Tool Room	
12. Reception Room			
		26. Tool Crib	
13. Switchboard			
		27. Product Supervision	
14.			
		28.	
15.			
		29.	
		30.	
Total General Office Area	800 sq. ft.	Total Production Service Area	2700 sq. ft.

Fig. 8–21. Plant service

PLANNING SHEET

Estimated by A. M. James _____ Date ___Nov. 15___

Personnel Services	Est. sq. ft.	Physical Plant Services	Est. sq. ft.
31. Health and Medical Facilities		46. Heating facilities	
		47. Ventilating Equipment	
32. Food Service			
a. kitchen		48. Air conditioning Equipment	
b. dining 50 x 15	750		
c. vending machines		49. Power Generating Equipment	
33. Lavatory			
a. showers 5 x 20 = 100		50. Telephone Equipment Room	
b. locker room 50 x 15 = 750			
urinals 10 x 10 = 100		51. Maintenance Shops	500
w. basin 5 x 20 = 100	1050		
stools		52. Air Compressors #51	
34. Smoking area			
35. Lounge Area		53. Scrap Collection Area	
36. Recreation Area		54. Vehicle Storage	
37. Parking (outside)		55. Fire Protection	
		a. extinguishers	
38. Time Clock			
a. bulletin boards		c. equipment	
		d. sprinkler valves	
39. Fire Escapes			
		56. Stairways	
40. Drinking Fountains			
		57. Elevators	
41. Telephones			
		58. Plant Protection	
42.			
		59.	
43.			
		60.	
44.			
45.			
Total Personnel Service Area	1800 sq. ft.	Total Physical Plant Service Area	500 sq. ft.

area planning sheet.

9

Planning and Analyzing
the Materials Flow Pattern

Introduction. Previous chapters have dealt with the "preliminaries" and discussed the many items of importance in planning the materials flow pattern. The task now remains of actually developing the flow pattern from the material and data accumulated. The Assembly Chart in Chapter 4 provided a glimpse of what the flow pattern might look like, but it did not consider all the factors presented in Chapters 6, 7, and 8. The problem now is to continue from the Assembly Chart concept to a more complete and accurate flow pattern, embodying proper consideration of the many factors developed in the previous chapters. However, it will be found that the construction of the Assembly Chart and its preliminary view of the flow pattern has been helpful as a background for the discussion of the various factors considered in Chapters 6, 7, and 8.

Flow Planning Procedure Outlined. Although there is no formally accepted procedure for planning the materials flow pattern, it will be found helpful to proceed in an orderly manner. Following such a pattern will help to avoid overlooking any of the important factors which must be taken into consideration. It will also assure the use of the right techniques, from among the several used in varying planning situations.

The suggested materials flow planning procedure to be detailed in this and the next chapter is outlined below:

1. Review factors to be considered (from Chapters 6, 7, 8)
   a) General
   (1) Levels of activity
   (2) Movement of personnel
   (3) Working conditions
   (4) Cost
   b) Product
   (5) Volume of production
   (6) Number of parts

    c) Process
       (7) Specific requirements of activities
       (8) Number of operations
       (9) Sequence of operations
       (10) Number of subassemblies
       (11) Product vs. product layout
       (12) Quantity of equipment
       (13) Space requirements of equipment

    d) Flow Pattern and Materials Handling
       (14) Required flow between work areas
       (15) Preliminary materials handling plans
       (16) Location of shipping and receiving
       (17) Storage requirements
       (18) Aisle area
       (19) Desired location of departments
       (20) Desired location of service areas
       (21) Supervisory requirements
       (22) Production control
       (23) Flexibility
       (24) Expandability

    e) Building and Site
       (25) Building type
       (26) Number of floors
       (27) External transportation facilities

    f) Plant Service Areas (see Chapter 8 for details)
       (28) General
       (29) Serving production
       (30) Serving personnel
       (31) Serving the physical plant

The importance of these factors cannot be overemphasized. Since they cannot be repeated at every stage in the planning process, the plant layout engineer must be well enough acquainted with them to permit him to unconsciously consider them throughout the entire planning process. For this reason, it may be well to review the previous chapters (6, 7, and 8) before proceeding with the detailed flow planning. Whenever practicable, appropriate factors will be reconsidered as they apply to the flow planning process.

    2. Analyze Materials Flow. This step involves the use of one or a combination of several charting techniques to aid in establishing proper interrelationships between various activity areas.

    3. Determine Space Requirements. This involves the calculation of the approximate number of square feet required for each activity or function.

    4. Plan Area Allocation. In this step, the space requirements are converted into actual area and space relationships.

This chapter will deal primarily with flow planning and analysis techniques (step 2, above). The following chapter will continue with the space requirements and area allocation planning procedure.

Flow Planning and Analysis Techniques. There are many commonly used techniques that are helpful in the flow planning process. Some are "peculiar" to plant layout, some are particularly useful in the materials handling phase, some are "borrowed" from the field of motion economy or work simplification. Although most of the techniques were originally devised for analytical purposes, they are also useful in the planning process. The more common techniques are:

1. *Assembly Chart*
2. *Operation Process Chart*
3. *Flow Process Chart*
4. *Multi-Product Process Chart*
5. *Flow Diagram*
6. *From–To Chart (sometimes used as travel, or cross charts)*
7. *Activity Relationship Chart*
8. *Activity Relationship Diagram*
9. *Area Allocation Diagram*

Since it is obvious that all the techniques are not useful in every type of plant layout project, the chart in Figure 9–1 will serve as a guide to the selection of the appropriate techniques for various purposes. It will be observed that most of the techniques are equally useful in either the planning of a new layout project or the analysis of an existing layout.

Each of the above techniques will be commented on in this and the next chapter, although some will be presented in more detail in the chapters with which they are more closely related.

1. *Assembly Chart.* The Assembly Chart was discussed in Chapter 4 with instruction given for making and using it. This technique provides the first insight into the probable flow relationships *within* the production area. For an example, see Figure 4–11.

2. *Operation Process Chart.* This technique is the first to consider the individual operations on each part and/or assembly. It will provide a much more accurate "picture" of the *production* flow patterns than the Assembly Chart, since it adds the first quantitative data to the flow planning project. The Operation Process Chart "extends" the Assembly Chart by adding each and every operation to the graphical representation of the preliminary flow pattern previously developed. An example of the Operation Process Chart is shown in Figure 9–2.

The Operation Process Chart is one of the most useful techniques in manufacturing planning. Actually, it is a "diagram" of the manufac-

COMPARISON OF PLANNING & ANALYSIS TECHNIQUES USEFUL IN PLANT LAYOUT

TECHNIQUE	Especially Useful In			PRIMARILY APPLICABLE IN FIELD OF										
				PLANT LAYOUT								MATERIALS HANDLING		
	Planning	Analysis	Comparison or Evaluation	Preliminary Planning	Activity Relationship	Material Flow	Space Requirements	Area Allocation	Evaluation of Floor Path, or Plant Lay.	Recording Material Flow	Coordination	Planning	Analysis	Relationship between Work Areas
1 Assembly Chart	✓	✓		✓		✓						✓	✓	✓
2 Operation Process Chart	✓	✓	✓	✓		✓					✓	✓	✓	✓
3 Flow Process Chart	✓	✓	✓		✓	✓			✓	✓	✓	✓	✓	✓
4 Multi-Product Process Chart	✓	✓	✓		✓	✓				✓	✓	✓	✓	✓
5 Flow Diagram	✓	✓	✓		✓	✓	✓	✓	✓	✓		✓	✓	
6 "From-to" Chart	✓	✓	✓		✓	✓		✓	✓			✓	✓	✓
7 Activity Relationship Chart	✓	✓	✓	✓	✓			✓	✓		✓	✓	✓	✓
8 Activity Relationship Diagram	✓	✓	✓	✓	✓	✓	✓	✓	✓	✓		✓	✓	
9 Area Allocation Diagram	✓	✓	✓		✓	✓		✓	✓			✓	✓	

Fig. 9–1. Planning and analysis techniques useful in plant layout.

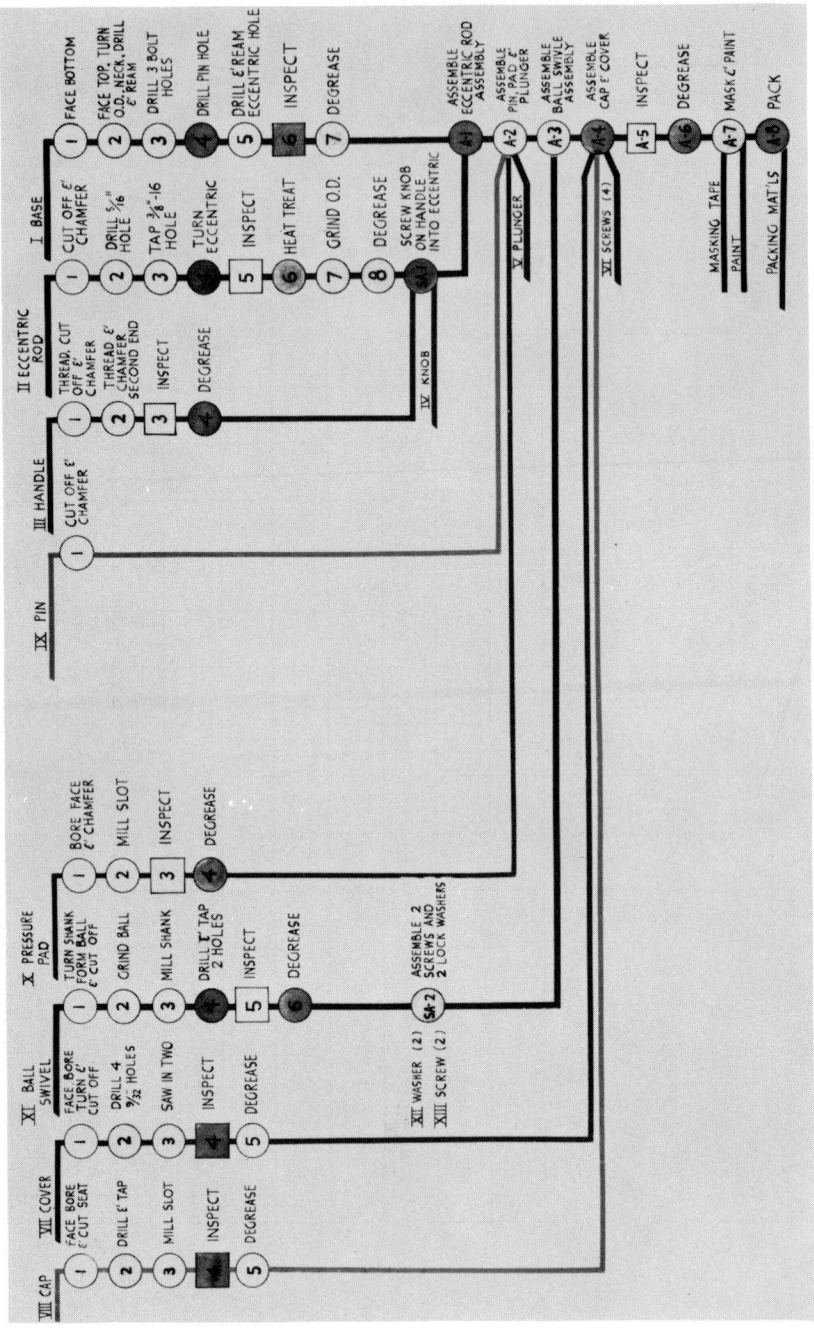

Fig. 9-2. Operation process chart for Powrarm.

turing process. It has been used in many ways as a planning and control device. With the addition of other data, it can be extremely useful in manufacturing management. Some of the advantages and uses of the Operation Process Chart are:

1. Combines Production Routings and Assembly Chart for a more complete presentation of information
2. Shows operations to be performed on each chart
3. Shows sequence of operations on each part
4. Shows order of part fabrication and assembly
5. Shows relative complexity of parts fabrication
6. Shows relationship between parts
7. Indicates relative length of fabrication lines and space required
8. Shows point at which each part enters into process
9. Indicates desirability of subassemblies
10. Distinguishes between purchased and manufactured parts
11. Aids in planning individual work places
12. Indicates number of employees required
13. Indicates relative machine, equipment, and personnel concentration
14. Indicates nature of materials flow pattern
15. Indicates nature of materials handling problem
16. Indicates possible difficulties in production flow
17. Records manufacturing processes for presentation to others

Some suggestions in making an Operation Process Chart are given in the following paragraphs.[1]

Material, either purchased or upon which work is performed during the process, is shown by horizontal material lines feeding into the vertical flow lines. Figure 9–3 is a graphic representation of this principle.

One of the parts going to make up the completed product is selected for charting first. Usually a chart of the most pleasing appearance will be obtained by choosing the component on which the greatest number of operations is performed. If the chart is to be used as a basis for laying out a progressive assembly line, the part having the greatest bulk to which the smaller parts are assembled should be chosen.

When the component which is to be charted first has been chosen, a horizontal material line is drawn in the upper right-hand portion of the chart. A description of the material is recorded directly above this line. The description may be as complete as is deemed necessary. In order to identify the part itself, the name and identifying number are recorded in capital letters directly above the material description.

A vertical flow line is next drawn from the right-hand end of the horizontal material line. Approximately 1/4 inch from the intersection of the

[1] Adapted from *Operation and Flow Process Charts,* published by the American Society of Mechanical Engineers.

horizontal material line and the vertical flow line, the symbol is drawn for the first operation or inspection which is performed. To the right of this symbol, a brief description of the event is recorded, such as "bore, turn, chamfer, and cut off" or "Inspect material for defects." To the left of the symbol is recorded the time allotted for performing the required work. Other pertinent information which it is considered will add to the value of the chart, such as the department in which the work is performed, male or female operator, cost center, machine number, or labor classification is recorded to the right of the symbol below the description of the event.

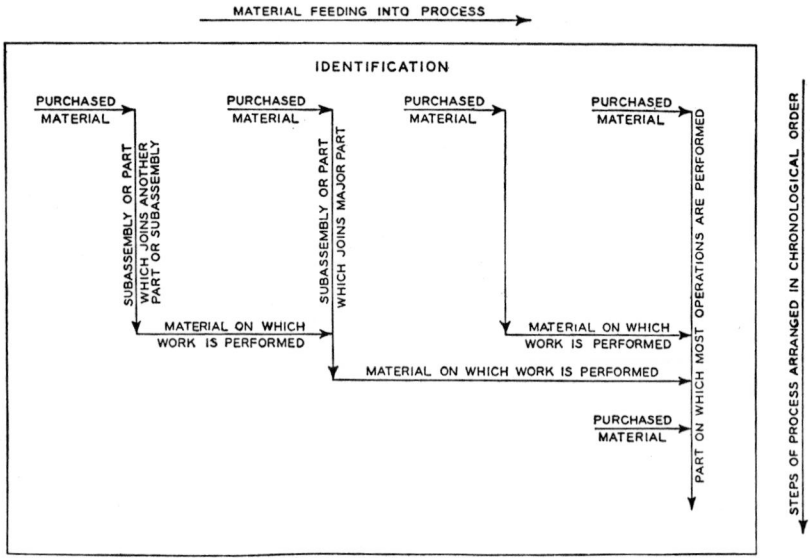

Fig. 9–3. Graphic representation of principles of operation process chart construction. (From "Operation and Flow Process Charts," by permission of the A.S.M.E.)

This charting procedure is continued until another component joins the first. Then a material line is drawn from the operation symbol to show the point at which the second component enters the process. If it is purchased material, a brief identification of the material is placed directly above the material line. If work has previously been done on the component in the plant, a vertical line is erected from the left-hand end of the material line. The material from which the component was made and the operations and inspections performed on it are then charted following the conventions described above. The same procedure is repeated as each new component joins one which is being charted. As each component joins the one shown on a vertical flow line to its right, the charting of the events which occur to the combined components is continued along the vertical flow lines to the right. The final event which occurs to the completed apparatus will thus appear in the lower right-hand portion of the chart. There should be a vertical flow line for each part upon which work is done in the plant.

Operations are numbered serially for identification and reference purposes in the order in which they are charted. The first operation is numbered O–1, the second O–2, and so on. When another component on which work has previously been done joins the process, the operations performed upon it are numbered in the same series. If the first component on the chart has had four operations performed upon it, they will be identified as O–1, O–2, O–3, O–4. If a second component then joins the first, the first operation performed on the second component will be identified as O–5. If two more operations are performed on the second component before it joins the first, they will be numbered O–6 and O–7. The first operation performed after the two components have come together would then be identified as O–8.

An operation number once used is never repeated on the same chart. If, after a chart has been completed, it becomes necessary to add an operation to the process between two operations, it is permissible to identify the new operation with the number of the preceding operation followed by the subscript "a." Thus an operation inserted between O–4 and O–5 would be identified as O–4a. (If desired, operation numbers from the part Routings may be used. This will permit closer correlation between Routings, the Operation Process Chart, and the layout. This method is used in Figure 9–2.)

Inspections may be numbered in the same manner in a series of their own. They are identified as Ins–1, Ins–2 and so on. The same numbering conventions used for operations are followed. Figure 9–2 illustrates a typical Operation Process Chart as it would appear when completed.

Do not try to relate the Operation Process Chart too closely to the Assembly Chart. The Assembly Chart was based on the Bill of Materials or Parts List only, with no knowledge of the operations to be performed. When more detailed information regarding the product is available, as on the Production Routing, more specific relationships between parts can be shown.

The accompanying sketches indicate what is meant in this connection. In a compressor crankcase, the bearings are pressed into position. This operation would appear on the Assembly Chart as in Figure 9–4. The proper way to depict the same operation on an Operation Process Chart is shown in Figure 9–5. This shows the interrelationship of parts more accurately.

In other words, what was shown on the Assembly Chart as operation 1 in the assembly, actually becomes operation 40 in the fabrication of part 1.

It will be seen from the completed Operation Process Chart that a definite flow pattern is beginning to shape up. In fact, with a little imagination, the layout is beginning to form itself in the mind of the plant layout engineer. He can see which parts will present the biggest planning problems and which ones will be less important. If additional information is charted on each operation, the chart will then indicate where the most equipment will be concentrated. The chart also points out which parts are closely related to each other and therefore should be fabricated in adjacent areas, and shows where subassembly is desirable, as outlined in the previous discussion.

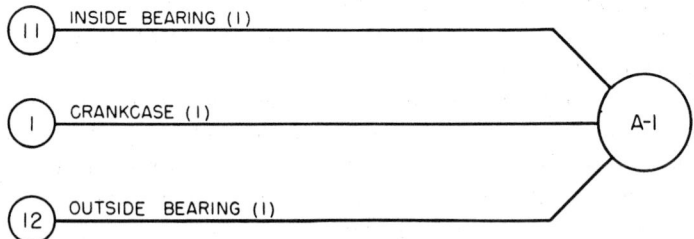

Fig. 9–4. Detail on assembly chart.

It is rather obvious that an Operation Process Chart would become unwieldy if made for a product containing a large number of components. For example, it has been calculated that a typical four-door automobile includes 13,512 parts—including bolts, nuts, washers, and cotter pins. This problem is overcome in two ways. The chart can be made showing only subassembly and assembly operations—with supplementary information on separate sheets. In this way, the writer has seen an Operation Process Chart for a diesel switch engine on a sheet of paper 36″ x 72″.

3. *Flow Process Chart.* One of the oldest and most common techniques for planning or analyzing the flow of materials is the Flow Process Chart. For planning purposes, it requires more knowledge of the proposed activity than do the Activity Chart or the Operation Process Chart, since it calls for identification of "move" or materials handling steps. However, since it can be assumed that the "move" *must* be made between any two operations, its insertion on the Flow Process Chart is an assurance that the materials handling steps will not be overlooked in subsequent planning steps. Figure 9–6 shows a typical Flow Process Chart. The basis for the

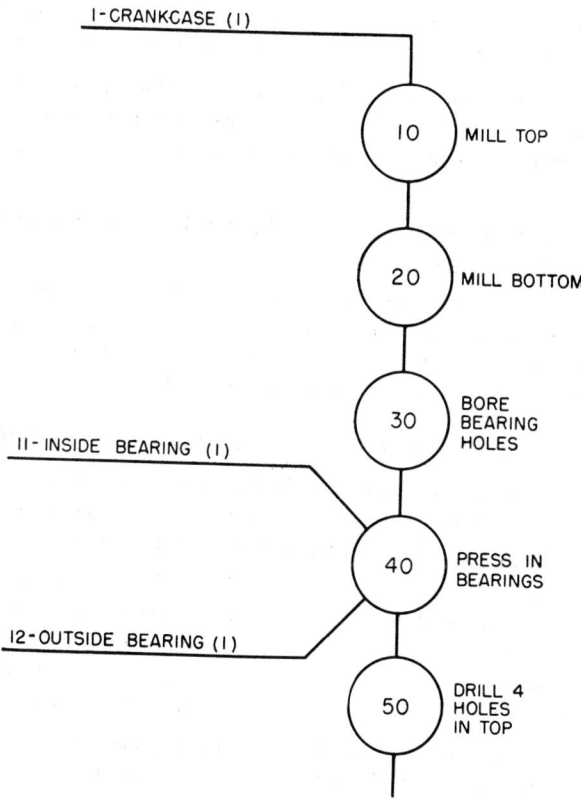

Fig. 9–5. Same detail, as expanded on operation process chart.

Flow Process Chart is the Process Symbols, developed by F. M. Gilbreth in the 1920's. These symbols, as used today, are: [2]

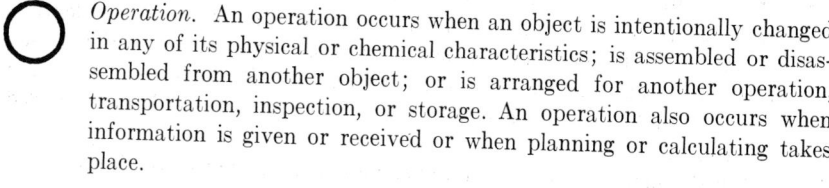

Operation. An operation occurs when an object is intentionally changed in any of its physical or chemical characteristics; is assembled or disassembled from another object; or is arranged for another operation, transportation, inspection, or storage. An operation also occurs when information is given or received or when planning or calculating takes place.

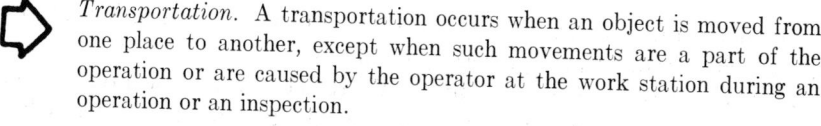

Transportation. A transportation occurs when an object is moved from one place to another, except when such movements are a part of the operation or are caused by the operator at the work station during an operation or an inspection.

[2] Maynard, H. B., "Industrial Engineering Handbook" (McGraw-Hill Book Co., Inc., 1956), p. 2–19.

Inspection. An inspection occurs when an object is examined for identification or is verified for quality or quantity in any of its characteristics.

Delay. A delay occurs to an object when conditions, except those which intentionally change the physical or·chemical characteristics of the object, do not permit or require immediate performance of the next planned action.

Storage. A storage occurs when an object is kept and protected against unauthorized removal.

Combined Activity. When it is desired to show activities performed either concurrently or by the same operator at the same work station, the symbols for those activities are combined, as shown by the circle placed within the square to represent a combined operation and inspection.

When making a Flow Process Chart, the procedure is as follows:

1. Fill in the heading to properly identify the process under observation.
2. Decide on the type of information desired and label the columns on the right for each type of data to be planned or analyzed, such as:

   a) Distance moved.   *f*) Method of handling.
   b) Number of men involved.   *g*) Frequency of move.
   c) Type of container.   *h*) Time per move.
   d) Time required.   *i*) Department number.
   e) Number of pieces handled.   *j*) Operation number

3. In the first column, on the first line, enter the step number.
4. Decide on the symbol which best represents the activity (or lack of it) at the *very* beginning of the process.
5. Insert a small number 1 *inside* the symbol (each *type* of symbol is numbered consecutively).
6. In the "description" column, enter just enough to indicate what is *not* told by the other columns.
7. Fill in the remaining columns to the right, with pertinent data.
8. Proceed through the entire process or series of steps until a logical or desired end point is reached. Remember, in selecting symbols and identifying steps, to "follow" *either* a person *or* an object—not both. When used as an *analytical* tool, the Flow Process Chart is a RECORD of an *existing* situation. When used as a *planning* tool, it is a record of what is intended to happen.
9. Fill in the summary box in the upper right-hand corner of the form.

Further details on the Flow Process Chart can be found in any motion study text or industrial engineering handbook.

4. *Multi-Product Process Chart.* Where more than one product flow is to be planned or analyzed at one time, the Multi-Product Process Chart will be found more useful than the Operation Process Chart. Figure 9–7 shows a typical Multi-Product Process Chart.

FLOW PROCESS CHART

PART NAME ___Gizmo___

PROCESS DESCRIPTION ___Machine base and assemble, and finish___

DEPARTMENT ___Machine shop, Assembly, and Finishing___

PLANT ___XYZ Products Co.___

RECORDED BY ___I. M. Looking___   DATE _____

SUMMARY		NO.
○ OPERATIONS		
⇨ TRANSPORTATIONS		
☐ INSPECTIONS		
D DELAYS		
▽ STORAGES		
TOTAL STEPS		
DISTANCE TRAVELED		

STEP	Operations Transport Inspect Delay Storage	DESCRIPTION OF PRESENT METHOD				
1	○⇨☐D▽	in storage at receiving				
2	○⇨☐D▽	to position at mach 2	walkie	6'		
3	○⇨☐D▽	at mach. 2				
4	○⇨☐D▽	into mach. 2	hand	4'		
5	①⇨☐D▽	turn				
6	○⇨☐D▽	to table	hand	4'		
7	○⇨☐D▽	on table				
8	○⇨☐D▽	to mach. 3	hand	4'		
9	②⇨☐D▽	drill				
10	○⇨☐D▽	to table	hand	4'		
11	○⇨☐D▽	on table				
12	○⇨☐D▽	into mach. 4	hand	3'		
13	③⇨☐D▽	drill				
14	○⇨☐D▽	to skid	hand	4'		
15	○⇨☐D▽	on skid				
16	○⇨☐D▽	to Assembly Dept.	walkie	10'		
17	○⇨☐D▽	at end of assembly bench				
18	○⇨☐D▽	onto bench to assy. position	hand	5'		
19	④⇨☐D▽	assemble				
20	○⇨☐D▽	to inspection position	hand	3'		
21	○⇨①D▽	inspect				
22	○⇨☐D▽	to skid at end of assy. bench	hand	8'		

Fig. 9–6. Typical flow process chart.

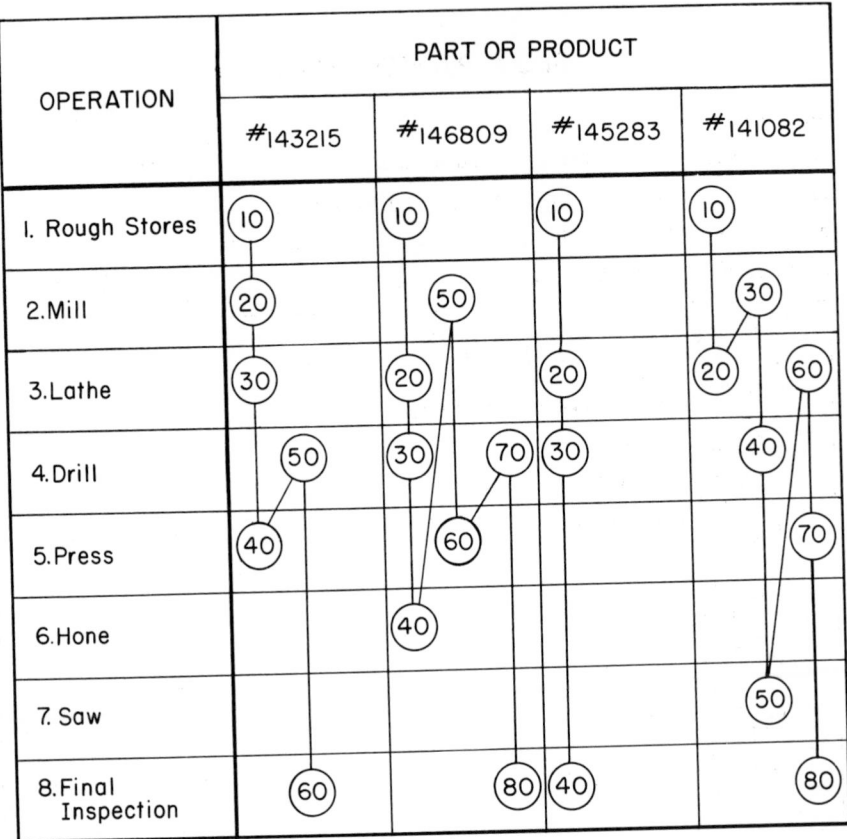

Fig. 9–7. A typical multi-product process chart.

The construction principles can be observed by examining the chart. It will be seen that it provides a comparative graphical representation of several related flow patterns. If such a chart is made of several "typical" parts moving through a plant, or of the major components of a product, the Multi-Product Process Chart will serve as a guide in establishing the materials flow. Backtracking can be observed by inspection, and the sequence of departments arranged most efficiently for the major items flowing through them.

5. *Flow Diagram.* A companion to the Flow Process Chart is the Flow Diagram. (See Figure 9–8.) This is a graphical representation of the flow pattern, drawn on a floor plan of the area involved. In making a Flow Diagram, merely transfer the symbols, numbers inside also, and draw a line to connect the symbols and show the path followed by the object or person. Each symbol should be drawn as nearly as is possible

Present Flow Pattern of XYZ Products Co.

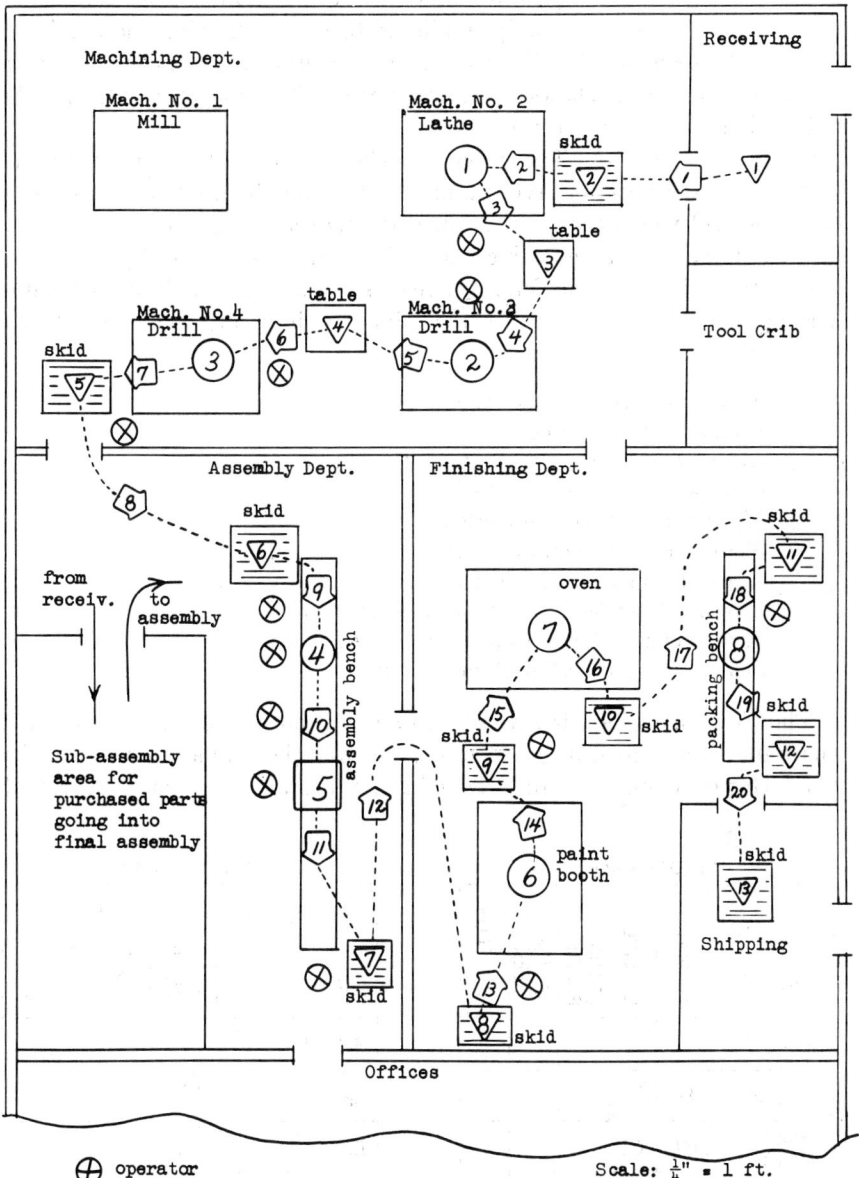

Fig. 9-8. Typical flow diagram (to accompany Fig. 9-6).

right where the step *actually* occurs or will occur. Die-cut symbol rulers or templates are commercially available to aid in drawing the symbols.

It will be seen that the Flow Diagram is helpful in both flow planning and analysis, since it shows the actual path of flow and frequently points out obvious problems or errors.

6. *From–To Chart.* The From–To Chart is one of the most recent techniques used in plant layout and materials handling work. It is especially helpful where many items flow through an area, such as in a job shop or large general machine shop. It is also useful in any situation where there is a relationship between several areas and an optimum arrangement of the areas is desired. Some of its many uses and advantages are:

1. Analysis of materials movement
2. Planning flow patterns
3. Determination of department locations
4. Comparing alternate layouts
5. Measuring flow pattern efficiency
6. Shortening manufacturing cycles
7. Visualizing materials movement
8. Showing dependency of one area on another
9. Shows volume of movement between areas
10. Shows interrelationship of product lines

The From–To Chart is actually an adaptation of the common mileage chart found on a road map. Figure 9–9 shows the similarity between the two. However, on the From–To Chart, the numbers usually represent

MILEAGE CHART

FROM \ TO	DETROIT	LANSING	GRAND RAPIDS	BATTLE CREEK	MUSKEGON
DETROIT					
LANSING	84				
GRAND RAPIDS	146	62			
BATTLE CREEK	113	48	62		
MUSKEGON	184	100	38	97	

FROM–TO CHART

FROM \ TO	STORES	SHEAR	BRAKE	PRESS	WELD
STORES					
SHEAR	2			3	
BRAKE	2	2		2	
PRESS	2	1	3		
WELD		2	3	1	

Fig. 9–9. The similarity between a common mileage chart and the From–To chart.

some measure of the materials flow between the locations involved. This measure might be the number of moves, distances, weights, volume, or some other factor—or a combination of factors.

The method of constructing a From–To Chart is as follows:

1. Analyze basic data to determine areas of activity, i.e., machine types, departments, buildings, etc. (see Figure 9–10).
2. Arrange areas into most likely looking "best" order [3] and enter in *same* order on both top and left side of From–To Chart form (see Figure 9–11).
3. Reduce basic data to usable form. (Figure 9–10 shows the treatment of Production Routings for 17 parts through a general machine shop. Numbers in squares represent operation on each machine type and sequence of operations, i.e., 5, 10, 20, 30, 40, etc.)
4. Post "moves" on From–To Chart form (Figure 9–11) as tally marks; i.e., on Part No. 1, the first tally mark would go *opposite* Rough Stores, and *under* Mill (to show move *from* Rough Stores *to* Mill). The next would be *opposite* Mill and *under* Lathe, and so on.
5. Prove recording by totaling number of tally marks in each square and totaling each column and row. Each column should equal each comparable row (except first and last, which will be reversed). Grand totals should check.

OBSERVATIONS ON THE FROM–TO CHART. Examination of Figure 9–11 will show that some of the entries are below the diagonal line. On the mileage table, these would serve no useful purpose; but on the From–To Chart, these entries represent *backtracking*. The entries above the line represent moves directly from one department to another, along the line of normal travel. But if a part travels from one department to another and then *back* to a "previous" department, the entry appears *below* the diagonal line.

It will also be noted that when the entries are in the squares *just* above the diagonal line, the parts have moved directly from one department to the next adjacent department. When they appear two spaces above the line, the part has "skipped" a department along the way. So, the objective is to have as many entries as close to the diagonal line as possible. This would indicate that most parts are moving directly from one department to the next in line—there would be a minimum of backtracking.

In actual use, the entries on the chart might be "weighted" to show quantity, weight, distance, etc., involved in each move. This would cause resulting totals in each square to reflect the volume of movement.

---

[3] If dealing with an *existing* situation, list areas in actual order of present flow of material, work, etc.

Part No.	Rough Stores	Mill	Lathe	Drill	Bore	Grind	Press	Hone	Saw	Final Inspection
1	5	10, 20; 30	40	70, 80; 90			50; 60			100
2	5		10, 20	30, 40; 50				60		70
3	5		10	20; 30; 40					10	50
4	5	70	20, 30; 40, 50; 60	80						90
5	5	50, 60	10, 20; 30	20, 40; 80	30	10	70, 90			100
6	5		20	40, 50; 60		40			10, 30	70
7	5		10							50
11	5		10, 20							20
12	5	10		20, 30						30
13	5		10	20			30			40
14	5						10			40
15	5	20					20			30
17	5		10				10			30
18	5		10				10, 20			20
19	5						10, 20			20
20	5									30
34	5									30

Fig. 9–10. Re-cap of operations on seventeen parts.

PLANT _Acme Manufacturing Co._ TRIAL NO. _1_ DATE _June 7_

FROM-TO CHART FROM (Contributor) \ TO (User)	1 Rough Stores	2 Mill	3 Lathe	4 Drill	5 Bore	6 Grind	7 Press	8 Hone	9 Saw	10 Final Inspection	TOTALS
1 Rough Stores		2	8			1	4		2		17
2 Mill			1	2			1			1	5
3 Lathe		1		4			1	1	1	3	11
4 Drill		2			1		2			5	10
5 Bore				1							1
6 Grind				1						1	2
7 Press				2						6	8
8 Hone										1	1
9 Saw			2			1					3
10 Final Inspection											
TOTALS		5	11	10	1	2	8	1	3	17	58 / 58

Fig. 9–11. From-To chart—Trial No. 1.

ANALYZING THE FROM–TO CHART. A quantitative "measure" of the efficiency of the area arrangement can be obtained by taking the "torque" of the system. This is done by totaling the values in the squares *just above* the diagonal line and multiplying *by one*, the values *two squares above by two*, etc. The same procedure is carried out for the values below the diagonal line. If desired, all of the "backtracking" moves might be multiplied by two to show "backtracking" as twice as *bad* as forward movement. This procedure is shown in Figure 9–12.

Forward		Reverse	
$1 \times (2 + 1 + 4 + 1) =$	8	$1 \times (2 + 1) =$	3
$2 \times (8 + 2 + 1)$	$= 22$	$2 \times (1 + 1) =$	4
$3 \times (2 + 6)$	$= 24$	$3 \times (2 + 1) =$	9
$4 \times (1 + 1 + 1)$	$= 12$	$6 \times (2)$	$= 12$
$5 \times (1 + 1)$	$= 10$	Sub-Total	28
$6 \times (4 + 1 + 5)$	$= 60$		
$7 \times (3)$	$= 21$		
$8 \times (2 + 1)$	$= 24$		
Sub-Total	181	Grand Total $= 209$	

Fig. 9–12. "Torque" calculations on From–To chart—Trial No. 1 (Fig. 9–11).

Since Figure 9–11 shows several entries below the diagonal line (representing backtracking) and some larger entries several squares *above* the line, a rearrangement might be attempted in order to find a better arrangement, or sequence of areas. By inspection, it appears that "Press" and "Final Inspection" might be moved "up" to get the larger values closer to the diagonal line. This is shown in Figure 9–13.

Recalculating the "torque" results in the improvement shown in Figure 9–14.

This new arrangement shows considerable improvement, since the objective is the lowest practicable *total* value. These rearrangements might be tried over and over again, until an optimum solution is reached. If a computor were available—and the optimum arrangement were of sufficient importance—one could try out *every* possible arrangement!

As can be seen from this brief preesentation, the From–To Chart is an extremely useful technique in flow planning. Many variations and adaptations will suggest themselves to the plant layout engineer.

7. *Activity Relationship Chart*. It has been pointed out previously that the flow of materials is the primary basis for layout planning. However, the location of the related service areas is of great importance—and in some cases, of more importance than the flow of materials. The service areas must be integrated with the over-all flow pattern so that necessary facilities are conveniently available.

PLANT _Acme Manufacturing Co._ TRIAL NO. _2_ DATE _June 7_

FROM–TO CHART

FROM (Contributor) \ TO (User)	1 Rough Stores	2 Lathe	3 Drill	4 Mill	5 Press	6 Final Inspection	7 Saw	8 Bore	9 Hone	10 Grind	TOTALS
1 Rough Stores		8	4	2	4		2				17
2 Lathe			2	2	1	3	1			1	11
3 Drill				1	2						10
4 Mill					1	5		1	1		5
5 Press						6					8
6 Final Inspection											
7 Saw						1				1	3
8 Bore						1					1
9 Hone						1					1
10 Grind											2
TOTALS		11	10	5	8	17	3	1	1	2	58 / 58

Fig. 9–13. From-To chart—Trial No. 2.

Forward

$$1 \times (8 + 4 + 1 + 1 + 6) = 20$$
$$2 \times (2 + 2 + 1) = 10$$
$$3 \times (2 + 1 + 5 + 1) = 27$$
$$4 \times (4 + 3) = 28$$
$$5 \times (1 + 1) = 10$$
$$6 \times (2 + 1) = 18$$
$$9 \times (1) = 9$$

Sub-Total   122

Reverse

$$1 \times (2) = 2$$
$$2 \times (1 + 2) = 6$$
$$3 \times (1) = 3$$
$$4 \times (1) = 4$$
$$5 \times (2 + 1) = 15$$

Sub-Total   30

Grand Total   152

Fig. 9–14. "Torque" calculations on From–To chart—Trial No. 2 (Fig. 9–13).

The Activity Relationship Chart is an ideal technique for planning the relationship between any group of related activities. It is helpful in such cases as:

1. Preliminary allocation of sequence for a From–To Chart
2. Relative location of work centers or departments in an office
3. Location of activities in a service-type business
4. Location of work centers in a maintenance or repair operation
5. Relative location of service areas within production facility
6. Showing which activities are related to each other
7. Preliminary analysis of relationship for Activity Relationship Diagram (Chapter 10)

The Activity Relationship Chart is similar to the From–To Chart, except that only one set of locations is indicated. In fact it is again similar to some road map mileage tables, except that quantitative numbers are usually replaced by qualitative letters and numbers. A typical Activity Relationship Chart is shown in Figure 9–15. As developed by Richard Muther,[4] the following relationship code indicates which activities are related to each other and how important each closeness relationship is. In addition, Muther has provided space in the lower half of each "box" to insert a code number representing the substantiating reason for each closeness relationship. Reasons will change for different situations and the list below is only to indicate typical reasons.

Closeness	Color	Typical Reasons
A—Absolutely necessary	Red	1. Use same equipment or facilities
E—Especially important	Orange	2. Use common records
I—Important	Green	3. Share same personnel
O—Ordinary closeness	Blue	4. Share same space
U—Unimportant	Uncolored	5. Degree of personal contact
X—Undesirable	Brown	6. Degree of paperwork contact
		7. Sequence of work flow
		8. Perform similar work
		9. Noise, dirt, fumes, vibration
		10. Interruption of personnel
		11. Urgency of contact
		12. Others as may be necessary

[4] Muther, Richard, "Systematic Layout Planning," Industrial Education Institute, Boston, 1961—Forms used by courtesy of Richard Muther.

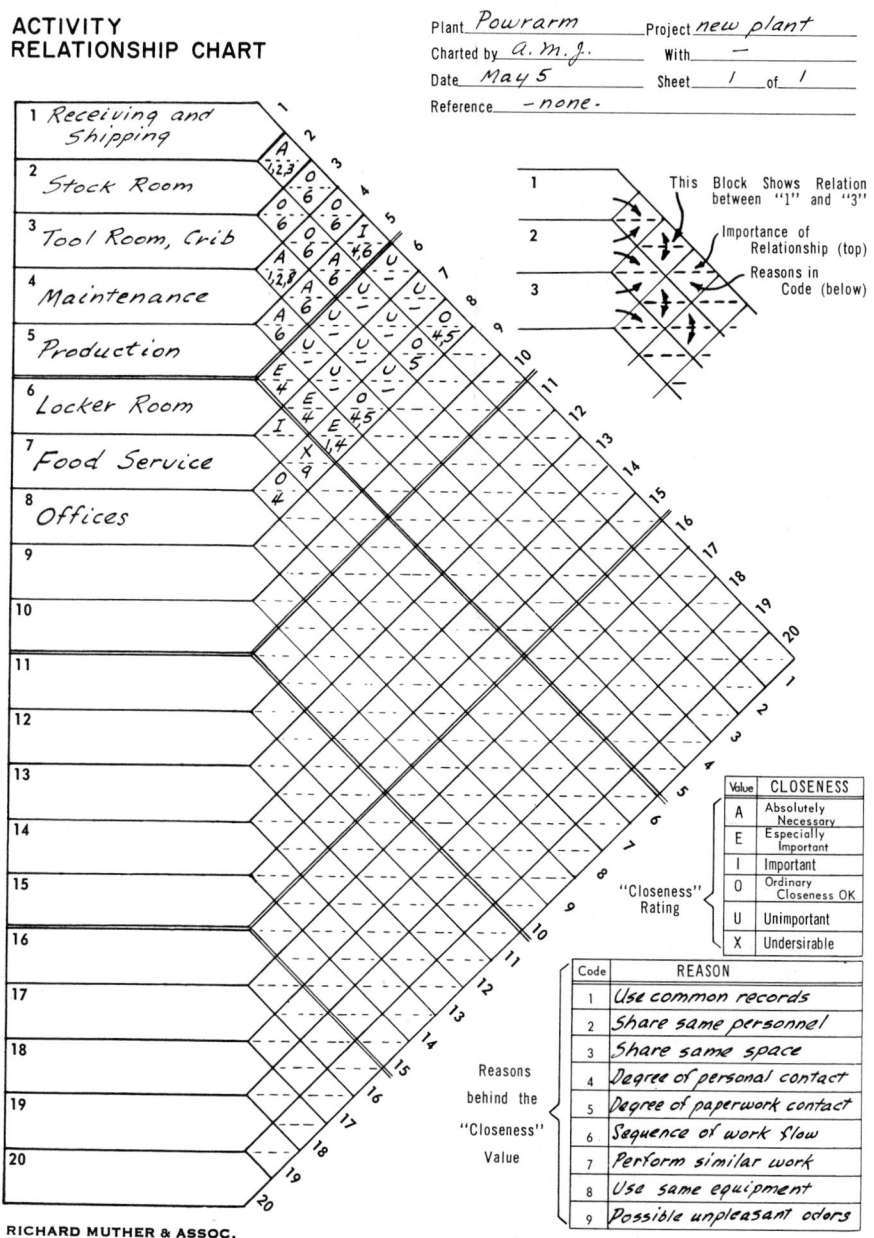

Fig. 9–15. Activity relationship chart for Powrarm plant.

On the Activity Relationship Chart blank form, the "Reason" column is left blank to permit entry of applicable substantiating reasons for each specific situation.

The codes are used as shown in Figure 9–16. As can be seen, the Activity Relationship Chart shows which activities are related to others and the importance of the relationship.

In making the chart, the procedure is as follows:

1. Identify activities.
2. List activities on chart (put production or operating activities near the top and group similar or related activities).
3. Establish ratings (by knowledge, calculations, discussion, or survey).
4. Evaluate and enter code letters and numbers.
5. Fill in substantiating reasons.

When the chart has been completed and all persons involved are satisfied with the ratings, it can be used as an excellent guide in the allocation of areas in the over-all flow pattern. It will also be used as a basis for the Area Relationship Diagram, later on.

It should be noted that the above analysis has *not* dealt with the detailed production flow, but considers "production" as a unit of activity. In many cases, "production" would be broken down into departments or work centers. An alternative would be to include only those production areas that are closely related to the other activities charted. Another alternative, where production activities are not closely related to service activities, would be to make a separate chart for the subdivisions of production.

Some of the other techniques previously discussed, such as the Operation Process Chart, From–To Chart, Flow Process Chart, etc., are commonly used to analyze or plan the flow within the production area.

Many other variations, adaptations, and conventions have been used with the Activity Relationship Chart and will suggest themselves to the plant layout engineer in the course of his work. Particularly useful is the addition of some form of quantitative data to the Activity Relationship Chart.

CONCLUSION

This chapter has presented those techniques which are primarily useful in planning or analyzing materials and activity flow. As indicated previously, not all would be used on a given project. Instead they would be selected to fit the problem at hand and used to supplement each other.

The next chapter will present the techniques used in space planning.

QUESTIONS

1. Why is it so important to *know* the factors to be considered in planning the materials flow pattern?
2. What are some of the important factors?
3. Briefly describe and differentiate between:
   a) Assembly Chart
   b) Operation Process Chart
   c) Flow Process Chart
   d) Flow Diagram
   e) From–To Chart
   f) Activity Relationship Chart
4. Give an example or two of proper uses or applications for each.
5. How would you construct an Assembly Chart or Operation Process Chart for a product composed of several hundred parts?
6. What is indicated on the From–To Chart when entries appear *below* the diagonal line? What is the procedure for correcting the situation?
7. What is meant by taking the "torque" of a From–To Chart? What does it accomplish?

10

Planning and Allocating Space

Introduction. The previous chapter has dealt with the problems involved in planning activity interrelationships. It now becomes necessary to think, not in general terms of activities, but more specifically, in the concrete terms of actual square feet of space available, required, or to be allocated to each activity, area, or function. This chapter will present the Activity Relationship Diagram and the Area Allocation Diagram as tools for the actual allocation of space to each plant functional area. This is the last "preliminary" planning step prior to the detailed planning of materials handling methods, individual work stations, and the final plant layout.

Factors for Consideration in Space Planning. Although the techniques presented in this chapter will aid in the development of space requirements, there are some factors which cannot be easily "calculated" into the planning process. They are primarily items with which the planner must be acquainted, and which he must have sufficiently in mind to permit him to plan them "into" the layout. Some of these factors are:

External Materials Handling Facilities. As pointed out in Chapters 6, 7, and 9, the external transportation facilities are a part of the over-all production flow pattern. Materials which are delivered to and finished products which are shipped from the plant must be moved in coordination with the internal plant activities. Therefore the location of receiving and shipping facilities must be integrated with the location of public transportation facilities and the intended flow of materials within the plant. As indicated in Figure 10–1, the over-all flow pattern is extremely broad in concept; and this must be kept in mind continuously during the flow planning process.

Expansion. A very common fault in plant layout planning—or lack of it—is the failure to plan for the fact that the enterprise *may* grow and require additional facilities. Whether this becomes necessary due to increased volume, new products, or any other reason, it is extremely wise to make plans at the very beginning for the *possibility* of future growth. One has only to look about at the industrial monstrosities which have been built piece-by-piece with no thought but for the immediate space needs.

Additional space can be obtained by any of several methods:

1. Use additional space already available.
2. Obtain and use adjacent or nearby buildings.
3. Construct mezzanines or balconies.
4. Purchase or design building to facilitate expansion.

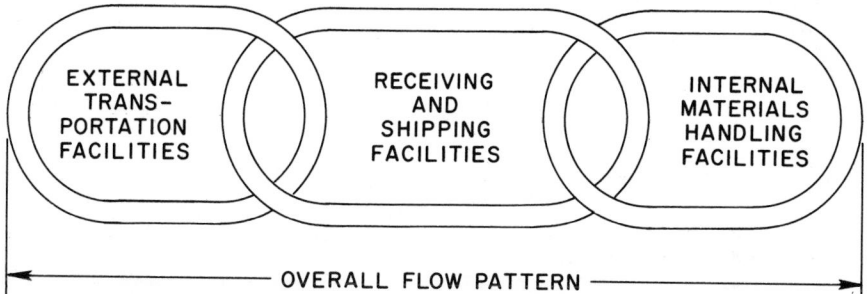

OVERALL FLOW PATTERN

Fig. 10–1. Relationship between external transportation facilities and the overall flow pattern.

Since the latter is preferable, and more within the scope of this text, these are some of the factors to consider in buying or planning for expansion:

1. Building shape—probably rectangular to facilitate construction of additions
2. Location of building on property—located with adequate space for expansion and available in the logical or proper directions
3. Construction—build with removable or demountable walls to provide easy access to future additions
4. Construction features—consider such possibilities as:
   a) Roof bearing on columns, not walls
   b) Module, or bay size to permit easy duplication and to accommodate possible future equipment and facilities
   c) Location of utilities to serve not only present needs but also future requirements:
      (1) Electrical distribution center
      (2) Toilets, etc.
      (3) Air compressor
      (4) Heating and/or steam source
      (5) Sewer, roof, and floor drainage
      (6) Water supply for processes, toilets, and sprinkler system
   d) Installation of oversize conduit, piping, etc., and stubbed or capped at end for ease of extension
5. Location of offices and other service areas to serve equally well *after* expansion

Figures 10–2 through 10–12 illustrate some of the above factors and features.

Fig. 10–2. Mezzanine toilet facilities. (By permission of The Austin Company.)

Flexibility. Although a plant or department may be planned for the production of a certain quantity of a certain part, there are occasions when it may be necessary to alter original plans. As was indicated previously, this change may be for one of several causes:

1. Design change
2. Increased or decreased demand for part
3. Adding a new product to the line

Many of the changes thus called for may be more easily made if they are anticipated in the original planning. A common way of facilitating the rearrangement of productive equipment is to install utility systems into which service connections are easily tied, when the building is constructed. Good examples are the electrical ducts and the cutting-compound pipe lines which may be installed overhead, down the centers of bays. Such arrangements permit machines to be "plugged-out," moved to a new location, and "plugged-in" almost at will. Figure 10–6 shows

Fig. 10–3. Mezzanine office area over a toilet. (By permission of The Austin Company.)

the use of such an overhead system to simplify the disconnecting and reconnecting of a machine to a power source. Still another method is to install cellular steel beams as an integral part of the floor. Through the cells or channels utility lines are run. The cells may be tapped into with very little trouble at almost any place in the floor. Figure 10–7 shows a cut-away view of this cellular type of flooring.

An interesting story is told concerning the flexibility of such systems. An employee in a certain plant left his machine during his lunch hour.

Upon returning after his meal, he discovered that the machine and all traces of it had vanished. In its place was a new machine, and another employee already at work. The first machine had been moved to a new location several hundred feet away, although he had not been told about the plan, and was there ready for him to continue his work.

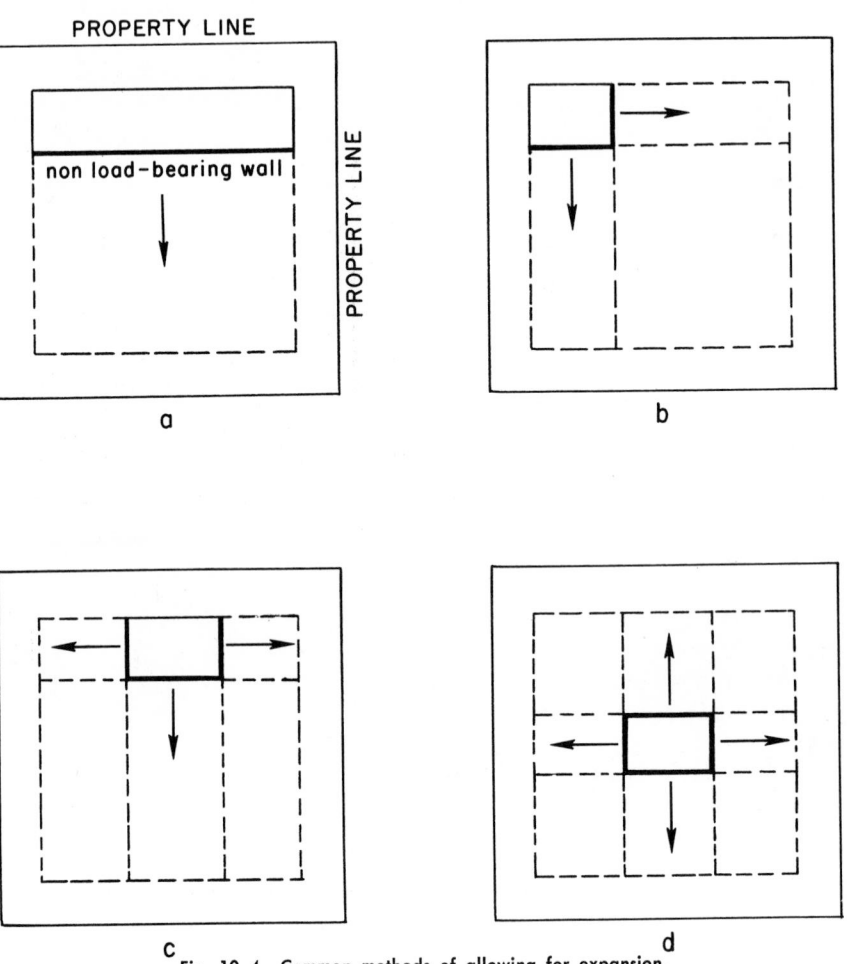

Fig. 10-4. Common methods of allowing for expansion.

Other ways in which flexibility can be maintained are by means of self-contained machines which can be moved around to take advantage of existing facilities, as explained above. Mobile equipment is used by the American Seating Company, which makes sheet metal parts of various kinds, in limited quantities on one line of large presses. Smaller presses

Fig. 10–5. "Portable" partitions. (By permission of E. F. Hauserman Co.)

Fig. 10–6. Electric power connections placed overhead for flexibility in machine relocation. (By permission of Trumbull Electric and Manufacturing Co.)

for intermediate operations are mounted on skids and moved in and out, as called for, by a lift truck. Three of these presses are shown in Figure 10–8.

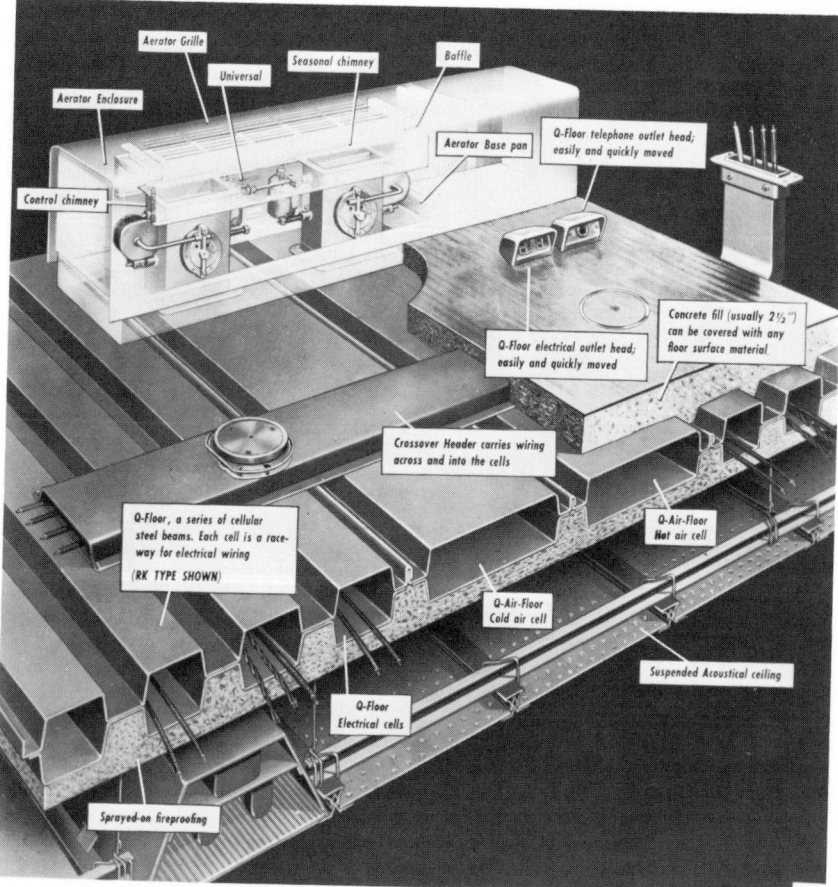

Fig. 10–7. Q-flooring construction for utility distribution. (By permission of H. H. Robertson Co.)

Another sheet-metal plant has installed a special mounting pit along which any of the many presses required may be mounted in the order required. Pits for large and small presses are shown in Figures 10–9 and 10–10.

Use of Roof. It should be remembered that the plant contains six levels of activity, as discussed in Chapter 6. One of these levels is the roof. It is commonly used to support drying ovens, water tanks, electrical and air conditioning equipment, etc. Also, do not overlook the possibility of other levels, i.e., within the trusses, and a basement, or utility tunnel. Some plants have personnel corridors, employee and service facilities below the manufacturing floor. A central, cross-wise, or perimeter tunnel may also be adequate for utility lines. This is very common in modern, one-floor, "sprawling" school buildings.

Fig. 10–8. Small presses mounted on skids for spotting between larger presses by fork lift trucks. (By permission of American Seating Co.)

Inter-Building Handling. Even the fact that plant buildings may be widely separated need not interfere too much with materials flow between them. Although surface transportation is most common, many buildings are connected to each other, either underground or overhead. Figures 10–11 and 10–12 show such possibilities.

Activity Relationship Diagram. The Activity Relationship Diagram is a logical next step after constructing the Activity Relationship Chart. It is based on the latter and is the first attempt to actually represent individual activities by "space"—even though only as dimensionless "blocks" at this

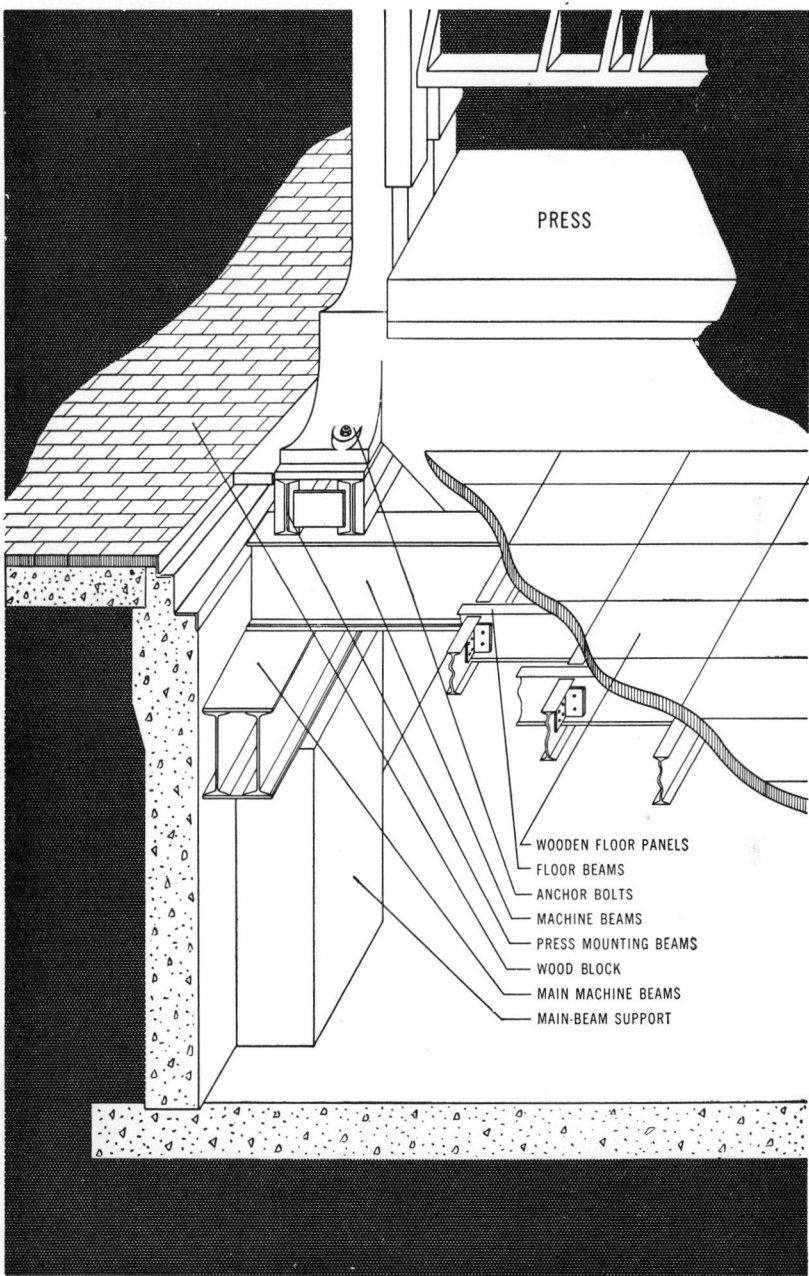

PRESS

WOODEN FLOOR PANELS
FLOOR BEAMS
ANCHOR BOLTS
MACHINE BEAMS
PRESS MOUNTING BEAMS
WOOD BLOCK
MAIN MACHINE BEAMS
MAIN-BEAM SUPPORT

Fig. 10–9. Cut-a-way section of a large press pit. (By permission of Factory Magazine.)

point in the planning process. The Activity Relationship Diagram is in reality a block diagram indicating an approximate activity relationship and again may show production as a single "block" of space—or several as indicated in Chapter 9. The Activity Relationship Diagram is constructed as follows:

1. Analyze the Activity Relationship Chart (Figure 9–15) with the aid of the worksheet shown in Figure 10–13.

2. Enter activity areas in left column.

3. Enter "Degree of Closeness" code letter (A,E,I,O,U,X) in the six spaces under the title.

4. Enter in each "square" the *numbers* (from Figure 9–15) of the areas related to each of those in the left column—by *degree* of closeness; i.e., for No. 5 Production, is "A" to Numbers 2, 3, and 4; "E" to 6, 7, and 8; and "I" to 1.

5. Transfer data from worksheet to the block templates shown in Figure 10–14, using corners of templates as indicated, to enter data: i.e., for No. 5, Production:

Fig. 10–10. Tunnel under floor of a small press department. (By permission of Factory Magazine.)

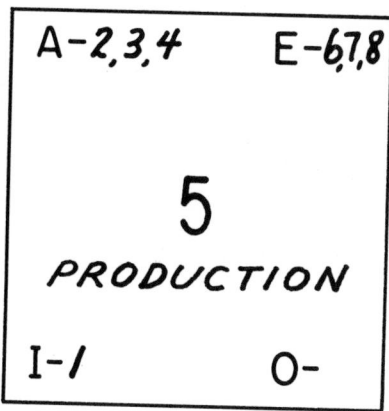

Undesirable relationships ("X") may be entered in red pencil on the block template, over the activity number.

6. Cut out "block templates" from form as shown in Figure 10–14.

7. Arrange block templates into an Activity Relationship Diagram, matching first the "A's," next the "E's," etc., in the most appropriate arrangement; i.e., No. 5 Production should be closest to 2, 3, and 4; next closest to 6, 7, and 8, etc. So, No. 5 should be "surrounded" by 2, 3, and 4, etc. Figure 10–15A illustrates a possible arrangement satisfying most of the closeness requirements. As with many of the other techniques, there is probably no "one best" arrangement. Other trials should be made until all concerned are satisfied. In fact, an adaptation of the From–To Chart could be constructed and the relationships assigned numerical values—as shown under From–To Charts—to "prove" the "best" answer.

In cases where there are a large number of activities and relationships, it is desirable to divide them into *groups* of related activities and work first with the larger groups—as when the production area is large and complex, or there are a larger number of service areas than in the accompanying illustration, then, the larger areas may be more easily related to each other—and the smaller areas *within* the larger areas.

An alternative technique, developed by Richard Muther,[1] uses a combination of lines, symbols, and colors, and results in a diagram as shown in Figure 10–15B. In this figure, the symbols are modifications of the conventional process symbols, and the number of lines between symbols represent the importance of the closeness; i.e., 4 lines = A, 3 = E, 2 = I, etc. "Wiggly" lines are used to show undesired relationships.

[1] Muther, *op. cit.*, Chap. 6.

Fig. 10–11A. Underground tunnel between buildings for utilities and personnel passage. By permission of The Austin Company.)

Fig. 10–11B. Underground passageway for employees, from plant entrance to various production areas (via stairs up) and service areas on basement level. (By permission of The Austin Company.)

Fig. 10–12. Overhead handling between buildings. (By permission of American Monorail Co.)

WORKSHEET FOR ACTIVITY RELATIONSHIP DIAGRAM

ACTIVITY AREA	DEGREE OF CLOSENESS					
	A	E	I	O	U	X
1 Receiving and Shipping	2	–	5	3, 4, 8	6, 7,	–
2 Stock Room	1, 5	–	–	3, 4, 8	6, 7,	–
3 Tool Room and Tool Crib	4, 5	–	–	1, 2	6, 7, 8	–
4 Maintenance	3, 5	–	–	1, 2, 8	6, 7	–
5 Production	2, 3, 4	6, 7, 8	1	–	–	8
6 Locker Room		5	7		1, 2, 3, 4	8
7 Food Service	–	5	6	8	1, 2, 3, 4	
8 Offices		5		1, 2, 4, 7	3	6
9						
10						
11						
12						
13						
14						
15						
16						

Fig. 10–13. Worksheet for activity relationship diagram for Powrarm factory.

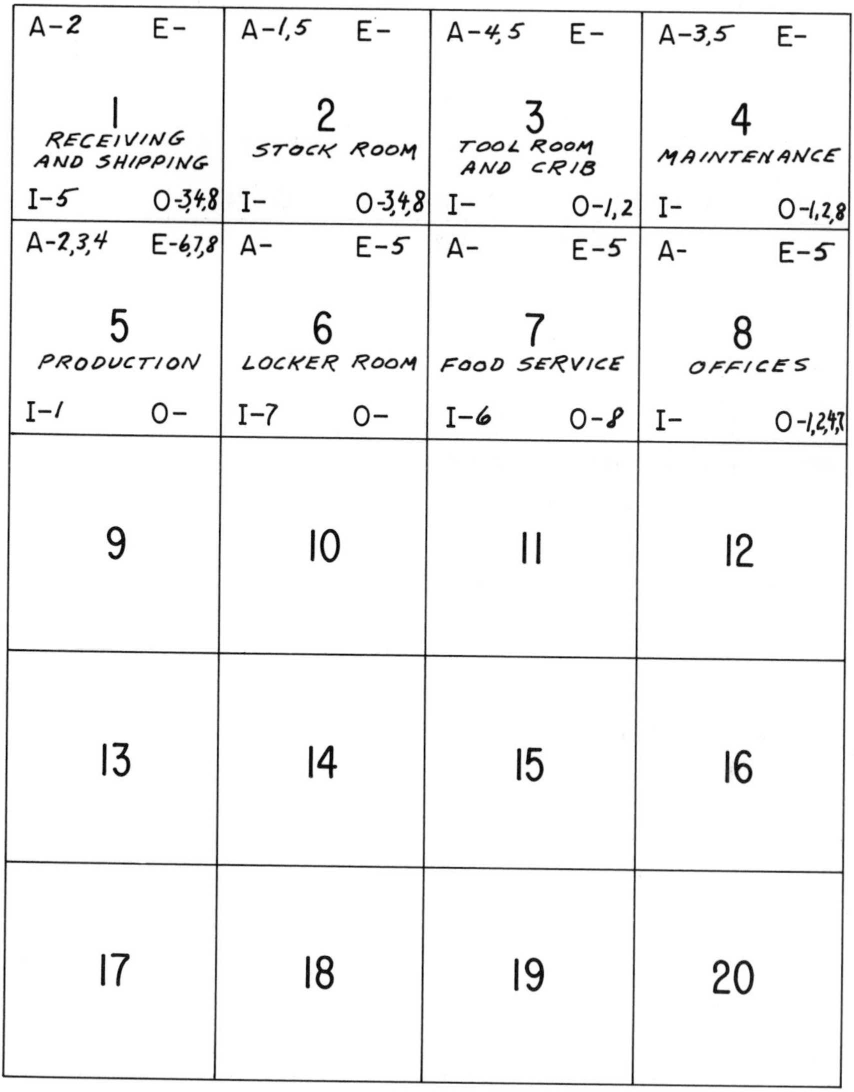

A–2 E–	A–1,5 E–	A–4,5 E–	A–3,5 E–
1 RECEIVING AND SHIPPING	**2** STOCK ROOM	**3** TOOL ROOM AND CRIB	**4** MAINTENANCE
I–5 O–3,4,8	I– O–3,4,8	I– O–1,2	I– O–1,2,8
A–2,3,4 E–6,7,8	A– E–5	A– E–5	A– E–5
5 PRODUCTION	**6** LOCKER ROOM	**7** FOOD SERVICE	**8** OFFICES
I–1 O–	I–7 O–	I–6 O–8	I– O–1,2,4,7
9	**10**	**11**	**12**
13	**14**	**15**	**16**
17	**18**	**19**	**20**

Fig. 10–14. Activity relationship diagram block templates for Powrarm factory.

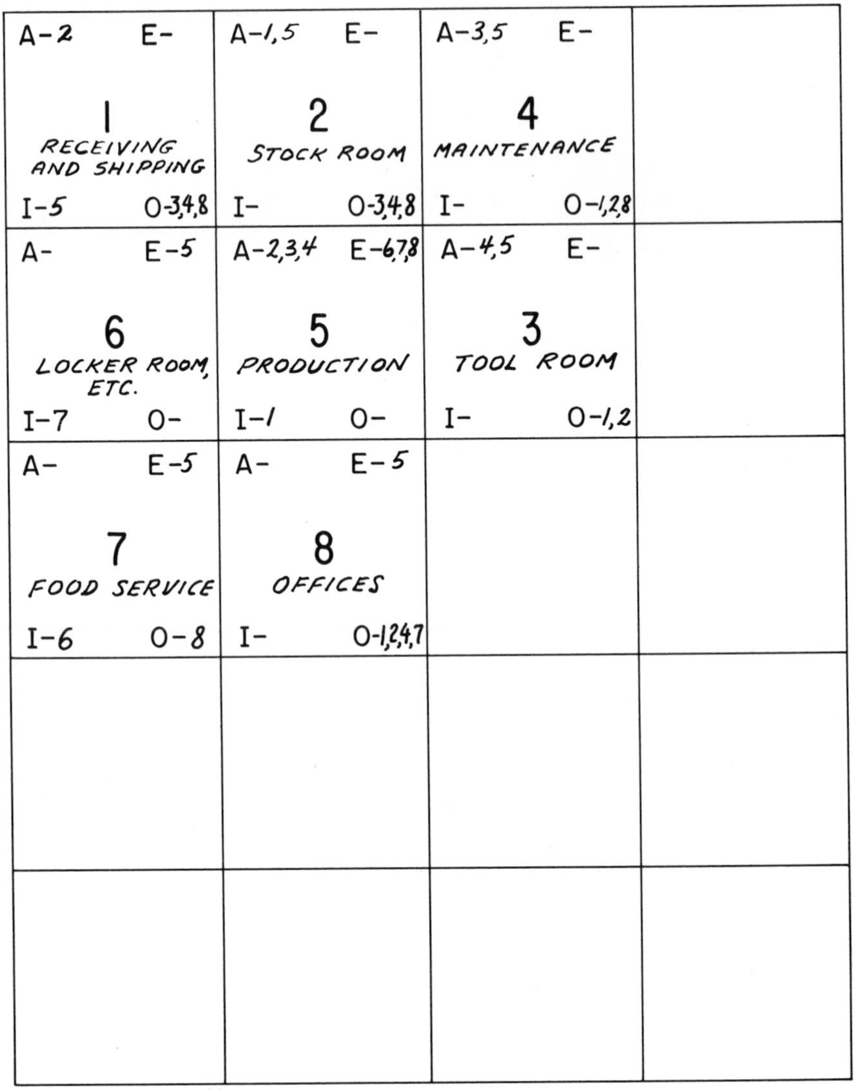

A-2 E- **1** RECEIVING AND SHIPPING I-5 O-3,4,8	A-1,5 E- **2** STOCK ROOM I- O-3,4,8	A-3,5 E- **4** MAINTENANCE I- O-1,2,8	
A- E-5 **6** LOCKER ROOM, ETC. I-7 O-	A-2,3,4 E-6,7,8 **5** PRODUCTION I-1 O-	A-4,5 E- **3** TOOL ROOM I- O-1,2	
A- E-5 **7** FOOD SERVICE I-6 O-8	A- E-5 **8** OFFICES I- O-1,2,4,7		

Fig. 10–15A. Activity relationship diagram for Powrarm plant.

The Muther approach is not unlike that suggested by De Villeneuve,[2] and later by Hoffman[3] and Downs.[4] They have all developed similar flow diagrams, with activity areas connected by lines or bands of varying width or thickness. The width of the line indicates the volume of flow between areas and aids in properly interrelating them in the early stages of layout planning.

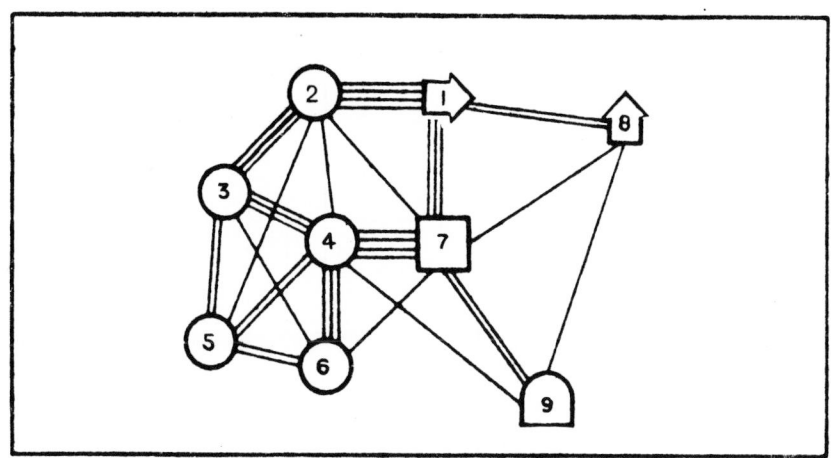

Fig. 10–15B.   Activity relationship diagram as developed by Muther.

The Activity Relationship Diagram has been helpful in planning the preliminary relationships between activity areas. The next step is to convert the activity areas from block templates to estimated space requirements.

Estimating Space Requirements.   The Area Allocation Diagram adds estimated space requirements to the concept of the Activity Relationship Diagram and leads one step closer to the final plant layout. Before this can be accomplished an estimated area must be determined for each activity being considered in the layout project. This has already been discussed for plant service areas in Chapters 7 and 8. Area requirements for those activities can be obtained from the Plant Service Area Planning Sheet (Figure 8–21) or estimated or calculated on that form at this point in the planning process.

[2] De Villeneuve, Louis, "The Quantitative Flow Chart," in proceedings of 2d biennial Packaging and Material Handling Institute, University of Southern California, 1952.

[3] Hoffman, John R., "An Evaluation of Quantitative Techniques in Plant Layout," privately circulated.

[4] Downs, George, "Best Way to Layout a Job Shop," *Factory Management and Maintenance,* Nov. 1956.

PRODUCTION SPACE REQUIREMENT SHEET

NO.	Activity, Dep't, Area or Item	Oper. No.	Machine or Equipment	SPACE REQUIREMENTS							
				Machine, etc. L × W = A +	Auxil. Equip. L × W = A +	Operator Space A + 3' × L = A +	Material Space L × W = A = SUB-Total	Sub-total × 150% Allowance =	No. of Mach.=Operation	Total Sq.Ft. per Operation	Total per Area
I	Base	10	LeBlonde Eng. Lathe	3x6=18	2x8=16	3x6=18	3x5=15	67	100	1	100	
		20	W & S Turret Lathe	4x7=28	2x20=40	3x7=21	(incl.)	89	134	3	402	
		30	Drill Press	3x4=12	2x2=4	3x3=9	(incl.)	25	38	1	38	
		40	Drill Press	3x4=12	2x2=4	3x3=9	(incl.)	25	38	1	38	
		50	Drill Press-2 spindle	3x5=15	2x2=4	3x3=9	(incl.)	28	42	1	42	
		60	Inspection Bench	2x6=12	2x2=4	3x6=18	(incl.)	34	51	1	51	
		70	Degreaser	3x10=30	–	3x10=30	(incl.)	60	90	1	90	761
III	Handle	10	W&S Turr. Lathe (with bar stock attachment	4x15=60	–	3x15=45	3x12=36	141	212	1	212	
		20	W&S Turret Lathe	4x7=28	–	3x7=21	–	49	75	1	75	
		30	Inspection Bench	2x6=12	–	3x6=18	–	30	45	1	45	
		40	Degreaser	(uses same equipment as Part No. I)						–	–	332

Fig. 10–16. Production space requirement sheet for Powrarm factory.

Estimated space requirements for production and related areas must now be determined. One way of doing this is by calculation of the estimated space required for each piece of plant equipment or related group of equipment. This can be accomplished with the help of the Production Space Requirement Sheet, as shown in Figure 10–16. It is filled out as follows:

1. Enter data from Production Routings, or equivalent, in columns 1, 2, 3, and 4 to identify the work areas involved.

2. Enter space requirement estimates in columns 5, 6, 7, and 8 (all entries in feet).

   — col. 5 = maximum length × maximum width of machine
   — col. 6 = maximum length × maximum width of auxiliary equipment such as tables, benches, etc.
   — col. 7 = maximum length of machine × 3' for operator working area
   — col. 8 = actual size of stock containers, etc.

3. Add columns 5, 6, 7, and 8; enter total in column 9 for subtotal per machine.

4. Multiply subtotal by 150 per cent. This allows access space for materials handling, maintenance and personnel movement, columns, work space share of necessary aisle area, etc. Enter this figure in column 10.

5. Enter number of machines of each type in column 11 (from calculations as shown in Chapter 4). Multiply this number by the figure in column 9 and enter result in column 12.

6. Follow the same procedure for all operations and determine total for each area, department, activity, etc. Enter area totals in column 13.

This procedure will give the estimated total number of square feet required for each department, activity or production area.

An alternate and simpler method for preliminary calculation is to use a predetermined number of square feet to represent a "typical" machine or piece of production equipment. This, of course, would vary with the type of plant and production process. A quick calculation from a present layout (total square feet allocated for *production* ÷ number of machines) would give an adequate figure for planning purposes. For a typical machine shop type of operation, it has been found practicable to use 100 to 150 square feet per machine.

At this point it is necessary to recap all space requirement estimates on the Space Requirement Work Sheet, Figure 10–17. Requirements for the General Office, Production Office, Personnel and Physical Plant areas are obtained from the Plant Service Area Planning Sheet (Figure 8–21). Requirements for production areas are obtained from (1) Production Space Requirement Sheet (Figure 10–16) or (2) estimate of average requirements as indicated above and shown in the example in Figure 10–17.

TOTAL SPACE REQUIREMENT WORK SHEET

FOR ___Powrarm___ PLANT_____

BY___A. M. James___ DATE _Nov. 15_____

Activity or Area	Estimated Square Feet		Module Size 20 X 20 = 400	
	Individual Areas	Sub-Totals	No. Mod.	Size of Area Templates
A. General Services	800			
		800	2	20 x 40
B. Production Services				
20, 22, 23 Rec., Shipping, Whsg.	800		2	20 x 40
21 Stock	1400		$3\frac{1}{2}$	20 x 70
24, 25 Tool Room, Tool Crib	500	2700	$1\frac{1}{4}$	20 x 25
C. Personnel Services				
32 Food Service	750		$1\frac{7}{8}$	20 x 50
33 Locker Room	1050		$2\frac{1}{2}$	20 x 50
		1800		
D. Physical Plant Services				
51 Maintenance	500		$1\frac{1}{4}$	20 x 25
		500		
E. Production	6500	6500	$16\frac{1}{4}$	60 x 108
F. Other				
GRAND TOTALS	12,300	12,300	$30\frac{5}{8}$	

Fig. 10–17. Total space requirement worksheet for Powrarm factory.

After having made the recap of space requirements for all areas, it is necessary to prepare templates to represent the calculated "blocks" of space. For example, Figure 10–17 would call for the following "block" templates:

1.* Receiving, shipping, etc.	800 sq. ft.
2. Stock room	1,400
3. Tool room and crib	500
4. Maintenance	500
5. Production	7,500
6. Lavatory, etc.	500
7. Food service	300
8. General offices	800
	12,300 sq. ft.

Assuming a 20- by 20-foot "module," these templates could be constructed as follows:

1.* Receiving and shipping	20 ft. × 40 ft.
2. Stock room	20 × 70
3. Tool room and crib	20 × 25
4. Maintenance	20 × 25
5. Production	60 × 108
6. Lavatory, etc.	20 × 50
7. Food Service	20 × 50
8. General office	20 × 40

*Numbers from block designation used on Activity Relationship Chart in Figure 9–15.

Using a "block template" worksheet (Figure 10–14), the above areas can be laid out, letting each square represent a 20- by 20-foot area, as shown in Figure 10–18.

Area Allocation Diagram. The next step is to cut out the area templates and arrange them so that they will match (as closely as possible) the Area Relationship Diagram in Figure 10–15A. Of course, this will require some compromises, as well as some possible changes in area shape and sizes. The final result might appear as in Figure 10–19. Note the similarity between Figure 10–19 and Figure 15–9A, the final layout.

Depending upon the final bay size chosen, the block templates might assume a slightly different arrangement. However, the foregoing procedure will be found an ideal method for arriving at an allocation of activity areas and a basis for the detail planning activities to be covered in subsequent chapters.

A similar technique for use in space allocation is the unit area template, developed by Richard Muther [5] to extend his Activity Relationship Diagram (Figure 10–15B). The unit area template concept is similar to the block template except that a specific "block" is broken up into a num-

[5] Muther, Richard, *op. cit.*, Chap. 8.

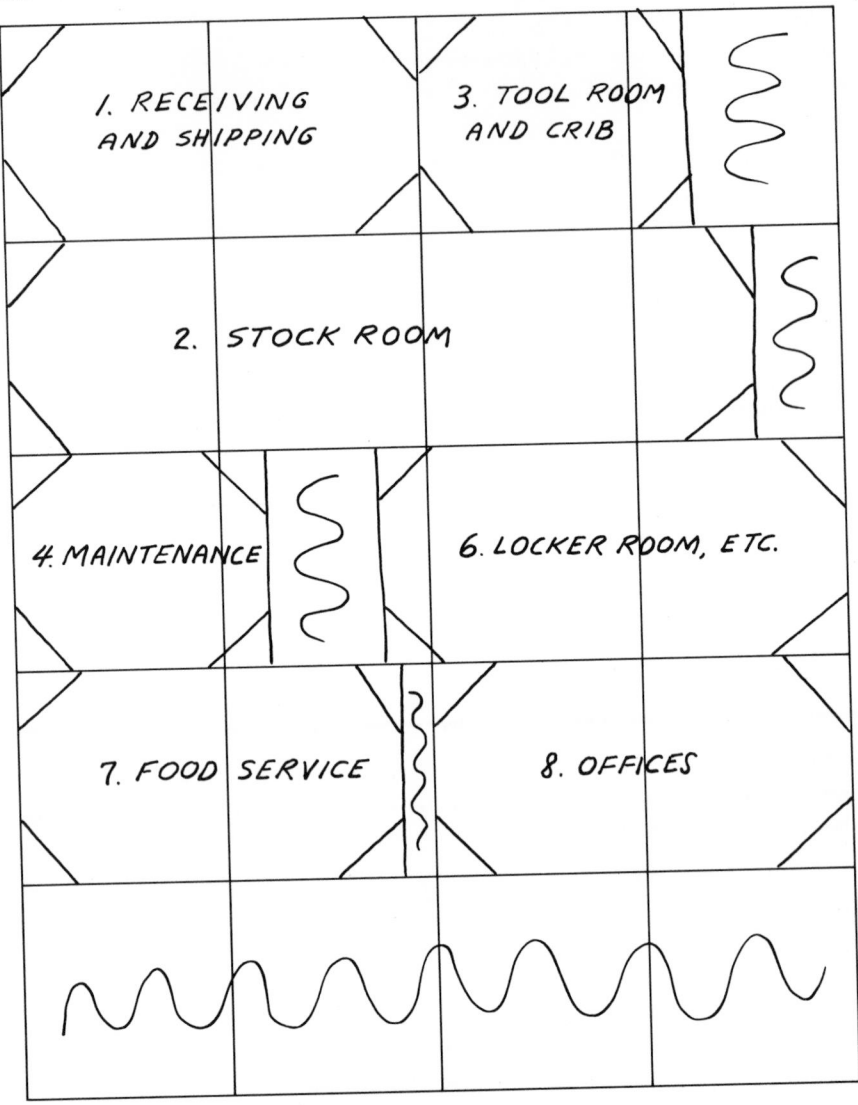

Fig. 10–18. Area templates

ber of smaller units (unit areas). That is, *one* 20- by 20-foot block would become a number of smaller rectangles, or squares, such as the following indicates:

$$1 \text{ block template @ } 20' \times 20' = 400 \text{ sq. ft.}$$
$$4 \text{ unit area templates @ } 10' \times 10' = 400 \text{ sq. ft.}$$
$$16 \text{ unit area templates @ } 5' \times 5' = 400 \text{ sq. ft.}$$

5. PRODUCTION

for Powrarm factory.

The outstanding advantage of the unit area template is that it allows a greater degree of freedom and flexibility in adjusting the various areas to the shape of the space available or desired. As used by Muther, the unit area templates are made of $\frac{1}{32}$-inch plastic, or even wood or tiles. He also adds a color code and letters or numbers to identify the areas involved.

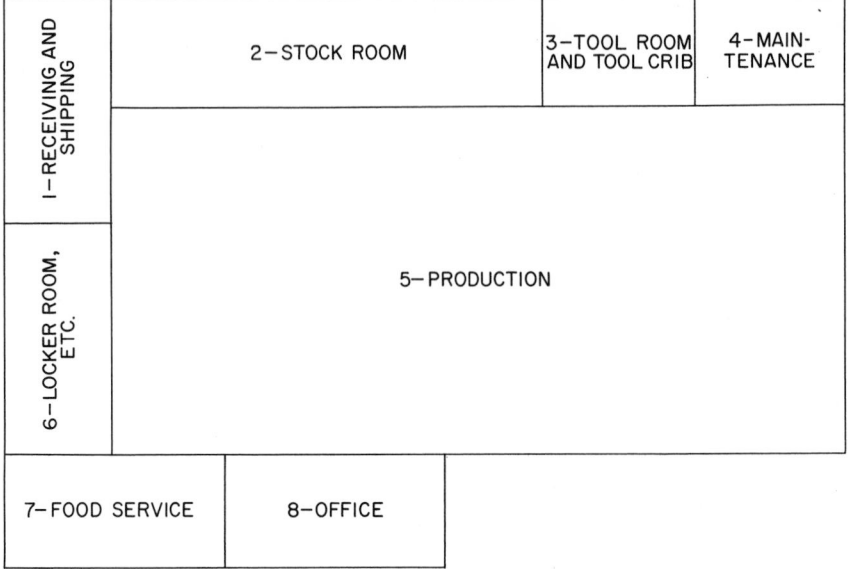

Fig. 10–19. Area allocation diagram for Powrarm factory.

CONCLUSION

The foregoing procedures have resulted in the development of a fairly definite allocation of activity areas—definite both as to relationship and size. Although the procedure may have appeared somewhat lengthy and detailed, it has been orderly and as accurate as was practicable with the amount and type of data commonly available. Each technique presented has contributed its share to this orderly procedure—and moved the project one step closer to the desired goal.

Now that activity, area, and space relationships have been worked out, it is necessary to plan the details *within* each area—both service and production. Subsequent chapters will consider information and procedures necessary for this detailed planning.

However, first it will be necessary to take a "side trip" into the field of materials handling to become acquainted with the equipment and techniques used in the detailed planning. Chapters 11, 12, and 13 will consider materials handling. Chapter 14 will return to the individual work station phase of layout planning.

QUESTIONS

1. How do the external materials handling or transportation facilities affect the flow pattern?
2. Why is possible future expansion a factor in flow planning?
3. What are some of the ways in which future expansion can be allowed for in the original planning process?
4. Differentiate between expansion and flexibility. What are some similarities?
5. In what ways could one provide for flexibility in the planning of a factory or commercial building?
6. What uses can be made of the "space" on a building roof to free interior space for other purposes?
7. What is meant by an Activity Relationship Diagram? Block template?
8. Distinguish between an Activity *Relationship* Diagram and an Area *Allocation* Diagram. What is the specific use, or purpose, of each?
9. How does the *area* template differ from the *block* template?

11

Introduction to Materials Handling

Definition.[1] Materials handling has been defined many times and in many ways. However, the net conclusion is usually that "materials handling is handling materials." In general, this means any material, anywhere, by any means. Various definitions merely attempt to delimit the activity in one way or another. A more meaningful definition would be in terms of the factors making up materials handling: motion, time, place, quantity, and space. Such a definition follows:

1. *Motion*. Parts, materials, and finished products must be moved from location to location. Materials handling is concerned with moving them in the most efficient manner, at the lowest cost.
2. *Time*. Each step in any manufacturing process requires that supplies are on hand the moment they are needed. Materials handling must assure that no production process or customer need will be hampered by having materials arrive on location too late or too early.
3. *Place*. Material is of little value in any industrial activity unless it is in the proper location. Materials handling has the responsibility of delivering the desired material to the right place.
4. *Quantity*. Rate of demand varies between steps in the manufacturing process. Materials handling has the responsibility of being sure that each location continually receives the correct quantity of material—parts, pounds, or gallons.
5. *Space*. Storage space, both active and dormant, is a major consideration in any building, since space costs money. Space requirements are greatly influenced by the efficiency of materials handling planning.

Scope. The common concept of materials handling is most likely associated with industrial plant activity. However, it should be remembered that a sizable portion of the total materials handling activity is not in manufacturing but in the fields of distribution, service industries, agriculture, and construction. In any case, it will be agreed by most all

[1] Adapted from Apple, James M., "Lesson Guide Outline on Material Handling Education" Unit 1 (Material Handling Institute, 1961).

concerned that there exists much more materials handling activity and cost than is either desirable or necessary for the efficient and economical operation of nearly any enterprise. This is rather evident if one examines the range and amount of handling in a typical manufacturing situation. Such a study might show the following materials handling operations on a typical item:

A. Receiving and Stock Storage
    1. Transport to unloading
    2. Unload
    3. Move to quantity check
    4. Move to inspection
    5. Transport to stock storage (or point-of-use)
    6. Place in stock storage
    7. Take out of stock storage
    8. Move to point-of-use

B. Fabrication
    9. Place in position at use point
    10. Move between operations
    11. Move to temporary storage
    12. Place in temporary storage
    13. Take out of temporary storage
    14. Move to next point-of-use
    15. Take out of position at completion point
    16. Move to assembly, storage, or shipping

C. Assembly
    17. Place in location near assembly
    18. Move to assembly station
    19. Put part on product
    20. Remove product from assembly line
    21. Move to packing and shipping

D. Packing and Shipping
    22. Place in storage
    23. Take out of storage
    24. Move to packing
    25. Move to shipping
    26. Move to temporary storage
    27. Move to check-count
    28. Load on carrier
    29. Move to customer locations

Even though there are a total of **29**, or even more, "handlings" indicated above, it is *not* an exaggeration. And rather obviously, it is expensive! Note also that there are only a relatively few *productive* operations. In fact, it is commonly acknowledged that materials handling activities account for 30–35 per cent of all production costs. Instances are on record where the figure has been as high as 62 per cent. Whenever goods are manufactured, material is handled and, all too frequently, rehandled. Here, then, is an ideal place for the plant layout engineer to take a big slice out of the product cost. The chart in Figure 11–1 gives some idea of the materials handling problem faced by industry.

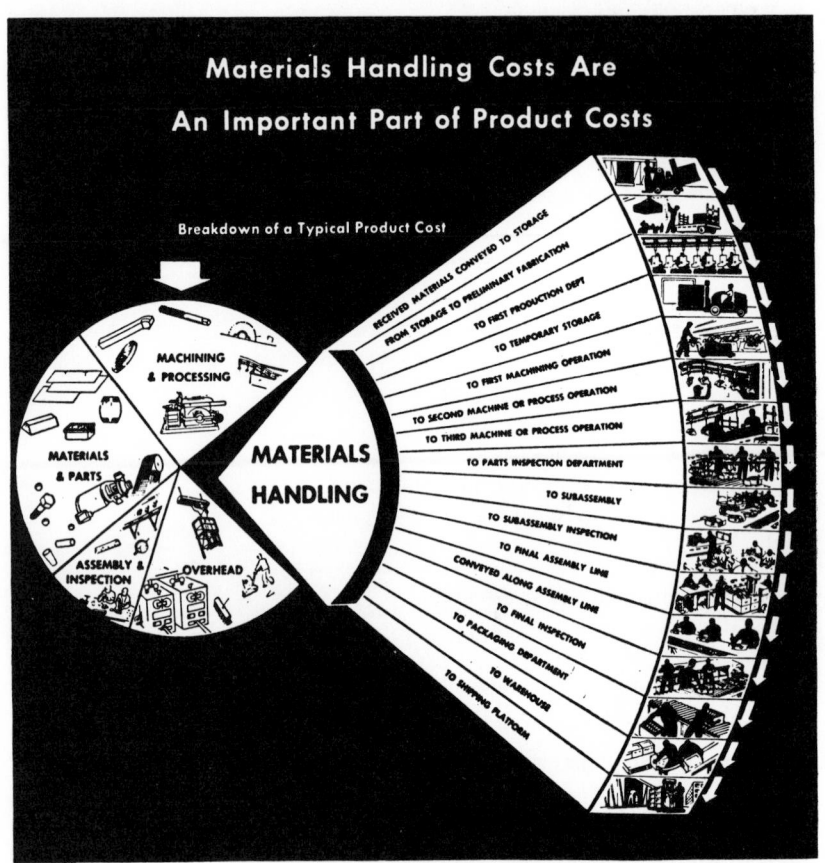

Fig. 11–1. Extent of materials handling activity. (By permission of Mill and Factory.)

It has been estimated that an item is being worked on only 20 per cent of the time it is in a plant. The other 80 per cent of the time is used up in storage or handling time. One authority states that 22 per cent of industry's manpower is used in handling materials.

Another idea of the scope of the materials handling problem is gained from a study by a leading periodical. A survey of manufacturing and distribution establishments tabulated footage of conveyors in use, as follows:

Gravity roller and wheel conveyor	7,678,584 ft.
Live roller conveyor	2,673,074
Belt conveyor	26,546,715
Trolley and tow conveyors	12,703,549
Vertical conveyors	8,039,498
Screw and pneumatic conveyors	6,133,830
Other types	4,113,531
	67,888,781 ft.

Of this total (over 13,000 miles!), 98 per cent is in manufacturing and 2 per cent in distribution.

Objectives of Materials Handling. The general objective of materials handling has been stated as follows: [2] ". . . to transport materials from point to point, without retrogression, with a minimum of transfers, and deliver them to their appropriate workplaces or production centers, in a manner to avoid congestion, delays, and unnecessary handling."

More specific objectives, in terms of expected advantages, are: [3]

1. Reduced Costs
   a) Lower inventory and production control costs
   b) Better space utilization
   c) Minimum of handling
   d) Shorter production time cycle
   e) Larger unit loads and less cost per piece handled
   f) Reduced demurrage
   g) Higher production per square foot or per employee

2. Reduced Waste
   a) Less spoilage
   b) Less damage by improper handling
   c) Upgrading scrap by selective handling

3. Increased Productive Capacity
   a) Assured constant rate of production
   b) Coordinated handling system
   c) Better control of material
   d) More effective use of manpower
   e) Automatic handling
   f) Less idle machine time
   g) Eliminate production bottlenecks

4. Improved Working Conditions
   a) Safer working situations

[2] Alford, L. A., and J. R. Bangs, *Production Handbook* (The Ronald Press Co., New York, 1947).
[3] Adapted from *Basic Concepts of Material Handling* (Material Handling Institute, 1958).

b) Less fatigue

c) Improved personnel comfort

d) Upgrading employees to more productive work

5. Improved Distribution

a) Quicker delivery to customer

b) Increased production volume, due to lower costs and selling price

c) Reduced damage claims

It is apparent that the above objectives are of major importance in the efficient operation of any business enterprise. It is to assure the carrying out of these objectives that the plant layout engineer devotes a large portion of his efforts to materials handling planning.

How Materials Handling Affects Plant Layout. As has been pointed out in previous chapters, the materials flow pattern is the basis for an efficient plant layout. However, the flow pattern is *static*. It is the materials handling equipment which causes the materials to flow and enables the flow pattern to become *dynamic*. Therefore, it is of utmost importance that the materials handling problem be considered concurrently with the plant layout problem. Chapter 12 will present a selection of commonly used materials handling equipment, and Chapter 13 will discuss materials handling analysis and planning procedures.

Principles of Materials Handling.[4] As an aid in amplifying the objectives of materials handling and applying materials handling to the layout planning procedure, the principles of materials handling will prove extremely helpful. A principle is a rule, fundamental, or other statement of an observed truth. Over a period of years, materials handling men have learned from experience that certain fundamental truths exist in materials handling as in other fields.

In all fields of human activity, contemporary practitioners rely on the experience of their predecessors. This is true in government, politics, medicine, law, and engineering—to mention only a few. It would be as foolish for the practicing materials handling man to overlook the principles of materials handling as it would for anyone else to overlook the things which those who have gone before him have found to be true and had accomplished with success.

The principles of materials handling then represent an accumulation of knowledge, built up over a period of years by others who have been practicing in the field. They have tried out or discovered various relationships and found them to be true, successful, worthwhile, and tending to reduce costs. As they were repeatedly applied and found to "hold up under fire," they were passed on to others and eventually written down.

[4] Adapted from Apple, James M., *op. cit.*, Unit 2.

The following principles represent a composite of materials handling experience representing literally hundreds of years of practice by engineers in every field of industrial and commercial activity. The principles are arranged in logical groups, related to various areas of activity in the materials handling field. They are presented as guides to action and suggestions for obtaining economical materials handling.

1. General.

a) Keep all handling at a minimum.
b) Handle as many pieces in one unit as is practical.
c) Design handling aids into large, heavy, or bulky objects.
d) Eliminate unnecessary handling by proper planning, scheduling, and dispatching.
e) Reduce rehandling time to a minimum.
f) Study all materials handling problems in relation to plant layout and vice versa.
g) Plan for over-all economy.
h) Materials handling operations are only as efficient as the physical layout of the plant.
i) Modify existing building facilities to permit full use of available capacity.
j) Ideal manufacturing exists when all production operations are performed while material is moving.
k) Move the greatest weight or bulk the least distance.

2. Relating to Materials Flow.

a) Provide for movement of materials in as direct a path as possible through the plant.
b) Design the flow pattern to facilitate the manufacturing process.
c) Maintain a continuous, uniform, maximum rate of materials movement.
d) Plan to minimize backtracking.
e) Allow for flexibility of the process.
f) Plan for a practical minimum of space between related operations.
g) Materials should flow over direct mechanical routes whenever practical.
h) Plan for machine controlled materials movement to assure constant flow.
i) Apply the "line" production technique when practical.
j) Have incoming materials delivered directly to work areas, when practical.
k) Allow for a bank or float of materials between operations to permit uninterrupted flow when production is intermittent.
l) Make use of gravity whenever practical.
m) Combine operations whenever practical to eliminate handling between them.
n) Place related activities and departments near each other.
o) Plan for processes involving heavy or bulky materials to be near receiving area.
p) Consider probability of future expansion or contraction of production activity.

3. Relating to Methods.

   a) Plan for straight line moves.
   b) Combine inspection, storage, and processing within the transportation.
   c) Keep handling to a minimum.
   d) Reduce lengths of all moves.
   e) All handling should be analyzed for possible improvement by elimination, combination, or simplification.
   f) Avoid transfers from floor to container, or vice versa, or from container to container.
   g) Assemble product on crate bottom or pallet to facilitate handling.
   h) Use equipment to supply or remove materials at the proper rate.
   i) Provide for automatic processing of parts.
   j) Provide for mechanical handling to and from the workplace.
   k) Plan for mechanical removal of scrap.
   l) Plan for storage of a minimum amount of materials at the workplace.
   m) In planning individual operations, remember the necessary relationships with preceding and succeeding operations or work areas.
   n) Allow area for storage of the maximum amount of work to be on hand at an individual work area—ahead of the operator, or awaiting removal.
   o) Handle as many pieces as practical in one unit.
   p) Never pile anything directly on the floor without a container, skid, or pallet underneath.
   q) Deliver materials to the right place on the first move.

4. Relating to Utilization of Manpower.

   a) Make proper use of manual handling—which in many cases is the most efficient.
   b) Plan proper methods for all manual handling.
   c) Long, hard, or hazardous manual handlings should be studied for improvement possibilities.
   d) Frequent, repetitive, short, irregular moves should be studied for mechanization possibilities.
   e) Containers should be designed to provide prepositioning as well as easy disposal of objects.
   f) Avoid delays of operators caused by waiting for materials.
   g) Avoid use of direct labor for handling.
   h) Install equipment to permit operators to spend full time on production.
   i) Install equipment to replace heavy physical exertion.
   j) Use equipment to assure operator of his share of the work—no more, no less.
   k) Reduce size of handling unit to minimize fatigue or increase speed of handling.
   l) Productivity is increased as handling operations become easier and safer.
   m) Deliver materials directly to the operator to reduce walking required.

5. Relating to Receiving, Shipping, and Storage.

   a) Use mechanical devices as much as is practical.

b) Care in loading and unloading will prevent damage.

c) Keep pick-up and delivery points to a minimum.

d) Provide means for leveling truck and dock heights.

e) Standardize dock heights.

f) Deliver materials directly to point-of-use.

g) Keep a minimum of material in storage.

h) Plan storage facilities for easy accessibility.

i) Use uniform containers to aid in counting of parts.

j) Keep materials in storage a minimum amount of time.

k) Utilize live storage, on racks or conveyors.

l) Keep materials in storage as short a time as is practical.

m) Make full use of building cube to obtain maximum storage at lowest cost.

6. Relating to Containers and Unit Loads.

a) Use containers to consolidate materials to be handled into unit loads.

b) Design containers for use in shipping, receiving, in-plant handling as well as at the point-of-use.

c) Consider collapsible containers to save storage space when empty and to reduce transportation cost on return trip.

d) Keep container weight at a minimum.

e) Use standardized containers throughout the entire cycle.

f) Keep number of containers at a minimum.

g) Use the product, package, or container as a pallet.

h) Use pallet size to best utilize space in trucks, trailers, and railroad cars.

i) Expendable pallets or containers eliminate cost of return trip.

j) Use of pallets permits packages of lower strength.

k) The four-way pallet offers greatest flexibility.

l) Have supplier ship in unit containers to be delivered to the workplace.

m) Arrange to receive materials from vendors in unit packages for easy handling.

n) Use materials directly from the vendor's container.

o) Redesign container to reduce voids, increase weight or size of unit load, or reduce number of handlings or trips.

p) Design container to permit automatic handling.

q) The degree of enclosure provided by a container should be the minimum necessary to protect and/or restrict movement of the item.

r) Keep ratio of dead weight to pay load at a minimum.

s) Economy of handling is obtained as the size of the handling units is increased.

t) Assemble materials into unit loads as soon as possible and keep in that form as long as possible.

u) When necessary, redesign packages or cartons for better assembly into unit loads and retain the unit load form to use all possible cube and prevent product damage.

v) Make the unit load as large as possible considering the limitations of buildings, handling equipment, production areas, volume of materials required, and common carrier dimensions and capacities.

MATERIALS HANDLING ANALYSIS
– PRELIMINARY SURVEY CHECK SHEET –

Company _____ Plant _____ Bldg. _____ Area_____

Compiled By _____ Date _____

Indicators of Ineffective Materials Handling	Check		Comments, Suggestions for Improvement, etc.
	Yes	No	

GENERAL
1. Crowded Conditions - - - - - - - - -
2. Lack of provision for expansion -
3. Empty floor space - - - - - - - - - -
4. Poor housekeeping- - - - - - - - - -

RECEIVING, SHIPPING & STORAGE
1. Demurrage - - - - - - - - - - - - - -
2. Truck tie-ups - - - - - - - - - - - -
3. Cluttered docks- - - - - - - - - - - -
4. Manual loading & unloading - - - -
5. Excessive temporary storage - - -
6. Material piled directly on floor - -
7. Wasted "cube" - - - - - - - - - - - -
8. Disorderly storage - - - - - - - - - -

PRODUCTION
1. Unexplainable delays & idle time
2. Stock control difficulties - - - - - -
3. Decreased production in an area -
4. Bottlenecks in production - - - - -
5. Backtracking - - - - - - - - - - - - -
6. Material piled directly on floor - -
7. Obstacles in materials flow - - - -
8. Scheduling difficulties - - - - - - -
9. Low production density,
   i.e., production/sq. ft. - - - - - -
10. Idle equipment - - - - - - - - - - - -
11. Related operations spread over
   an unnecessarily large area - - -
12. Use of "process layout," when
   "product layout" could be used
13. Improper location of feeder, or
   sub-assembly lines - - - - - - - -
14. Inspection not integrated with
   production - - - - - - - - - - - - - -
15. Improperly located service areas
16. "Vanishing" aisles - - - - - - - - -
17. Zig-Zag flow lines- - - - - - - - - -
18. Non-uniform rate of flow - - - - - -

MATERIALS HANDLING METHODS
1. Hard, hazardous work, being done
   by hand - - - - - - - - - - - - - - -
2. Excessive materials handling
   equipment repairs- - - - - - - - - -
3. Unnecessary handling- - - - - - - -

Fig. 11–2. Materials handling analysis,

Indicators of Ineffective Materials Handling	Check		Comments, Suggestions for Improvement, etc.
	Yes	No	
MATERIALS HANDLING METHODS (continued) 4. Long hauls - - - - - - - - - - - - - - - 5. Uneconomical handling methods a. manual - - - - - - - - - - - - - - - - b. failure to use gravity - - - - - - c. overlooking inexpensive handling equipment or devices - - 6. Two-man lifting jobs - - - - - - - - 7. Frequent manual handling of similar materials - - - - - - - - - 8. Failure to use standard containers for in-plant handling - - - - - 9. Failure to use standard m.h. equipment for in-plant handling - 10. Rehandling - - - - - - - - - - - - - - - 11. Non-integrated materials handling equipment - - - - - - - - - 12. Materials being moved one piece at a time - - - - - - - - - - - - - - - - 13. Materials not delivered right to the work place - - - - - - - - - - - - MATERIALS 1. Damaged materials - - - - - - - - - - 2. Excessive scrap - - - - - - - - - - - UTILIZATION OF MANPOWER 1. Excessive injuries - - - - - - - - - - 2. Employee complaints - - - - - - - - 3. Large numbers of men moving materials - - - - - - - - - - - - - - - 4. Handling done by skilled labor - - 5. Safety hazards - - - - - - - - - - - - 6. Two-man lifting jobs - - - - - - - - 7. Operators walking for matls. - - - - COSTS 1. High overhead costs - - - - - - - - - 2. High indirect labor payroll - - - - - 3. Unexplainable cost increases - - -			

SUMMARY OF SUGGESTIONS FOR IMPROVEMENT

preliminary survey check sheet.

7. Relating to Equipment.

a) Select each piece of equipment to fit into the over-all handling system.

b) Use enough equipment to correlate materials handling with production schedules.

c) Use equipment to prevent damage to parts being handled.

d) Design equipment to carry materials in a position to save space.

e) Use equipment requiring no fixed floor space.

f) Install only safe equipment.

g) Make maximum use of gravity for movement.

h) When loading or unloading time is a factor, use equipment where power unit is separate from load unit.

i) Plan to keep equipment operating as much time as practical.

j) Conveyor drives should be adjustable to allow for changing production schedules.

k) Before buying new equipment, be sure present equipment is being fully utilized.

l) Make use of standard equipment as much as possible.

m) Provide for alternate methods in case of breakdown.

n) Make use of conveyors for floats and banks.

o) Consider all characteristics of the move before selecting equipment.

p) Do not exceed the rated capacity of equipment.

q) Do not overmechanize for the sake of mechanizing.

r) Install materials handling equipment which is flexible and can serve a variety of uses or applications.

s) Increase flexibility by means of accessories and attachments.

t) Mobile equipment must be kept moving as much of the time as is possible.

u) Replace equipment and methods when expense of replacement is exceeded by economies effected in a reasonable period of time.

v) Operate equipment at the fastest economical and safe speed.

w) The productivity of equipment is increased if repairs and maintenance are anticipated and scheduled.

x) Check and revise maintenance schedule when production rates or shifts increase.

8. Relating to Cost.

a) Unit handling cost is reduced as the number of pieces handled at one time is increased.

b) Handling cost is usually a function of distance and weight.

c) Select equipment on a basis of over-all cost—not first cost.

d) Consider the leasing of equipment for trial or peak periods.

e) Install materials handling equipment whenever its cost can be recovered within a reasonable time.

f) Economy of handling is obtained by making full use of available plant and equipment capacity.

g) Maintain the lowest possible ratio of equipment investment to units of materials handled.

MATERIALS HANDLING CHECK SHEET

RECEIVING & STORAGE

PLANT			LOCATION	
DEPARTMENT				
OPERATION				

ITEM	CHECK OPERATION FOR THE FOLLOWING	CHECK YES	NO	EXPLANATION
1.	Are materials (other than bulk materials) received from the vendor in unit uniform packages for easy handling?			
2.	Can the material be used directly from vendor's package?			
3.	Can the material be unloaded and delivered to stores, and later to the workplace without unnecessary manual handling?			
4.	Can the material be delivered directly to the workplace without storing?			
5.	Can the material be stacked without manual handling?			
6.	Is the stock on hand too great?			
7.	Is the stock on hand too small?			
8.	Are the bins or racks the right size for holding the material?			
9.	Can a complete bin or rack of material be moved from the storeroom to the workplace to save rehandling?			
10.	Is the material stacked as high as practicable?			
11.	Is the material mixed with other material?			
12.	Is the storage place congested?			
13.	Are piles of material tied when necessary to prevent falling?			

Fig. 11–3. Receiving and storage check sheet.

In going over the above list of principles, it is immediately apparent that many of them are in direct conflict with each other! This is because each is directed toward a particular objective, and it is not always possible to completely fulfill several different objectives in a specific situation. In such cases, the conflicting objectives and principles must be resolved in the most practical and economical manner.

Applying the Principles. Two things are certain about the above principles:

1. They are extremely useful and have been proved in practice over a period of many years.
2. They are of *no* value *if* left in a textbook, notebook, or folder in a file drawer.

However, there are several ways in which the practicing materials handling or plant layout engineer can make use of this accumulated experience:

1. Study the principles for use when required.
2. Reproduce the list for handy reference.
3. Reproduce by categories in the form of check sheets. Use for survey purposes in desired situations. Typical check sheets are shown in Figures 11–2 and 11–3. As shown on the check sheets, it is frequently advisable to reword the principles in simpler or in question form to aid in using the check sheet.

CONCLUSION

As was pointed out in the definition of plant layout in Chapter 1, materials handling is an integral part of plant layout. This has been emphasized in previous chapters, as preliminary layout planning techniques were presented. It is re-emphasized in this chapter in which the broad scope of materials handling activity has been pointed out. The principles of materials handling were presented as an aid in the process of integrating materials handling into the plant layout planning process.

Chapter 12 will present selected types of materials handling equipment and indicate their particular advantages and applications.

QUESTIONS

1. What is materials handling?
2. What are the four major phases of manufacturing activity in which materials handling is an important factor?
3. Approximately what per cent of production cost does materials handling account for?
4. What is the *over-all* objective of materials handling? the *specific* objectives?
5. How does materials handling affect plant layout?

6. What is a "principle"? How does it come into existence?
7. Give some examples of materials handling principles under each of the major groupings.

   a) General
   b) Relating to materials flow
   c) Relating to methods
   d) Relating to utilization of manpower
   e) Relating to receiving, shipping, and storage
   f) Relating to containers and unit loads
   g) Relating to equipment
   h) Relating to cost

8. Make up a list (from the text) of those principles which are most closely related to plant layout and which could be "planned" into the layout. *Save* this list for use later in the layout planning process.
9. How can the principles of materials handling be most easily applied?

12

Materials Handling Equipment

Introduction. As has been pointed out previously, a materials flow pattern is *static*. It is the movement of materials that makes the flow dynamic and productive. It is, in most cases, the materials handling equipment that causes the material to flow through the plant. However, the selection of the right equipment for each necessary move is a complex task. This chapter will present in outline form a consideration of some of the more important types of equipment commonly used in manufacturing plants. The following chapter will discuss techniques for selecting the proper equipment for a given situation.

Basic Equipment Types. According to the *Materials Handling Handbook*,[1] there are over 430 kinds of materials handling equipment. These are divided into nine major categories, as follows:

1. Conveyors
2. Cranes, elevators, and hoists
3. Positioning, weighing and control equipment
4. Industrial vehicles
5. Motor vehicles
6. Railroad cars
7. Marine carriers
8. Aircraft
9. Containers and supports

Fortunately for the practicing plant layout engineer, many of these are not used within the typical manufacturing plant; and a large number of them are relatively specialized pieces of equipment.

This chapter will present a few of the more common ones from classifications:

1. Conveyors
2. Cranes, elevators, and hoists
4. Industrial vehicles
9. Containers and supports

[1] Bolz, H. A., and Hagemann, G. E., *Materials Handling Handbook* (New York: The Ronald Press Co., 1958).

Those to be presented on the following pages are as follows:

A. Conveyors for Handling over a Fixed Path
    1. Apron
    2. Arm
    3. Belt
    4. Bucket
    5. Car-type
    6. Chain
    7. Chute
    8. Flight
    9. Monorail
   10. Pallet loader
   11. Pneumatic
   12. Power and Free
   13. Pusher bar
   14. Roller
   15. Screw
   16. Slat
   17. Suspended tray
   18. Tow
   19. Trolley
   20. Wheel

B. Equipment for Handling over a Fixed Area
   21. Bridge crane
   22. Gantry crane
   23. Hoist
   24. Jib crane
   25. Stacker crane

C. Vehicles for Handling over a Variable Path
   26. Dolly
   27. Crane truck
   28. Fork lift truck
   29. Hand lift truck
   30. Industrial tractor
   31. Mechanical table
   32. Narrow aisle truck
   33. Platform truck
   34. Portable elevator
   35. Side loading truck
   36. Straddle carrier
   37. Platform hand truck

D. Containers and Supports
   38. Pallet

39. Pallet box
40. Racks and supports
41. Shipping container
42. Shop box
43. Skid
44. Skid box

The above list contains an adequate selection of equipment types for a large majority of handling problems in the field of manufacturing. On the following pages will be found descriptions, illustrations, and characteristics of each type.

CONVEYORS [2]

The conveyor has become the symbol of the industrial might of the United States; it is synonymous with "mass-production." The continuous, mechanized handling of materials by conveyors provides the integrated flow coupled with the precise timing which forms the very backbone of orderly production.

Conveyors are available for the handling of every sort of bulk material; every size, weight or shape of package; and for every kind of object.

Conveyors move materials to, through, and from processing machines whose capacities may be rated in ounces—or in tons. Conveyors themselves may become an integral part of such a machine, or they may form the processing machine by themselves.

Conveyors will pass the lightest or the heaviest casting from one machine operation to the next with a speed, ease, and accuracy never approached by human hands. Conveyors permit the plant operator to obtain the fullest capacity production possible from his processing and manufacturing equipment.

Conveyors provide the means of timing and pacing of manufacturing operations so essential to quantity production and mass-assembly. Conveyors maintain a constant, measured flow of materials; they provide moving, out-of-the-way storage for parts and subassemblies with unfailing delivery of the right thing at the right place at the right time and, yet, their flexibility is such that production schedules for an entire plant may be set in a matter of seconds with no more than the adjustment of a dial or the push of a button; conveyors utilize "air rights" by moving along ceilings or they may make use of space beneath a floor which would be wasted otherwise; they reduce and even eliminate in many cases the chance for human errors in sequence of, or timing of, operations; they provide a constant visual check of the progress of a production schedule; they reduce work-in-process inventories to a minimum; and conveyors

[2] Adapted from *Conveyor Terms and Definitions* (2d ed., Washington, D.C.: Conveyor Equipment Manufacturer's Assn., 1958).

are a significant factor in the reduction of industrial accidents through the elimination of lifting and carrying and by making it unnecessary for man to even approach dangerous areas.

In general, a conveyor is defined as a horizontal, inclined, or vertical device for moving or transporting bulk materials, packages, or objects in a path predetermined by the design of the device and having points of loading and discharge fixed or selective.

Fig. 12–1. Apron conveyor carrying ore. (By permission of Link-Belt Company.)

Apron Conveyor. *Description.*[3] A conveyor whose carrying surface consists of overlapping metal aprons or pans, attached at their ends to two strands of chain running in steel guides. Beaded slat edges and turned up ends result in a minimum of spillage. (Figure 12–1.)

[3] Descriptions are adapted from *Conveyor Terms and Definitions* (see footnote 2) or *Material Handling Engineering Directory* (Cleveland: Industrial Publishing Co.; published annually).

Characteristics.

1. Ideal for bulk materials in large quantities.
2. Used for severe service conditions.
3. Operates at 60 to 100 feet per minute.
4. Can be used as inclines up to 45 degrees with deep pans and/or cleats.
5. Discharges over head end.
6. Will handle 80 to 290 tons per hour.
7. Handles either fine or lumpy materials.

Arm Conveyor. *Description.* A conveyor consisting of an endless belt, or one or more chains, to which are attached projecting arms, or shelves, for handling packages or objects in a vertical or inclined path. (Figure 12–2.)

Fig. 12–2. Arm elevator carrying 200 lb. kegs of washers. (By permission of Link-Belt Company.)

Characteristics.

1. Used vertically or on incline.
2. Handles barrels, boxes, logs, bags, pipe, rolls, etc.
3. Raises or lowers loads.
4. Automatically discharges.
5. One unit may lift as well as lower.
6. Chain speed 30 to 60 feet per minute.

Belt Conveyors. *Description.* GENERAL. An endless fabric, rubber, plastic, leather, or metal belt operating over suitable drive, tail end, and bend terminals and over belt idlers or slider bed for handling bulk materials, packages, or objects, placed directly upon it. (Figures 12–3A, B, C, D.)

Characteristics.

1. Top and return runs of belt may be utilized.
2. Will operate on level, incline up to 28 degrees, or downgrade.
3. Belt may be fabric, rubber, metal, woven wire, etc.
4. Belt supported on flat surface is used as carrier of objects or as basis for an assembly line.
5. Belt supported by flat rollers will carry bags, bales, boxes, etc.
6. Belt supported by concave or troughing idlers is used to handle bulk materials.
7. Metal mesh belts are used for applications subjected to heat, cold, or chemicals.
8. Speeds range from 3 to 200 feet per minute.

CLOSED BELT. Moving, endless, flexible belt, or belts, which may be formed into a tubular shape by joining of edges and which are opened while in motion to receive load, closed to convey or elevate, and opened to discharge.

FLAT BELT. A type of belt conveyor in which the carrying run of the conveyor belt is supported by flat belt idlers or by a flat surface.

TROUGHED BELT. A belt conveyor with the conveyor belt edges elevated on the carrying run to form a trough by conforming to the shape of the troughed carrying idlers or other supporting surface.

Bucket Conveyor. *Description.* A conveyor for carrying bulk materials in a vertical or inclined path, consisting of an endless belt, chain or chains, to which elevator buckets are attached, the necessary head and boot terminal machinery and supporting frame or casing. (Figure 12–4.)

Fig. 12–3A. Closed belt, or "zipper" conveyor. (By permission of Stephens-Adamson Manufacturing Co.)

Fig. 12–3B. Flat belt conveyor. (By permission of The Logan Company.)

Fig. 12-3C. Troughed belt conveyor. (By permission of Link-Belt Company.)

Fig. 12-3D. Portable belt conveyor transferring parts from one operation to the next. (By permission of Rapids-Standard Co.)

Fig. 12–4. Bucket conveyor. (By permission of Link-Belt Company.)

Characteristics.

1. Commonly used for coal, sand, and other bulk items.
2. Used with or without casings.
3. Centrifugal-discharge or continuous bucket types.
4. Will operate from 45-degree slope to vertical.
5. Can be equipped with movable tripper, mounted on wheels, and operating above a succession of bins.
6. Operates on horizontal, vertical, or inclined path.
7. Ideal for hot and abrasive materials.

Car-type Conveyor. *Description.* A series of cars attached to and propelled by an endless chain or other linkage running on a closed track. (Figure 12–5.)

Characteristics.

1. Endless, so that loads continue over fixed path until removed.
2. Commonly used in foundries for molds.
3. Used in small scale in canning and bottling plants as carriers for containers.
4. Used as feeders for assembly lines.
5. Used for assembly when fixture must return to first station.

Fig. 12–5. Car-type conveyor. (By permission of Link-Belt Company.)

Chain Conveyor. *Description.* One or more strands of endless chain operating on suitable tracks or guides. Load is placed on and carried by chain surface or by special carriers fastened to the chain. (Figures 12–6A, B, C.)

Characteristics.

1. Load may be carried directly on chains.
2. Carriers or fixtures may be mounted on chains.
3. Pushers mounted on chain may propel load.

Fig. 12–6A. Chain-type conveyor. (By permission of Link-Belt Company.)

Chute. *Description.* A slide made of metal or other material and shaped so that it guides objects or materials as they are moved from one location to another. May be used on horizontal or inclined planes, or as a spiral between extreme levels. (Figure 12–7.)

Characteristics.

1. Used to move objects, usually short distances, from one place to another.
2. Usually slopes downward slightly to take advantage of gravity in moving objects.
3. Running surfaces may be metal, wood, or composition.
4. May be open or closed.
5. Often serves to connect roller or other conveyors located on different levels, especially between floors.

Fig. 12–6B. Flat top chain conveyor. (By permission of Link-Belt Company.)

Fig. 12–6C. Rolling chain conveyor. (By permission of Jervis B. Webb Co.)

Fig. 12–7. Gravity chute. (By permission of The Logan Company.)

Flight Conveyor. *Description.* A type of conveyor comprising one or more endless propelling media, such as chain, to which flights are attached and a trough through which material is pushed by the flights. (Figure 12–8.)

Fig. 12–8. Flight conveyor. (By permission of The Jeffrey Mfg. Co.)

Characteristics.

1. Used for bulk materials ranging from ashes and coal to gravel and grain—but which are not too abrasive.
2. Often installed under floor to remove chips from machine tools.
3. Moves horizontally, or down inclines, or up inclines not exceeding 45 degrees.
4. Discharge can be at the end of flight conveyor or at any desired intermediate points.
5. May be single or double chain driven.

Monorail Conveyor. *Description.* An overhead single track system supporting load carrying trolleys. (Figures 12–9A, B, C.)

Characteristics.

1. May be hand operated, or trolleys may be power-driven.
2. Travel limited to track installation.
3. Track may incorporate switches, lifting or lowering sections, turntables, crossovers and swinging sections.

4. Track may be pipe, flat bar, or formed structural members.

5. May be combined with trolley conveyor to result in "Power and Free" conveyor (see below).

Pallet Loader. *Description.* An automatic or semiautomatic machine, consisting of synchronized conveyors and mechanisms to receive objects from conveyor(s) and place them onto pallets according to a prearranged pattern. (Figures 12–10A, B.)

Fig. 12–9A. Monorail conveyor. (By permission of Cleveland Tramrail and Engineering Co.)

Characteristics. Figures 12–10A and B show views of an automatic pallet loader which stacks cartons or boxes in standard patterns on pallets fed to the loading position by the machine itself from a stack within the machine, replenished by the operator as the pallets are filled with standard loads. A conveyor system, regulated by "cartridges" for the various kinds of loads to be built up, supplies the cartons and will automatically turn those which it is desired to interlock so as to steady the load. The

Fig. 12–9B. Monorail conveyor. (By permission of American Monorail Co.)

Fig. 12–9C. Monorail conveyor. (By permission of Cleveland Tramrail and Engineering Co.)

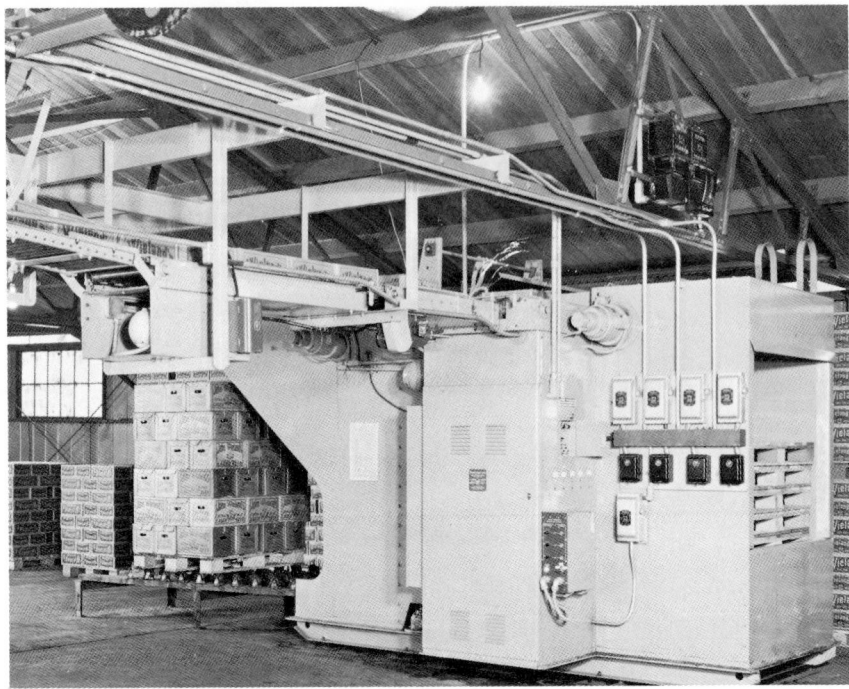

Fig. 12–10A. Pallet loader for arranging cartons (at top), into pallets (at right), into a unit load (at left). (By permission of Lamson Corporation.)

Fig. 12–10B. Top view of pallet loader showing method of arranging the pallet pattern. (By permission of Lamson Corporation.)

boxes are thus laid in a pattern in a single layer on a stripper plate in the machine, below which is a pallet to be loaded. When a layer has been formed, the stripper plate is automatically withdrawn from beneath the boxes, allowing them to drop ¾-inch onto the pallet.

The pallet is dropped a distance corresponding to the height of the layer of boxes; a second layer is built up according to the pattern set for this next layer; and the second layer, when completed, is dropped, by withdrawal of the stripper plate, upon the previous layer. The pallet

Fig. 12–11A. Pneumatic tubes for carrying records. (By permission of Lamson Corporation.)

then drops down to allow the stripper plate to return for the third layer, and so on until the pallet is fully loaded. It is then automatically ejected to a conveyor leading from the machine, and another pallet is pushed into its place to be loaded in the same manner. The conveyor may carry the loaded pallet away to a storage or shipping area, or a fork truck may be used to take it from the conveyor for disposal.

Such pallet loaders will handle smooth, flush cartons or boxes from 9 to 24 inches in length and 8⅜ to 18 inches in width. Rigid pallets are used, from 40 to 50 inches in width, from 32 to 48 inches in length, and from 4 to 7 inches thick. Pallet loads of 3,000 lb. total or 1,000 lb. per layer may be handled, of maximum width 53 inches, length 50 inches,

height 71 inches measured from the bottom of the pallet. Capacity is up
to 35 cartons or boxes per minute, according to size and stacking pattern.

Pneumatic Conveyor. *Description.* An arrangement of tubes or ducts
through which materials are carried by a pressure or vacuum system.
(Figures 12–11A, B.)

Characteristics.

1. Provide mechanical messenger service for mail, prints, orders, small parts,
   etc., contained inside carriers.
2. Carry samples to laboratories.
3. Carry small or costly dies, tools, gages, and other equipment from toolrooms to operating departments and back.
4. Ideal for large quantities of finely divided or dusty material which is blown
   or sucked through tubes.

Fig. 12–11B. Pneumatic tubes for carrying small tools. (By permission of Lamson Corporation.)

Power and Free Conveyor. *Description.* A conveyor system in which the load is carried on individual trolleys on the lower of two tracks. An upper track is installed where power is desired for moving or diverting the trolley. (Figure 12–12.)

Characteristics.

1. "Free" trolleys move by gravity or by "pushers" supported from trolley conveyor on upper level.
2. Interconnections may be manually or automatically controlled.
3. Track switches may divert trolleys from "power" to "free" tracks.
4. Dispatching may be automatically controlled.
5. Gravity "free" tracks may be installed between two "power" tracks for storage.
6. Speeds may be varied from one "power" section to another.
7. See also monorail and trolley conveyors.

Fig. 12–12. Power and free conveyor, showing "power" rail above and "free" rail below. (By permission of Jervis B. Webb Co.)

Pusher Bar Conveyor. *Description.* Two endless chains cross-connected at intervals by bars or rotatable pushers which propel the object along the bed or trough of the conveyor. (Figure 12–13.)

Characteristics.

1. Used for raising or lowering.
2. Operates on inclines up to 60 degrees.
3. Used as boosters in gravity roller lines.
4. Does automatic loading and unloading.
5. Particularly adapted to handling packages, cartons, or other containers.
6. Handles up to 100 units per hour.

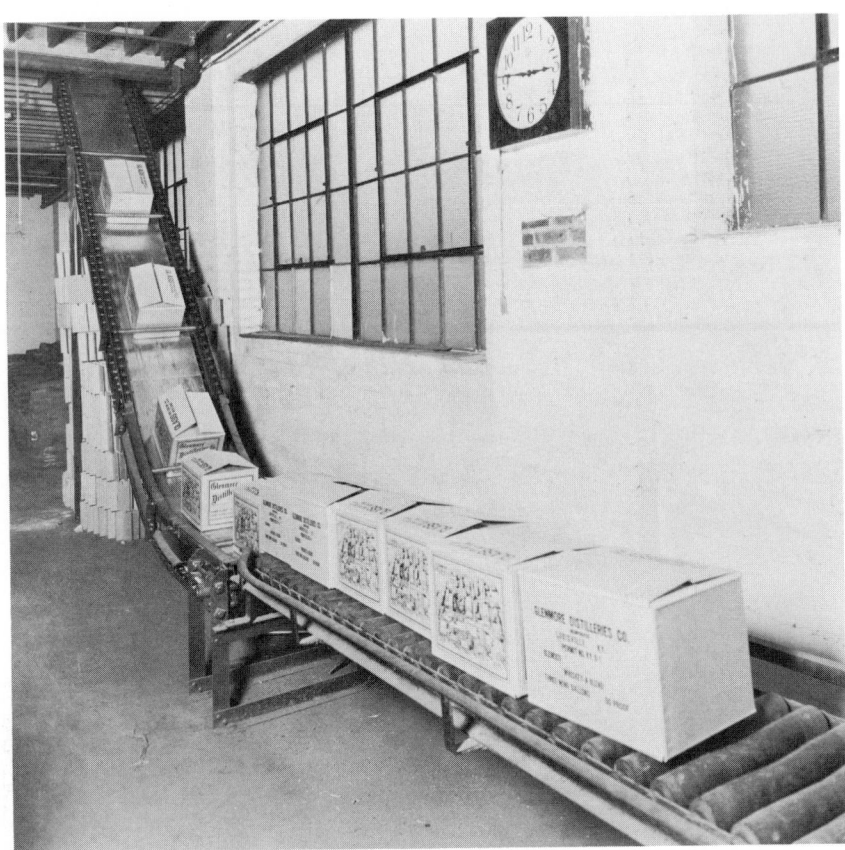

Fig. 12–13. Pusher bar conveyor. (By permission of The Logan Company.)

Roller Conveyor. *Description.* A series of rollers mounted between side rails, over which objects are moved manually, by gravity, or by power. (Figures 12–14A, B, C, D.)

Characteristics.

1. For movement of materials between work areas for short or relatively short distances.
2. Can be level with load pushed.
3. Can have slight down grade and let gravity move loads.
4. Can be driven with belts or chains.
5. Used to carry objects having a smooth, firm traveling surface.
6. Can move fragile objects, or objects with uneven surfaces, if supported in containers.

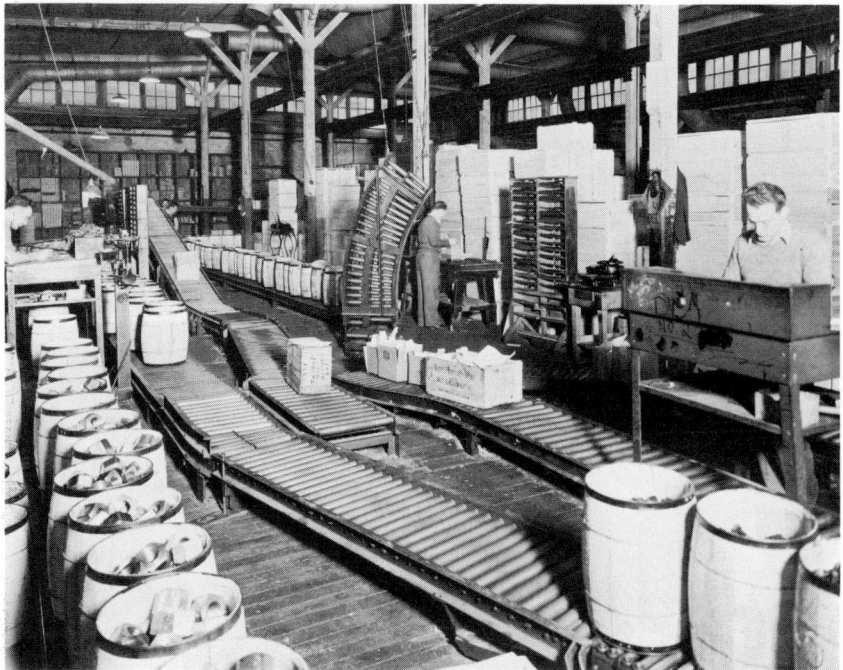

Fig. 12–14A. Gravity roller conveyors showing switch and lift sections, with slat conveyor in background. (By permission of The Logan Company.)

Screw Conveyor. *Description.* Conveyor screws rotating in a suitably shaped stationary trough or casing. (Figure 12–15.)

Characteristics.

1. Move bulk materials along length of trough, or casing.
2. Compact and easily fitted into close quarters.
3. Can operate in horizontal, vertical, or inclined path.

Fig. 12–14B. Live roller conveyor (note drive belt *under* rollers). (By permission of Standard Conveyor Company.)

Fig. 12–14C. Roller rack. (By permission of Rapids-Standard Co.)

Fig. 12–14D. Roller spiral conveyor. (By permission of The Logan Company.)

Fig. 12–15. Trough-type screw conveyor. (By permission of Jeffrey Mfg. Co.)

Slat Conveyor. *Description.* A conveyor whose carrying surface consists of wood or metal slats, fastened at their ends to two strands of chain running in a suitable track or guide. (Figure 12–16.)

Characteristics.

1. For handling heavy objects and packages.
2. Used as a mobile floor section.
3. Load can be placed directly on slats or in containers.
4. Carries horizontal, on incline up to 35 degrees with cleats, or down.
5. Placed at work height or floor level.
6. Used as basis for assembly lines.

Fig. 12–16. Slat conveyor. (By permission of Link-Belt Company.)

Tow Conveyor. *Description.* An endless chain supported by trolleys from an overhead track or running in a track above, flush with, or under the floor with means for towing trucks, dollies, or cars. (Figure 12–17.)

Characteristics.

1. Used in warehouses as a medium for distributing incoming shipments or gathering items to fill outgoing orders.
2. Used as a continuous moving storage for supplying manufacturing areas.
3. Trucks can be automatically picked up, switched, or dropped.
4. May be used for "scheduled" delivery to or removal of items from departments or areas.

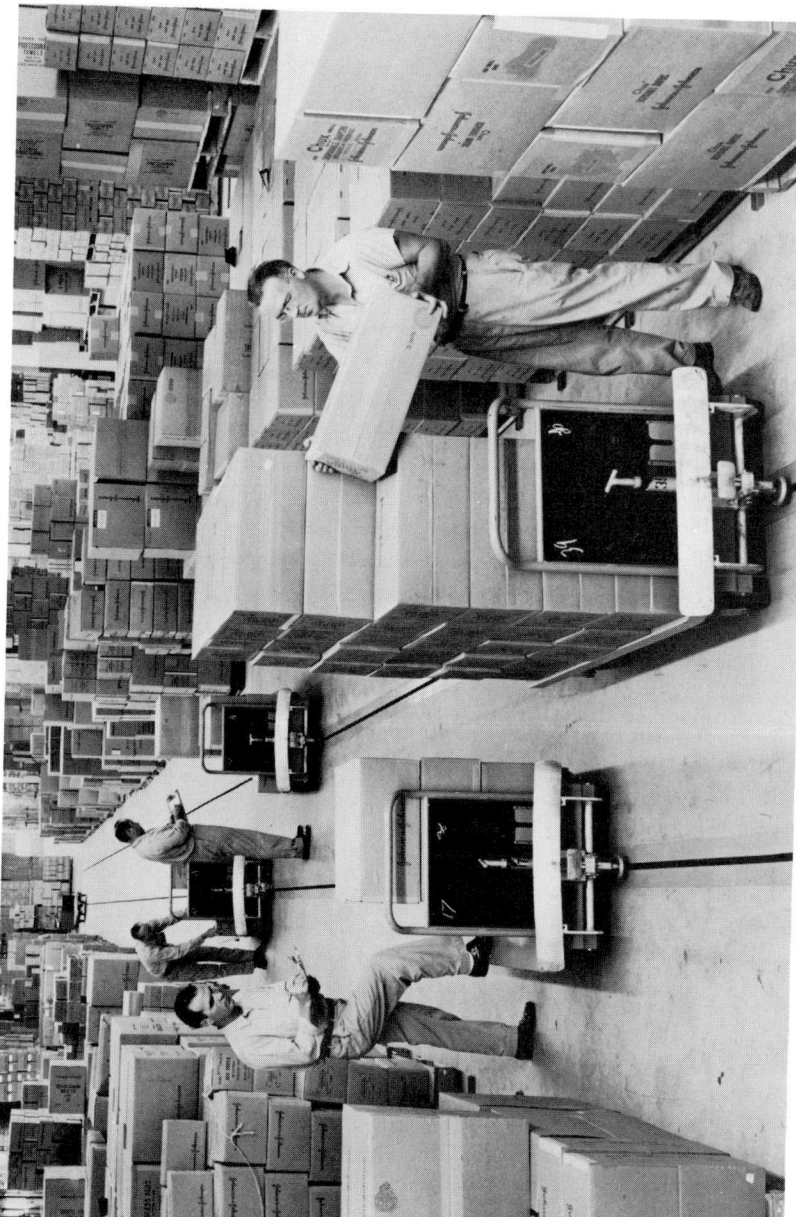

Fig. 12-17A.   Tow-line conveyor installed under the floor.   (By permission of Jervis B. Webb Co.)

Fig. 12–17B. Tow-line conveyor installed overhead. (By permission of Link-Belt Company.)

Suspended Tray Conveyor. *Description.* A vertical conveyor having one or more endless chains with suitable pendant trays, cars, or carriers which receive objects at one elevation (s) and deliver them to another elevation (s). (Figures 12–18.)

Characteristics.

1. Can raise or lower loads from floor to floor.
2. Can be selectively and automatically loaded or unloaded.
3. May be single or multiple chain driven.
4. "Tray" may be a roller bed to facilitate loading and unloading.
5. Can be loaded or unloaded from either side.
6. Can provide continuous motion for supply or removal of objects.

Fig. 12–18. Suspended tray conveyor. (By permission of Link-Belt Company.)

Trolley Conveyor. *Description.* A series of trolleys supported from or within an overhead track and connected by an endless propelling medium such as chain, cable, or other linkage, with loads usually suspended from the trolley. (Figures 12–19A, B.)

Characteristics.

1. Used for such continuous operations as spray painting, baking, degreasing, etc.

2. Used as storage conveyors, saving floor space.

3. Used to supply assembly lines.

4. Used for long distance moves between fixed locations.

5. Saves floor space as it is suspended from overhead.

6. Will carry loads on level and up or down inclines.

7. Travel limited to track installation.

8. Track can be routed around or over obstructions and down to work stations from upper carrying level.

9. Frequently installed for interbuilding movement of materials.

10. See also tow conveyor.

Fig. 12–19A. Trolley conveyor. (By permission of Mechanical Handling Systems.)

Fig. 12–19B. Trolley conveyor. (By permission of Mechanical Handling Systems.)

Wheel Conveyor. *Description.* A series of wheels mounted in a frame over which objects are moved manually, by gravity, or by power, (Figures 12–20A, B, C, D.)

Characteristics.

1. For solid, smooth-bottom objects.

2. Usually operates by hand movement or gravity.

3. For light-weight objects.

4. Commonly used in portable applications.

5. Relatively inexpensive and light in weight.

6. Commonly used for cartons, boxes, etc., in warehousing, loading, and unloading operations.

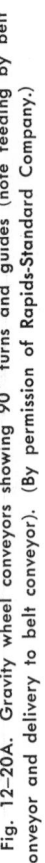

Fig. 12–20A. Gravity wheel conveyors showing 90° turns and guides (note feeding by belt conveyor and delivery to belt conveyor). (By permission of Rapids-Standard Company.)

Fig. 12–20B. Live wheel conveyor. (By permission of Rapids-Standard Company.)

Fig. 12–20C. Wheel rack, or live rack conveyor. (By permission of Rapids-Standard Company.)

Fig. 12–20D. Spiral wheel conveyor. (By permission of Rapids-Standard Company.)

OVERHEAD EQUIPMENT

Bridge Crane. *Description.* A lifting device mounted on a bridge which is supported at each end by trucks riding on runways installed at right angles to the bridge. Runways are installed on building columns, overhead trusses, or frames. Lifting device moves along bridge and bridge moves along runway. (Figure 12–21.)

Fig. 12–21. Bridge crane. (By permission of Manning, Maxwell, and Moore.)

Characteristics.

1. Covers any spot within the rectangular area over which the crane travels. Provides three-dimensional movement.

2. Used where intermittent handling of heavy objects is necessary, such as in machine shops, press departments, storage areas, for heavy die handling, etc.

3. With proper accessories (lift magnet, chain slings, grab buckets, hooks, etc.), can be used for handling almost any material.

4. Capacities up to 150 tons or more.

5. Hoist speed up to 50 feet per minute (for lower capacity cranes).

6. Bridge travel from 200 to 500 feet per minute.

Gantry Crane. *Description.* A bridge crane mounted on girders which are supported by legs or end frames, usually traveling on floor or ground level. (Figure 12–22.)

Characteristics.

1. May be "fixed leg," semigantry (one leg), or cantilever (load passes through legs) type.

2. Used over short distances for loading and unloading.

3. Capacities up to 300 tons or more.

Fig. 12-22. Single-leg gantry crane. (By permission of Cleveland Tramrail and Engineering Co.)

Hoist. *Description.* A device for lifting or lowering objects suspended from a hook on the end of retractable chains or cables. Usually supported from overhead by a hook or traveling on a track. (Figures 12–23A, B.)

Characteristics.

1. Usually used to serve a workplace where heavy objects are handled.
2. May be used to transfer objects from one workplace to another.
3. May supplement overhead traveling crane.
4. May be operated by hand, electricity, or air.
5. Very common and universally used in all industries.

Fig. 12–23A. Hand chain hoist. (By permission of Yale and Towne Mfg. Co.)

Fig. 12-23B. Powered chain hoist. (By permission of Yale and Towne Mfg. Co.)

Jib Crane. *Description.* A lifting device traveling a horizontal boom which is mounted on a bracket, column, pillar, or a track mounted truck. (Figure 12–24.)

Characteristics.

1. Permanent types usually serve a single workplace.

2. Used for loading or unloading machines or vehicles.

3. Portable type used in yards and maintenance work for lifting, lowering, and short hauls.

4. Frequently supplement overhead cranes.

5. Can rotate 360 degrees.

6. Inexpensive and versatile.

7. Capacities usually under 5 tons.

8. Boom lengths usually up to 20 feet.

Fig. 12–24. Jib crane. (By permission of Manning, Maxwell, and Moore.)

Stacker Crane. *Description.* A fork-lift attachment suspended from an overhead truck, which moves on a track system supported from columns or trusses. (Figures 12–25A, B.)

Characteristics.

1. Handles unit loads in very narrow aisles.

2. Useful for stock rooms, die racks, finished goods storage, etc.

3. Travel limited by tracks and clear height available.

Fig. 12–25A. Stacker crane. (By permission of American Monorail Co.)

Fig. 12–25B. Some common overhead materials handling equipment. (By permission of, and copyright by, Manning, Maxwell and Moore.)

INDUSTRIAL VEHICLES.

Dolly. *Description.* A wheeled carrier that supports the load to be conveyed. (Figure 12–26.)

Characteristics.

1. "Wheels" may be rollers, casters, wheels—or a combination.
2. For infrequent movement or relatively smooth surfaces.
3. Frequently custom constructed for specific applications.

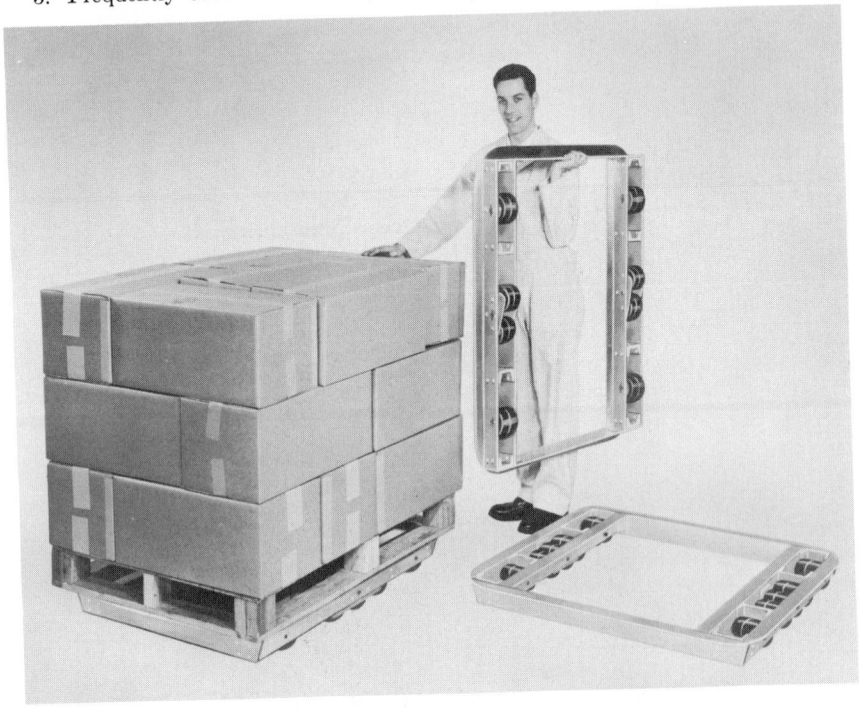

Fig. 12–26. Pallet dolly. (By permission of Magnesium Company of America.)

Crane Truck. *Description.* A self-propelled wheeled vehicle designed to carry a crane for lifting and transporting objects. (Figure 12–27.)

Characteristics.

1. Primarily for loading and unloading operations.
2. Frequently used in maintenance and repair work.
3. Best used over relatively short distances.
4. Ideal for handling unusual shapes and awkward items with slings, chains, etc.
5. Capacities up to 10,000 lb.
6. May be gasoline, diesel, or electric powered.

Fig. 12–27. Crane truck. (By permission of Yale and Towne Mfg. Co.)

Fork Lift Truck. *Description.* A cantilever-type self-propelled, wheeled vehicle carrying a load on two forks extending in front of the vehicle. A tilting vertical mast contains a mechanism for lifting and lowering the forks. (Figures 12–28A, B, C, D.)

Characteristics.

1. For handling pallets.

2. Capacities range up to 100,000 lb. for handling large dies in press departments and for other unusually heavy loads.

3. Used for:

   a) Primarily for lifting and stacking items on pallets or in palletized containers.

   b) Storing materials, usually where travel distances do not exceed 200 to 300 feet.

   c) Handling work between operations.

   d) Loading and unloading trucks, box cars, barges, ships, cargo planes, etc.

   e) Excellent for shipping, receiving, and warehousing activities.

4. Not best for long distance moves, as unit cost becomes high, often because return trips are without loads.

5. With attachments such as grabs, scoops, rams, tilt mechanism, or up-enders, can handle a wide variety of materials.

6. When equipped with telescoping mast, is used to stack pallet loads one on top of the other, or in pallet racks, at heights considerably above the floor, sometimes to a total of about 22 feet. Mast is lowered to go through doorways (in older buildings the clearance is often 7 feet) and when transporting loads, and raised for stacking loads.

7. May be gas, diesel, or battery operated.

Fig. 12–28A. Fork lift truck with radio controlled tractor in background. (By permission of Clark Equipment Co.)

Fig. 12–28B. Fork lift truck with drop-bottom shop box. (By permission of Union Metal Mfg. Co.)

Fig. 12–28C. Fork lift truck. (By permission of Clark Equipment Co.)

Fig. 12–28D. Fork lift truck with 180° rotating clamp. (By permission of Clark Equipment Co.)

Hand Lift Truck. *Description.* A hand-operated truck designed to raise loads on skids or pallets just high enough to clear the floor and move the load to its destination. Lift is by mechanical or hydraulic means and propulsion is by hand or power. Such trucks come in platform type for handling skids (platforms on legs) or fork type for handling pallets. (Figures 12–29A, B.)

Characteristics.

1. For moving stock between operations.

2. For loading or unloading trucks or box cars.

3. May supplement power trucks in feeding or removing loads.

4. For transporting materials into and out of storage areas.

5. Usually used for short or moderate distances, 50 to 200 feet.

Fig. 12–29A. Hand lift truck. (By permission of The Raymond Corp.)

Fig. 12–29B. Hand lift truck, power operated and propelled. (By permission of Clark Equipment Co.)

Industrial Tractor. *Description.* A self-propelled, wheeled vehicle designed for pulling loads on trailers or cars. (Figure 12–30.)

Characteristics.

1. Various types of trailers are used for handling different loads—may be platforms, bins, racks, etc.

2. Used for distances over 400 to 500 feet.

3. Handles greater tonnages than other truck systems.

4. Motive power is not tied up while trailers are being loaded or unloaded.

5. One tractor can keep three sets of trailers in use—one loading, one unloading, and one in transit, if loading and unloading labor is available at terminal points.

6. Useful for collecting or dispatching loads to a number of locations, often over regular routes as a shop express service.

7. May be gas, diesel, or battery driven.

Fig. 12–30. Industrial tractor, with trailer being loaded by fork truck, with a large shipping container. (By permission of Towmotor Corp.)

Mechanical Table. *Description.* A wheeled elevating platform or table built on a lifting mechanism for raising or lowering the table surface. (Figure 12–31.)

Characteristics.

1. For progressively raising or lowering the work feeding or receiving surface as load builds up or diminishes as with sheet metal, plywood, etc.

2. For aiding in placement or removal of heavy press dies.

3. May be permanently installed or portable.

Fig. 12–31. Mechanical lift table. (By permission of Southworth Machine Co.)

Narrow Aisle Truck. *Description.* A load lifting, lowering, and carrying truck making use of out-rigger supports for balancing loads (instead of the cantilever principle). Outriggers must straddle load, with lifting forks or platform between the outriggers. (Figures 12–32A, B.)

Characteristics.

1. For use in narrow aisles and restricted areas such as in warehouses, stock rooms, etc.

2. Can save a large amount of aisle space over ordinary trucks.

3. Must allow space under bottom load level for outriggers on such models.

Platform Truck. *Description.* A self-propelled vehicle on which the carrying surface is a flat platform about 6 inches off the floor. (Figures 12–33A, B, C.)

Characteristics.

1. For heavier loads, longer distances, more rapid, and more continuous service than hand-operated trucks.

2. Not self-loading.

Fig. 12–32A. Narrow-aisle fork lift truck (By permission of Automatic Transportation Co.)

3. Motive unit idle during loading and unloading operations as compared with fork or platform type, where load can be preassembled or disassembled.

4. Capacities up to 80,000 lb.

5. May be gas, electric, or diesel powered.

Fig. 12–32B. Narrow-aisle fork lift truck of special design. (By permission of Towmotor Corp.)

Fig. 12–33A. Platform truck. (By permission of Elwell-Parker Electric Co.)

Fig. 12–33B. Platform truck (being used also as a tractor). (By permission of Elwell Parker Electric Co.)

Fig. 12–33C. High lift platform truck. (By permission of Raymond Corporation.)

Portable Elevator. *Description.* A lifting and lowering device mounted on a wheeled base, with a vertical frame or mast to carry the mechanism and a carriage for supporting the load. Lifting may be done by mechanical, hydraulic, or electrical means. (Figure 12–34.)

Characteristics.

1. Inexpensive and uncomplicated.
2. Light in weight.
3. Highly maneuverable and portable.
4. Extremely versatile.
5. Capacities to 5,000 lb.
6. Lift up to 40 feet.

Fig. 12–34. Portable elevator. (By permission of Barrett-Cravens Company.)

Side Loading Truck. *Description.* A four wheeled truck that loads and unloads from the side by means of centrally mounted forks that move sideways outside the wheel-base to load and unload. Load is carried on two platforms, either side of the central fork. (Figures 12–35A, B.)

Characteristics.

1. Ideal for long, heavy loads such as pipe, structural steel, lumber, etc.

2. Primarily used for yard handling.

3. Capacities up to 30,000 lb.

Fig. 12–35A. Side loading fork truck. (By permission of Baker Industrial Trucks.)

Fig. 12–35B. Side loading truck for "indoor" work. (By permission of Automatic Div., Yale and Towne Mfg. Co.)

Straddle Carrier. *Description.* A self-propelled vehicle designed to straddle a load for picking up and carrying objects mounted on bolsters or skids. (Figure 12–36.)

Characteristics.

1. For unusually large loads, up to 96 inches wide, 102 inches high, and 50 feet long.

2. Handle up to 60,000 lb.

3. Travel on highways at up to 40 miles per hour.

4. May be gas or diesel powered.

5. Commonly used for pipe, steel billets, steel sheet, wallboard, lumber, and large shipping containers.

Fig. 12–36. Straddle carrier. (By permission of Clark Equipment Co.)

Platform Hand truck. *Description.* Manually pushed floor trucks whose beds are about 6″ to 12″ above the floor. Usually furnished with two rigid type casters and two smaller swivel casters, for easy maneuverability. Sometimes furnished with larger wheels at center of bed and a smaller diameter single swivel caster at each end, also for easy maneuverability. Trucks for special purposes have other wheel arrangements. Truck usually has end rack or racks to serve as handle(s) and to restrain loads. (Figure 12–37.)

Characteristics.

1. Inexpensive and versatile.

2. Probably the most common piece of materials handling equipment in use.

Fig. 12–37. Platform hand trucks. (By permission of Lewis-Shepard Products, Inc.)

CONTAINERS AND SUPPORTS

Pallet. *Description.* A load carrying platform designed to be picked up and carried by forks entering spaces provided by stringers between an upper carrying surface and usually a lower supporting surface. (Figures 12–28A, 28C, 29A.)

Characteristics.

1. May be made of wood, metal, formed wire, corrugated board.

2. Permits assembly of unit loads of a number of smaller items.

3. Provides better use of building cube, through stacking of unit loads.

4. Reduces handling time by virtue of the unit load.

5. Aids in orderly storage of materials.

Pallet Box. *Description.* A pallet upon which is constructed a box to confine the load. (Figure 12–38.)

Characteristics.

1. Permits unit loads of items that will not stack upon themselves, or of bulk materials.

2. Provides easy access to stored materials through openings in one side of pallet box.

3. May be made of wood, sheet metal, formed wire, or corrugated board.

4. May be collapsible.

Racks and Supports. *Description.* Frameworks designed to support unit loads in storage. (Figures 12–39A, B, C.)

Characteristics.

1. Increase utilization of storage space.

2. May be permanent (i.e., welded construction) or "flexible" (i.e., demountable and adjustable).

3. Can be designed to support pallets, skids, rolls, reels, drums, bars, boxes, etc.

4. May have shelves or rails for load supports or merely "lugs" on framework to permit a "drive-through" feature.

5. Reduce storage costs due to easier access, less damage to products, increased speed of handling, and use of less expensive handling equipment.

6. Facilitate controlling and taking of physical inventory.

Fig. 12–38. Wood pallet box. (By permission of General Box Co.)

Fig. 12–39A. Pallet rack. (By permission of Automatic Transportation Co.)

Fig. 12–39B. Pallet supports. (By permission of Paltier Corp.)

Fig. 12–39C. Pallet racks and stock picking truck, with belt conveyor feed line. (By permission of Paltier Corp.)

Shipping Container. *Description.* A large, or "jumbo," type container in which a number of smaller units are placed and sealed for shipment by rail, truck, air, or ship. (Figures 12–40A, B, C, D.)

Characteristics.

1. Vary in size from about 36 inches wide by 44 inches long by 27 inches high to 8 feet by 8 feet by 40 feet long.

2. Permit consolidation of many smaller packages or units into one large container.

3. Allow reduced packaging cost.

4. Carry lower freight and insurance rates.

5. Less damage to products in-transit.

6. Less pilferage of shipments.

7. Handled by fork trucks, cranes, straddle carriers, or specially designed lifts or hoists.

8. May be collapsible for convenience in return shipment.

9. May be made of wood or metal.

Fig. 12–40A. Shipping containers being unloaded from truck for transfer to flat cars. (By permission of Seatrain Lines, Inc.)

Fig. 12–40B. Shipping containers on flat cars for transfer to ship. (By permission of Seatrain Lines, Inc.)

Fig. 12–40C. Shipping containers in ship hold. (By permission of Seatrain Lines, Inc.)

Fig. 12–40D. Shipping containers built for fork truck handling, on flat cars. (By permission of Champion Company.)

Shop Box. *Description.* Any one of a number of varieties of relatively small containers for handling materials through the shop—sometimes known as tote pans. (Figures 12–41A, B.)

Characteristics.

1. May be made of sheet metal, wire, wood, fibre board, corrugated board, or plastic.

2. Permit easy handling of small parts.

3. May be consolidated into unit loads.

4. May be easily stacked or placed in racks.

5. Custom liners or inserts permit safe handling of odd shaped or fragile items.

Fig. 12–41A. Shop boxes in rack. (By permission of Bathey Mfg. Co.)

Fig. 12–41B. Shop boxes for transporting small parts. (By permission of Lyon Metal Products.)

Skid. *Description.* A load carrying platform supported from the floor by two parallel stringers or supports. Lifting device enters between the stringers. (Figure 12–33C.)

Characteristics.

1. Similar to the pallet.
2. Usually heavier and stronger than pallets.
3. Usually for use with heavier loads.
4. May be wood or metal.
5. May be built into a shipping container for ease of handling.

Skid Box. *Description.* A skid upon which is mounted a box to confine the load. (Figures 12–42A, B.)

Characteristics.

1. Similar to pallet box.
2. Usually for heavier service.
3. May be made of wood, sheet metal, or wire.

Fig. 12–42A. Skid boxes (before). (By permission of Union Metal Products.)

Fig. 12–42B. Skid boxes (after—note drop bottoms). (By permission of Union Metal Products.)

CONCLUSION

As was indicated in the beginning of this chapter, there are many types of materials handling equipment that have not been covered here. Those presented on the preceding pages are representative of the more commonly used types. Information on other types and adaptations of those shown here can be found in the "Materials Handling Handbook," published by The Ronald Press Company; the "Material Handling Engineering Directory and Handbook," published annually by the Industrial Publishing Corp.; and in "Conveyor Terms and Definitions" referred to in footnote 2 of this chapter. Industry literature and trade publications such as "Modern Materials Handling" and "Material Handling Engineering" are other excellent sources.

Chapter 13 will deal with the analysis of materials handling problems and the selection of the proper equipment for a specific handling task.

13

Materials Handling Planning and Equipment Selection

Introduction. It has been stated previously that a materials flow pattern —no matter how carefully planned—is static. It remains for the materials handling equipment, or other method of movement, to start the materials along the pattern or path and to convert the static pattern into a dynamic reality. However, the problem of determining the method of movement is a complex task, which must be thoroughly analyzed. Not only is the over-all materials handling problem itself broad in scope, but the range and variety of methods and equipment available is so great as to be somewhat overwhelming if the problem is not carefully considered.

Reviewing and summarizing the scope of the materials handling problem, it will be recalled that various handling activities are necessary in:

1. Getting materials to the plant
2. Unloading of carriers
3. Receiving of materials
4. Materials stores activities
5. In-plant distribution
6. In-process handling
7. In-process storage
8. Packing operations
9. Finished goods storage
10. Loading of carriers

Each of these stages in the over-all flow of materials may present one or many individual handling problems. So there may be as few as 10 handling problems per item of material, or even more than 29 indicated in Chapter 11.

It will also be recalled that Chapter 12 indicated as many as 430 types of materials handling equipment from which to choose in solving a specific problem.

This chapter will attempt to guide the reader in the solution of materials handling problems. It will suggest a planning (or analysis) procedure as well as a guide to the selection of the proper piece of equipment, where one is necessary.

Types of Materials Handling Problems. It will be recognized that a materials handling problem may involve:

1. The entire plant
2. A specific department
3. An individual workplace or situation

In each of the above cases, there is also the distinction between planning the materials handling for a new plant, department, or workplace; or of analyzing such a problem in an existing situation. This distinction suggests two general types of approach—synthesis or analysis.

It really matters little whether the problem is one of synthesis or one of analysis. The "procedure" is much the same—only the viewpoint is different. In the former, the problem must be *visualized,* the required data accumulated, and the solution synthesized. In the latter case, the problem *exists* and may be observed; but the facts must still be gathered and the solution arrived at, in many cases by synthesis also.

Whether it is for a brand new plant or an existing plant, the planning of a materials handling system for an entire plant is both a challenging

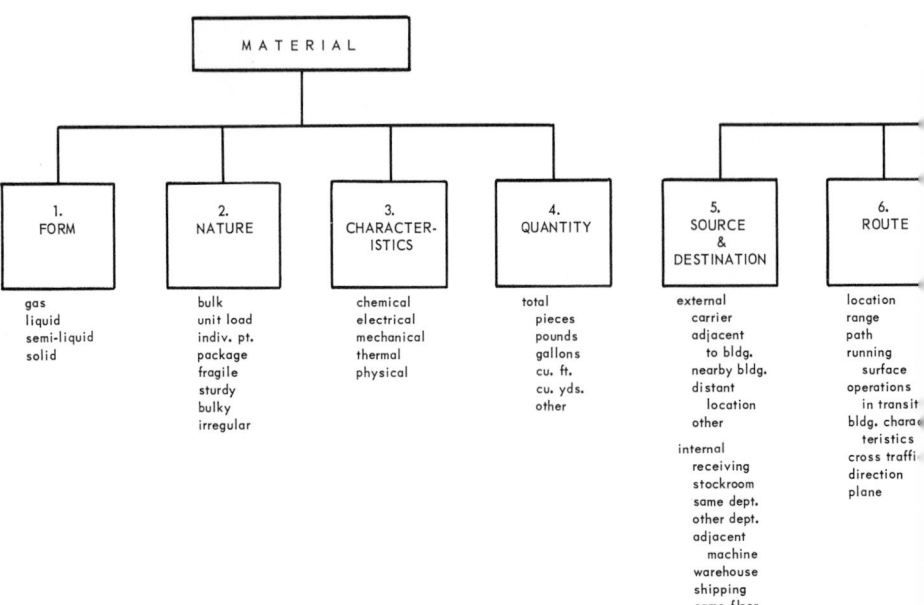

Fig. 13–1. Major factors involved in

and a complex project. And it is in terms of a *system* that the planning should be directed. By a system is meant a plan involving two or more pieces of equipment, operating interdependently.

In planning the materials handling for an entire plant, the engineer is actually solving a number of individual problems—but with the "system" concept always in mind. That is, the solution to each and every individual handling problem should be a part of an over-all, plantwide plan. This means, primarily, that each piece of equipment selected for an individual project must be compatible with the balance of the system, in terms of type, capacity, function, and adaptability, if later required for other purposes. It may also mean more careful selection of the equipment supplier, for convenience at a later date in adding equipment, as well as obtaining repair parts and service.

With the system concept in mind, the engineer may proceed to the actual planning or solution of the materials handling problem. He should always be aware of the fact that an over-all, plantwide system is usually composed of several departmental plans or systems. Each departmental plan, in turn, involves the solution of a related group of individual work-places.

Factors for Consideration in Solving a Materials Handling Problem. As has been indicated throughout this text, the solution to a materials handling

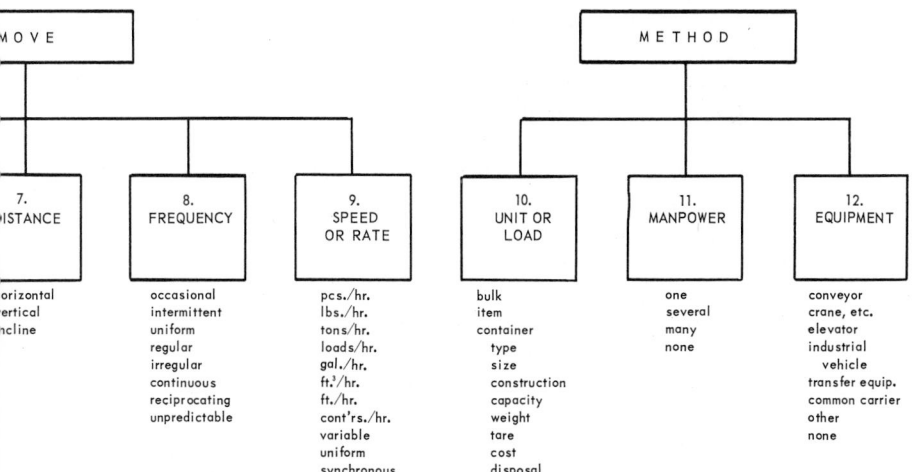

MOVE			METHOD		
7. DISTANCE	8. FREQUENCY	9. SPEED OR RATE	10. UNIT OR LOAD	11. MANPOWER	12. EQUIPMENT
orizontal	occasional	pcs./hr.	bulk	one	conveyor
ertical	intermittent	lbs./hr.	item	several	crane, etc.
ncline	uniform	tons/hr.	container	many	elevator
	regular	loads/hr.	type	none	industrial
	irregular	gal./hr.	size		vehicle
	continuous	ft.³/hr.	construction		transfer equip.
	reciprocating	ft./hr.	capacity		common carrier
	unpredictable	cont'rs./hr.	weight		other
		variable	tare		none
		uniform	cost		
		synchronous	disposal		

analyzing a materials handling problem.

problem is a complicated undertaking. It is not merely the buying of a conveyor or a fork lift truck and considering the problem solved. To do an adequate job requires the proper consideration of a multitude of factors —some simple, some complex; some closely related, some vaguely related. An idea of the magnitude of the over-all task is indicated in Figure 13–1. The major phases for consideration are:

1. The material
2. The move
3. The method

Each of these is subdivided in detail on the chart. Even though the task may seem insurmountable when studying the chart, it should become immediately apparent that no problem involves all of the factors—fortunately! Later in this chapter it will be shown that the factors involved in a specific problem can be fairly easily accumulated and reduced to workable terms.

General Procedure in Analyzing a Materials Handling Problem. As has been pointed out previously, an orderly procedure aids in the solution of any problem. The following will serve as a broad, over-all guide in approaching a materials handling problem: [1]

1. Determine and define the problem.
2. Make proper contacts with those involved in the problem and its solution.
3. Set up a method of approach and develop a work schedule.
   a) Learn the operation.
   b) Develop an accurate layout.
   c) Observe operation in detail.
   d) Secure comprehensive, factual data.
   e) Investigate methods of communication and control.
   f) Investigate anticipated results.
   g) Weigh and analyze all data.
   h) Develop improvements.
   i) Select equipment.
   j) Determine required structural changes.
   k) Plan necessary controls.
   l) Provide adequate communications.
   m) Develop operating procedures.
   n) Determine personnel requirements.
   o) Determine and compare costs, savings, and advantages.
   p) Consider intangible advantages.
   q) Summarize capital requirements and rate of return.

4. Prepare report or presentation.

[1] Hupp, Burr, "Analysis of Materials Handling Problems in Industry," privately distributed (adapted from).

5. Obtain approvals (revise as necessary).
6. Supervise installation.
7. Follow up after installation.

The above procedure will not be discussed in detail here, since much of it is "standard" practice and beyond the scope of this text. It will, however, serve as an adequate guide in attacking a materials handling problem; and certain phases of it will be covered below. Since this text concerns, in general, the planning of an entire plant, the materials handling planning will be likewise oriented. Thinking back over previous chapters, it will be recalled that much of the discussion centered about the development of an over-all flow pattern. It is this flow pattern which must now be implemented, and this becomes the definition of the present problem.

Basic Data Required. As was indicated in the discussion of factors involved in solving a materials handling problem, there is literally a mass of data which could be uncovered which would be relevant to any specific problem. The form shown in Figure 13–2 will aid in recording the necessary basic data on any selected problem. If there are several kinds of material, or types of moves, additional sheets may be necessary, or several similar or related items may be grouped together. Figure 13–2 shows the form filled in for *all* of the incoming materials for the Powrarm plant. Also considered as a "group" are all the moves involved in getting the materials from the common carriers to the stock room and/or their respective point-of-use. As the "Basic Data . . ." sheet is filled in, it will be found that the engineer's thoughts are gradually crystallized in the process! In fact, it is entirely possible, if he has enough background knowledge of materials handling, that he will have done a fairly adequate job of selecting basic equipment types.

However, in the solution of a more complex problem, or in a detailed analysis of a larger individual handling problem, many of the factors must be given greater consideration.

The Storage Analysis sheet (Figure 7–5) will be found extremely helpful in obtaining much of the data called for on the "Basic Data . . ." sheet. It should be referred to at this time to avoid recalculating many of the items.

Over-all Approach in Implementing the Flow Pattern. For use in planning the materials handling system for an entire plant, the above over-all general procedure can be somewhat reduced in scope and expanded in depth. This is done because the present project does not involve some of the details of a single, specific problem, but does require greater integration of the various handling situations to insure a compatible and integrated

BASIC DATA REQUIRED FOR MATERIAL HANDLING ANALYSIS

IDENTIFICATION

COMPANY ___Powrarm___ **BUILDING** _No. 1_ **COMPILED BY** _A. M. J._

LOCATION IN BLDG. _Rec._ **PLANT** ___—___ **DATE** ___Aug. 31___

STATEMENT OF PROBLEM ___handling of all incoming materials___

__from Receiving dock to Stock Room &/or point–of–use__

(fill in applicable data, referring to "Major Factors Involved in Analyzing a
Material Handling Problem")

A. MATERIAL Description _Castings, Bar Stock,_ Part No._____
                                            Misc. Hardware
                              Receiving and Storage Data

Source of materials __several__	Floor condition____good____
Deliv. to plant by_____truck_____	Stor. area size _20' x 70'_ 1400 sq. ft.
Dimen. of carrier_____vary_____	Useable vo. (cu. ft.)____28,000____
Units/delivery _____"_____	Volume req'd _____
Freq. of deliv._____daily_____	Normal inventory ___1 mo.___
Tonnage deliv. _____	Max. inventory ____1½ mo.____
Dist. from rec. to stor.__50 ft.__	Ave. inventory ____½ mo.____
Stor. area loc. Rough stores & asmbly	Amt. moved to pt. of use/move ___—___
Clear ceiling ht.____20 ft.____	Amt. stored at pt. of use _approx. 25%_
Floor type_____concrete_____	

MAJOR FACTORS

 1. Form__Castings, Bar Stock, Misc. Hardware__
 2. Nature_____—_____
 3. Characteristics
      a. size __2" dia x 12' long to 6" x 6" x 6"__ & misc.
      b. weight/unit _____—_____
      c. other _____
 4. Total Quantity

B. MOVE: Description _from dock to Stock Room &/or point–of–use_

 5. Source and Destination___see above_____
 6. Route
      a. location _____inside_____
      b. range____fixed point to varying points____

Fig. 13–2. Basic data required for materials

c. path ___relatively fixed for each item but varying for___
d. running surface_____good concrete_____different items
e. operations in transit_____none
f. cross traffic _____insignificant
g. direction or plane _horizontal & vertical (for stacking)
h. building characteristics
    1) truss ht. _____20 ft.
    2) truss strength ___—
    3) ceiling ht. ___22 ft.
    4) aisle width ____6 to 10 ft.
    5) column spacing___30' x 40'
    6) floor load capacity_____max. required
    7) elevators _____none
    8) sprinklers _____between truss chord & "ceiling"
    9) duct work ___none that interferes
    10) other _____—

7. Distance_____up to 100 ft.
8. Frequency_____variable
9. Rate, or Speed ___variable

C. METHOD

10. Unit handled
    a. bulk _____
    b. single item___bar stock – indiv. bars
    c. container ____castings & small parts

1) type _pallet box_		6) tare ___40 lbs.		
2) construction ___wood		7) quant./move___varies		
3) size_3' x 3' x 3'		8) container cost_$7.00		
4) capacity___18 cu. ft.		9) disposal of cont'r._____re–used		
5) wt. of load___varies		10) (other)_____		

    d. load characteristics ____—
    e. loading shock_____—
11. Manpower Req'd._____
12. Equipment and/or Method Indicated _____
    a. pallet boxes   e. shelving
    b. pallets   f. shop boxes
    c. pallet racks   g. 2–wheel hand truck
    d. bar stock racks

REMARKS

materials handling system. The following will serve as a guide to implementing the flow pattern. The "Basic Data . . ." sheet (see Figure 13–2) should be used for accumulating pertinent information.

1. Consider the *material*(s) to be handled.

   a) Identify and record materials characteristics.
   b) Decide on basic type of unit(s) to be handled (individual items, containers, etc.).
   c) Group similar and/or related materials or units for treatment as a single problem (as in Figure 13–2).

2. Consider the *move*(s) to be made.

   a) Examine flow patterns, Area Allocation Diagram, or Flow Process Charts to determine:
      (1) Source.
      (2) Destination.
      (3) Route.
      (4) Distance, etc.
   b) Determine frequencies of various moves (from volume requirements as discussed in Chapters 4 and 7).
   c) Calculate rates of movements (also from volume requirements).
   d) Break over-all problem into departments, areas, functions, or processes with similar or related types of handling problems (as in Figure 13–2).

   or

   Consider *each* move or series of related moves as a separate problem (i.e., handling of finished product from assembly to packing to storage).

3. Transfer key data to "Materials Handling Equipment Planning Sheet" (Figure 13–3) from "Basic Data ..." form.

   The "Move No." column may be used to identify a sequence of moves on one part or type of material or for "grouped" moves of several parts or materials. In the former situation, a Flow Process Chart would be extremely useful, and the "Move No." should correspond with the step number of the Flow Process Chart.

   It will be noted on the "Planning Sheet" that the method or equipment selected can be filled in, if it is known, or indicated by the engineer's past experience. *If not:*

4. Select the *method*(s) and *general* type(s) of equipment, based on equipment characteristics and limitations.

   a) Manual.
   b) Chute—generally for short distances, between machines, benches, or work stations.
   c) Conveyor.
      —When unit loads are uniform.
      —Where materials move or can move continuously.

—When rate of movement, unit loads, and location of route are not likely to vary.

—Where cross traffic can be by-passed by the conveyor.

—Fixed path.

—Point-to-point movement.

d) Cranes.

—Intermittent movements within a fixed area.

—Materials of variable size or weight.

—Movement of materials regardless of cross traffic or uniformity of load.

e) Industrial trucks.

—Where materials must be picked up and moved intermittently over various routes.

—Where materials are either of mixed size and weight or of uniform size.

—Where distances are moderate.

—When cross traffic exists.

—Where there are suitable running surfaces and clearances.

—Where the operation is principally handling.

—Where unit loads are applicable.

5. Check each selection for compatibility with the over-all materials handling system.

6. Group similar and/or related handling problems when necessary to justify an expensive piece of equipment.

7. Select *specific* pieces of materials handling equipment—as outlined below.

Selecting Specific Materials Handling Equipment. In the above procedure, the general type of materials handling equipment may have been selected, i.e., roller conveyor, overhead traveling crane, fork lift truck, etc. The task still remains, in many cases, of selecting a more specific type—and always of selecting *the* specific make and model.

An excellent illustration of the problem at hand is shown by Figure 13–4. The graph clearly shows the variation in man-hours by the six methods as:

Method	Man Hours/1,000 pcs.
A. Manual	36.5
B. 2-wheel hand truck	17.0
C. 4-wheel hand truck	12.0
D. Conveyor	10.0
E. Powered truck	5.5
F. Fork truck and pallets	1.0

Such a comparison is an excellent argument for selecting the proper method and equipment for each and every handling problem when it can be so obviously seen that the "wrong" method might require up to 36 times as much manpower.

MATERIALS HANDLING

Part of Mat'l. Description Powrarm Base

	MATERIAL								MOVE	
Move No.	Description	Size	Wt.	Vol.	Purch. Quant.	Units per Deliv.	Freq. of Deliv.	Vol. per Deliv.	Source	Destination
1	Casting	6x6x6	6#	1/8 cu. ft.	12,000	3000	1/wk.	375 cu. ft.	Receiving Platform	Rec. Insp.
2	"								Rec. Insp.	Stock Rm.
3	"								Stock Room	Machine Shop
4	"								Mach. Shop	LeBlond Eng. Lathe
5	"								LeBlond E. L.	W & S Turr. Lathe
6	etc., etc.									

Fig. 13–3. Materials handling

EQUIPMENT PLANNING SHEET

Part No. __1_____ Dept. or Area __Receiving, etc._____

Distance	Freq.	Quant. per Move	Unit. Handl.	Container				Manp. Req.	Man'l.	Chute	Conv.	Crane	Truck	Other	Comb.	Specific Type Selected
				type	Sixe	vol.	Wt.									
25 ft.	1/wk.	3000	pallet	pall.	3'x3' x3'	27 cu.ft.	450 lbs.	t r					x			Fork Lift
25'	1/wk.	3000	pallet	pall.	"	"	"	u c					x			Fork Lift
50'	2/day	300	pallet	pall.	"	"	"	k e					x			Fork Lift
20'	1/hr	75	pallet	pall.	"	"	"	r					x			Hand Lift
8'	cont.	1	1 cstg.	_	_	_	6#	_	x							Metal

METHOD (center header above Container)
Equip. or Meth. Indicated (header above Man'l / Chute / Conv. / Crane / Truck / Other / Comb. / Specific Type Selected)

equipment planning sheet.

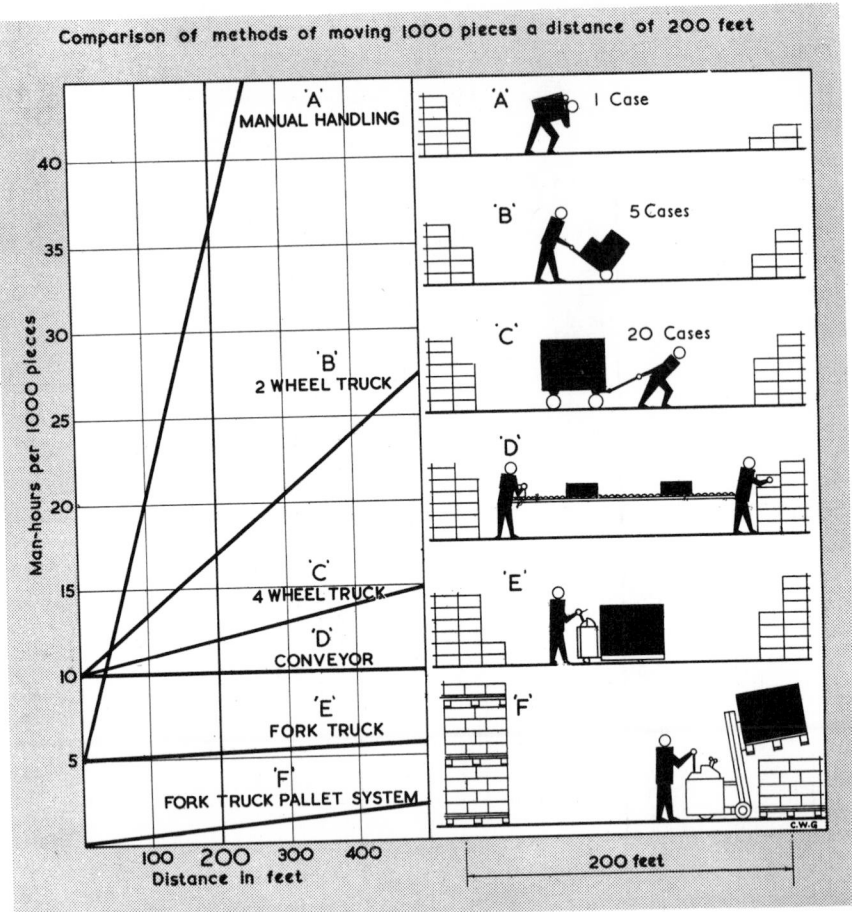

Fig. 13–4. Comparison of six methods of moving 1000 pieces 200 feet. (By permission of C. W. Glover.)

Selecting the Specific Type of Equipment. The selection of the specific type of handling equipment is at best a rather "unscientific" task. It depends heavily on the engineer's own knowledge of the many types of equipment available and, more specifically, those applicable to the problem at hand. The engineer must therefore:

1. Know, study, or have available the characteristics and limitations of the many types of *equipment.*

2. Know, study, or have available the characteristics of the *move* under consideration.

3. Be able to *resolve* the characteristics and limitations of the various equipment types with the characteristics of the move to be made.

As indicated above, much of the "selection" process is the result of the planner being able to draw from his background of experience, the information necessary to satisfy the needs of a particular problem. Consequently, there are many errors made due to the lack of an adequate background on the part of the planner.

Aids to Equipment Selection. To help and guide the planner, many charts, tables, and classifications of equipment characteristics have been prepared. All are helpful to a certain extent, but none can cover all of the possibilities, nor resolve all of the factors relevant to a problem. Figures 13–5 and 13–6 are examples of two such charts.

Figure 13–5 lists 90 types of materials handling equipment along the top. Along the side are 20 general limitations of the many equipment types, 11 properties of various materials, and 15 characteristics of the movement to be made. Although this is a limited number of the many characteristics presented in Figure 13–1, it covers most of the major items and will serve as a guide. To use the chart, first identify the limitations, properties, and characteristics of the immediate problem on the left-hand side of the table. Then "search" the columns to the right for those which contain "dots" opposite *all* factors identified at the left. For example, assume a problem such as the handling of automobile wheels from one location to another, as they move from operation to operation. This problem might have the following "characteristics":

1. Limitations of the *equipment*
   a) Fixed or mobile
   b) Supplemental *loading* and unloading necessary
   c) Ceiling height over 12 feet, aisle width over 6 feet, floor load adequate, curved path necessary
   d) Processed and inspected in transit

2. Properties of the *material*
   a) "Packaged" (i.e., a single unit)
   b) Sturdy
   c) 30 lb.
   d) Units

3. Characteristics of the *movement*
   a) Continuous
   b) Horizontal, up, and down
   c) May be 100 feet between operations
   d) Cross traffic can be by-passed

This problem may seem not too complicated, yet the chart shows *only* one type—live roller conveyor—that will suit the characteristics. However, this is where the "mechanical crutch" fails. *It* does not know that

GROUP 1

TO CARRY MATERIAL OVER A FIXED PATH BETWEEN FIXED POINTS

				CONVEYORS	ELEVATORS

Equipment columns (No. 1–36): 1 Spiral Chute · 2 Straight Chute · 3 Apron · 4 Portable Apron · 5 Push Bar · 6 Belt · 7 Portable Belt · 8 Pivoted Bucket · 9 Portable Bucket · 10 Chain · 11 Drag Chain · 12 Continuous Flow · 13 Chain Flight · 14 Portable Flight · 15 Floor · 16 Oscillating · 17 Reciprocating · 18 Gravity Roller · 19 Spiral Gravity Roller · 20 Live Roller · 21 Portable Roller · 22 Screw · 23 Slat · 24 Cable Trolley · 25 Wheel · 26 Sling · 27 Slat · 28 Pneumatic · 29 En-Masse · 30 Monorail · 31 Arm · 32 Bucket · 33 Self Propelled Bucket · 34 Suspended Tray · 35 Freight · 36 Portable

			VARYING FACTORS	No.
— 1 — **LIMITATIONS** **OF THE** **EQUIPMENT**	(a) EQUIPMENT MOBILITY		Either Mobile or Fixed	1
			Fixed	2
			Mobile	3
	(b) TRANSFER CHARACTERISTICS OF EQUIPMENT		Supplementary Loading Necessary	1
			Supplementary Unloading Necessary	2
			Mechanical Loading by Equipment Itself	3
			Mechanical Unloading by Equipment Itself	4
			Tiering Ability	5
	(c) BUILDING FACTORS AFFECTING EQUIPMENT		Ceiling Height Up To 12 Feet	1
			Ceiling Height Over 12 Feet	2
			Aisle Width Up To 6 Feet	3
			Aisle Width Over 6 Feet	4
			Distributed Floor Load Up To 200 Lb/Sq. Ft.	5
			Distributed Floor Load Over 200 Lb/Sq. Ft.	6
			Curved Path	7
			Short Turning Radius	8
	(d) OPERATIONS AFFECTING HANDLING		Processed In Transit	1
			Inspection In Transit	2
			Stored In Transit	3
			Weighed In Transit	4
— 2 — **PROPERTIES** **OF THE** **MATERIAL**	(a) TYPE OF MATERIAL		Semi-Fluid	1
			Bulk	2
			Packaged	3
	(b) NATURE OF MATERIAL		Fragile	1
			Sturdy	2
	(c) UNIT LOAD PART OR PACKAGE		1-100 Pounds	1
			100-1,000 Pounds	2
			1,000-5,000 Pounds	3
			5,000-20,000 Pounds	4
			Over 20,000 Pounds	5
	(d) UNIT LOAD		Unit Loads On Carrier	1
— 3 — **CHARACTERISTICS** **OF** **MOVEMENT**	(a) FREQUENCY OF MOVEMENT		Continuous	1
			Intermittent	2
			Occasional	3
	(b) NATURE OF MOVEMENT		Horizontal	1
			Up Incline	2
			Down Incline	3
			Elevating	4
			Lowering	5
	(c) LENGTH OF MOVEMENT		1-100 Feet	1
			100-300 Feet	2
			300-1,000 Feet	3
			Over 1,000 Feet	4
	(d) PLANT TRAFFIC		Where Cross Traffic Can Be By-Passed	1
			Movement Regardless Of Cross Traffic	2
			Cross Traffic Exists	3

Fig. 13–5. Materials handling equipment selector table (note: each dot indicates conditions

many types of conveyors can be altered or several types combined to satisfy the requirements of the problem. So actually, this problem *could* be solved by:

     3. Apron—with supplemental curves

     6. Belt—with supplemental curves

    18. Gravity roller—with power "boosters"

    23. Slat—with supplemental curves

    24. Trolley—cross-traffic can go under conveyor

    30. Monorail—cross-traffic can go under conveyor

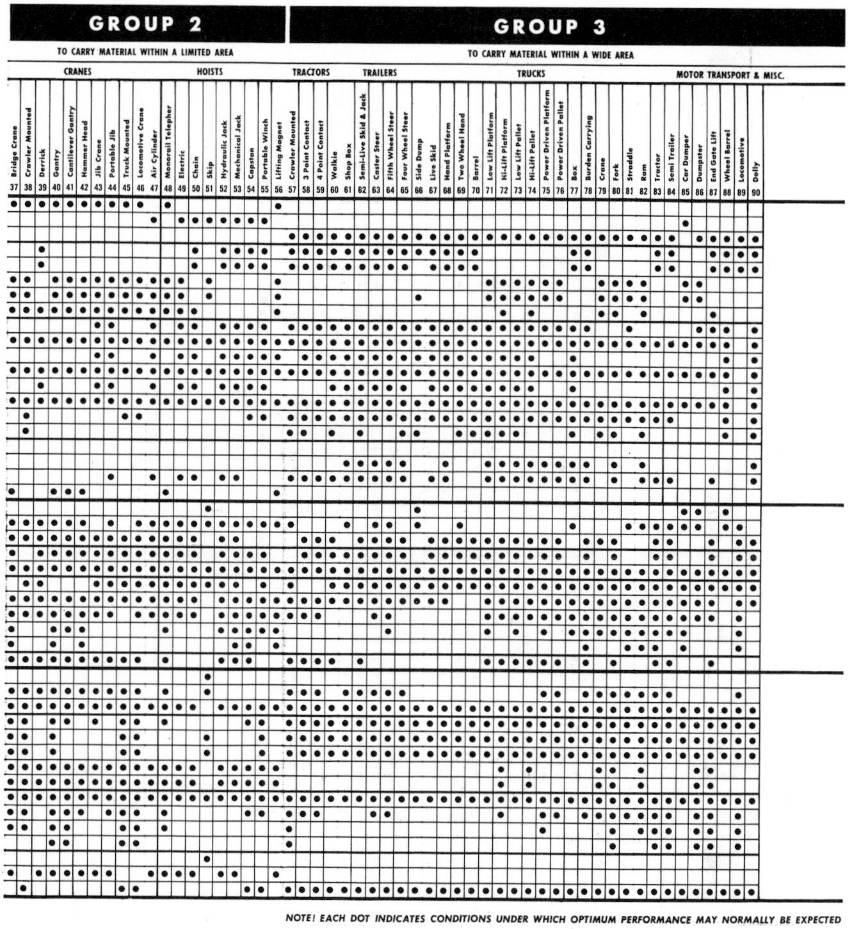
GROUP 2
GROUP 3
TO CARRY MATERIAL WITHIN A LIMITED AREA
TO CARRY MATERIAL WITHIN A WIDE AREA
CRANES
HOISTS
TRACTORS
TRAILERS
TRUCKS
MOTOR TRANSPORT & MISC.
37 Bridge Crane
38 Crawler Mounted
39 Derrick
40 Gantry
41 Cantilever Gantry
42 Hammer Head
43 Jib Crane
44 Portable Jib
45 Truck Mounted
46 Locomotive Crane
47 Air Cylinder
48 Monorail Telepher
49 Electric
50 Chain
51 Skip
52 Hydraulic Jack
53 Mechanical Jack
54 Capstan
55 Portable Winch
56 Lifting Magnet
57 Crawler Mounted
58 3 Point Contact
59 4 Point Contact
60 Walkie
61 Shop Box
62 Semi-Live Skid & Jack
63 Caster Steer
64 Fifth Wheel Steer
65 Four Wheel Steer
66 Side Dump
67 Live Skid
68 Hand Platform
69 Two Wheel Hand
70 Barrel
71 Low Lift Platform
72 Hi-Lift Platform
73 Low Lift Pallet
74 Hi-Lift Pallet
75 Power Driven Platform
76 Power Driven Pallet
77 Box
78 Burden Carrying
79 Crane
80 Fork
81 Straddle
82 Ram
83 Tractor
84 Semi Trailer
85 Car Dumper
86 Dumpster
87 End Gate Lift
88 Wheel Barrel
89 Locomotive
90 Dolly
NOTE! EACH DOT INDICATES CONDITIONS UNDER WHICH OPTIMUM PERFORMANCE MAY NORMALLY BE EXPECTED

under which optimum performance may be expected). (By permission of Mill and Factory Magazine.)

Figure 13–6 is a similar chart, but in more detail, and for a more specialized problem area—handling bulk materials. It is used in much the same way, as can be readily observed by studying the chart.

Selecting the Specific Piece of Equipment. Having determined the type of equipment, it now becomes necessary to determine the specific make and model, that is, to compare two or more alternatives. Three major types of factors must be considered in comparing the alternatives. They are as follows:

1. Investment required
2. Operating expenses
3. Intangible factors

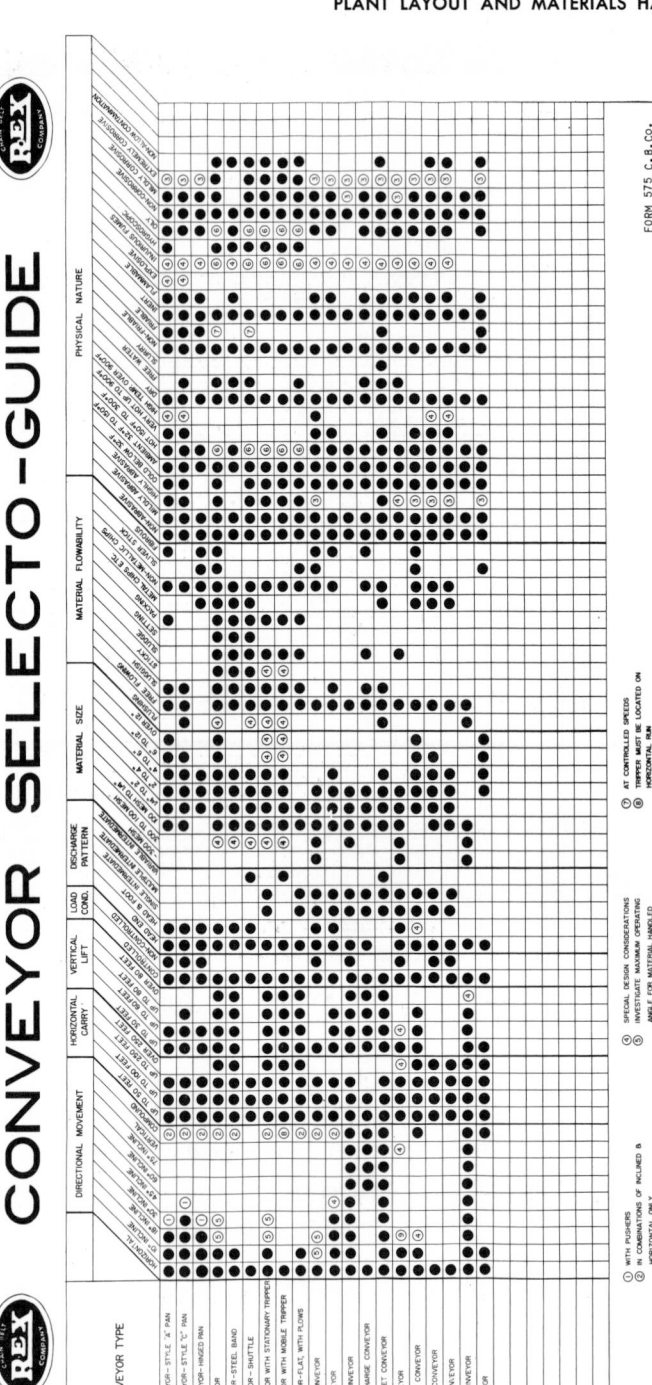

Fig. 13-6.　Conveyor Selecto-guide.　(By permission of Chain Belt Company.)

The form shown in Figure 13–7 will aid in arriving at the investment cost and operating expenses. Total annual charges accumulated at the bottom will serve as a guide to the selection of either the best of several alternative methods or the least expensive of several makes of equipment. The depreciation table at the bottom of the form assumes the "straight-line method." If desired, alternative methods could be substituted, such as the "declining balance."

However, the decision should not be made on the basis of cost alone. There are a number of intangible factors which should be considered, some of which may be more important than the cost factors in a given situation. Some of the intangible factors to be weighed are: [2]

1. Possible future expansion plans
2. Flexibility or adaptability for other uses
3. Standardization (does the proposed equipment fit into or match existing —or other proposed—equipment)
4. Company fiscal policy regarding investments
5. Trend of equipment costs on the market
6. Effect of savings on taxes
7. Durability of equipment
8. Relationship between labor saving and labor turnover rate
9. Availability of trained operator for new equipment
10. Safety considerations
11. Expected amount of downtime
12. Effect of increased overhead on cost of materials handled
13. Availability of repair parts
14. Value of necessary spare parts
15. Quality and availability of service
16. Postsale aid from manufacturer
17. Charges to operation after equipment is fully depreciated
18. Equipment manufacturer's reputation
19. Possible damage or breakage of materials or product due to proposed equipment
20.. Affect of proposed equipment on inventory taking or stock checking
21. Estimated length of time equipment will be used or life of job
22. Per cent of time equipment will be used
23. Complexity of equipment
24. Availability of proposed equipment

It will be seen in studying the above list of intangible factors that many of them are of extreme importance and could outweigh some—or even all—of the cost factors.

An interesting approach to equipment selection is the diagrammatic "formula" shown in Figure 13–8. This method of determination produces

[2] Adapted from "Selecting the Material Handling System," W. B. McClelland, privately distributed.

ANALYSIS OF ANNUAL MATERIALS HANDLING EQUIPMENT COSTS

Based on ____ working days per year

Item or account	Method 1			Method 2			Method 3		
	8 hrs	16 hrs	24 hrs	8 hrs	16 hrs	24 hrs	8 hrs	16 hrs	24 hrs
INVESTMENT									
Invoice price of equipment									
Installation charges									
Maintenance facilities									
Fueling or power facilities									
Alterations to present equipment									
Freight and other transportation									
Design work									
Supplies									
Others									
Credits									
TOTAL INVESTMENT									
FIXED CHARGES									
Depreciation (____yrs.)									
Interest on investment (____%)									
Taxes (____%)									
Insurance (____%)									
Supervision personnel									
Clerical personnel									
Maintenance personnel									
Other									
TOTAL FIXED CHARGES									

VARIABLE CHARGES

Operating personnel

Power and/or fuel

Lubricants

Maintenance labor

Parts and materials

Other

TOTAL VARIABLE COSTS

TOTAL ANNUAL CHARGES

ESTIMATED MATERIALS HANDLING EQUIPMENT DEPRECIATION CHARGES

METHOD NO._____   TYPE OF HANDLING EQUIPMENT _____

Description of Property	Original Installed Costs	Estimated Salvage Value	Amount to Depreciate	Estimated Life in Years	Annual Depreciation Charge Each Year					
					1st	2nd	3rd	4th	5th	6th

From: "Financial Factors in Selection of Handling Equipment," R. C. Brady, FLOW, Apr. 1955

Fig. 13-7. Analysis of annual materials handling equipment costs. (By permission of Flow Magazine.)

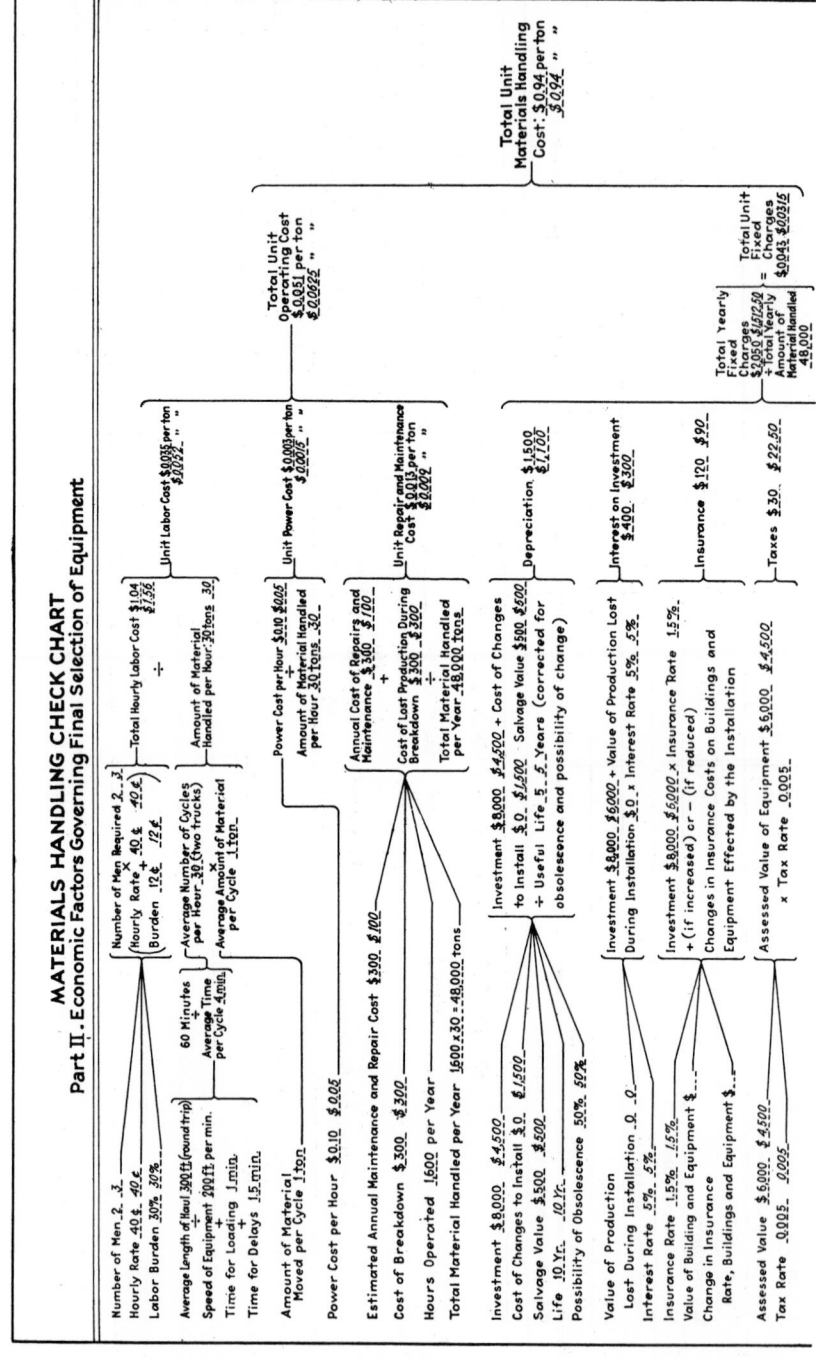

MATERIALS HANDLING CHECK CHART

Part II. Economic Factors Governing Final Selection of Equipment

Cost of Breakage $_____
Per Cent Saved or Lost $_____ } Cost of Increase (+) or Decrease (−) in Breakage of Product Due to Handling System $_____

Cost of Accidents $_____ Per Cent Saved or Lost $_____ } Cost of Increase (+) or Decrease (−) in Accidents to Workmen Due to Handling System $_____

Value of Investment Gained or Lost $_____
Interest, Depreciation, Insurance, Tax Rate $_____ } Depreciation, Interest, Insurance and Taxes on Inventory $_____

Cost of Taking Inventory $_____
Per Cent Saved Taking Inventory $_____ } Increased (+) or Decreased (−) by Handling System Plus Increased (+) or Decreased (−) Cost of Taking Inventory $_____

Amount of Floor Space _____
Unit Value of Floor Space _____ } Yearly Value of Floor Space Gained (−) or Lost (−) for Productive Operations $_____

Number of Machine Hours Saved or Lost _____
Value per Machine Hour $_____ } Idle Machines $_____

Building Maintenance $_____
and Building Changes $_____ } Repairs to Floors, Installation of Safety Devices, Changing Wall and Door Openings, Strenghtening Superstructures, etc. $_____ } Building Maintenance Changes $_____

⟶ Indirect Charges $_____

Case Study—II

Part II continues our hypothetical case, shows how comparative cost figures are obtained. All figures serve merely to illustrate the method. Roman figures for trucks; italic for tramrail. Computation of costs begins with labor. Two drivers are needed for the trucks. One man can operate the tramrail, but two more men are needed to get pile material in the warehouse. To get unit labor costs for trucks and tramrail now becomes a matter of multiplying number of men by hourly rate, adding burden, and dividing by amount of material handled per hour.

Similarly, by following the method outlined in the chart, we get comparative costs for power, maintenance, depreciation, interest, insurance, taxes. Comparative unit operating cost figures—remember, they are purely hypothetical—now look like this:

	Trucks	Tramrail
Labor	$0.0350	$0.0620
Power	0.0030	0.0015
Maintenance	0.0130	0.0090
Operating Cost	$0.0510	$0.0625

Computing our hypothetical fixed charges we get the following:

	Trucks	Tramrail
Depreciation	$1,500.00	$1,100.00
Interest	400.00	300.00
Insurance	120.00	90.00
Taxes	30.00	22.50
Fixed Charges	$2,050.00	$1,512.50

Dividing annual fixed charges by 48,000, the number of tons handled per year, we arrive at $0.043 and $0.0315 respectively as fixed charges per ton for trucks and tramrails. Final figures now read as follows:

	Trucks	Tramrail
Operating	$0.0510	$0.0625
Fixed	0.0430	0.0315
Total	$0.0940	$0.0940

Unit costs are exactly the same! That can happen in a hypothetical case study. It would probably never happen in actual plant practice. If it does—and if the results at this stage do not point conclusively to one or another of the types of equipment being studied—the next step is to tackle the final section of Part II, which we have chosen to label "Indirect Charges."

No attempt has been made to carry the hypothetical case study through this stage to an ultimate conclusion because such factors as floor space, safety, breakage, inventories, etc., vary widely with conditions. Enough of the method has been indicated, however so that the reader may determine how these indirect charges bear upon the problem. Upon that answer will depend the final selection of handling equipment.

Fig. 13–8. Diagrammatic method of comparing equipment alternatives. (By permission of Factory Magazine.)

Handling Method	Man-Hours Per Load (Loaded) COL. 1	Man-Hours Per Load (Unloaded) COL. 2	Man-Hours Per Load (Other) COL. 3	Man-Hours Per Load (Total) COL. 4	Loads Per Year (Table IV) COL. 5	Man-Hours Per Year (Theoretical) COL. 6	Manual Utilization Factor COL. 7	Man-Hours Per Year (Actual) COL. 8	Dollars Per Man-Hour COL. 9	Dollars Per Year COL. 10
Manual	0.005	0.005	—	0.01	15,360	153.6	0.85	180.7	2.00	361.40
Two-Wheel Hand Truck	0.005	0.005	—	0.01	3,840	38.4	0.85	45.2	2.00	90.40
Monorail	—	—	—	—	—	—	—	—	—	—
Walkie Pallet Truck	0.005	0.005	—	0.01	480	4.8	0.85	5.6	3.00	16.80

TABLE I — LABOR COSTS

Equip.-Hours Per Load (Loaded) COL. 1	Equip.-Hours Per Load (Unloaded) COL. 2	Equip.-Hours Per Load (Other) COL. 3	Equip. Hours Per Lo Per Load (Tota COL.
—	—	—	—
0.005	0.005	—	0.01
0.002	0.002	—	0.00
0.005	0.005	—	0.01

TABLE II — INVESTMENT

Fig. 13–9. Simplified approach to selection of materials handling equipment. (By permission

the expected unit cost of handling. Decision is based on the lowest unit cost.

A third technique is shown in Figure 13–9, in which costs are tabulated in a fashion somewhat similar to that shown in Figure 13–7.

The foregoing aids to the selection of materials handling equipment should result in an equitable determination of the proper piece of equipment for each handling task.

Other Analytical Techniques. In some instances, the materials handling problem may be more complex or of greater extent than can be solved with the procedures outlined above. In such cases, the analyst may want to use some of the more refined techniques or approaches to materials handling analysis. Since detailed consideration of these techniques is beyond the scope of this text, the bibliography offers references for further investigation.

CONCLUSION

As has been emphasized earlier, the planning of materials handling requirements and the selection of the necessary equipment is a complex and frequently exasperating task. This is partially true because there is no formula, "sure-fire" procedure, or any other easy way to accomplish the task. In general, the solution of materials handling problems depends primarily on knowledge and experience in the area, along with the help provided by proper analytical techniques and procedures.

This chapter has attempted to outline a procedure to guide the analyst, along with some of the more practical techniques.

				Yearly Investment Costs				
Equip.-Hours Per Year (Theoretical)	Equipment Utilization Factor	Equip.-Hours Per Year (Actual)	Dollars Per Eq.-Hour (Table V)	Dollars Per Year	Contain-ers Required	Dollars Per Container	Dollars Total Invest-ment*	Dollars Per Year (15% Of Col. 13)
COL. 6	COL. 7	COL. 8	COL. 9	COL. 10	COL. 11	COL. 12	COL. 13	COL. 14
—	—	—	—		3 Bskt.	20	60	9.00
38.4	0.85	45.2	0.00664	0.30	9 Bskt.	20	180	27.00
61.4	0.98	1920	0.1406	270	3 Bskt.	20	60	9.00
4.8	0.85	5.76	0.1406	0.81	66 Bskt. 4 Pall.	20	1320 16	200.40

*Investment costs for containers are based on minimum required.
If known, container inventory assigned to job should be used.

of Modern Materials Handling Magazine.)

			Yearly Operating Costs	Total Yearly Costs
Dollars Per Year (All Jobs)	Equip.-Hours Per Year (All Jobs)	Dollars Per Eq.-Hour (Rate)	Equip.-Hours Per Year (Col. 8, Table II)	Dollars Per Year	Sum Of Tables I, II, III
COL. 1	COL. 2	COL. 3	COL. 4	COL. 5	
—	—	—	—		370.40
10	1920	0.0052	45.2	0.23	117.93
480	1920	0.25	1920	480	759.00
480	1920	0.25	5.76	1.44	219.45

TABLE III — OPERATING COSTS

QUESTIONS

1. What is the difference in approach to a materials handling problem concerning (a) an entire plant, (b) a specific department, (c) an individual workplace?
2. What is meant by synthesis or analysis, in reference to the solution of materials handling problems?
3. What is meant by a materials handling system?
4. What are the three major phases of a materials handling problem in which factors must be considered? What are some of the major factors under each?
5. In general, when would you select a
   a) Conveyor
   b) Crane
   c) Industrial truck
   Suggest examples where a combination would be necessary.
6. What is there about selecting materials handling equipment which causes it to be "unscientific," and makes it rather difficult for the inexperienced person?
7. What three groups of factors must be considered in the final selection of a specific piece of materials handling equipment?
8. Suggest some of the items comprising each of the above groups.
9. What are some disadvantages or pitfalls of using forms or formulas such as those in Figures 13–8 and 13–9?

14

Operation and Work Area Planning

Introduction. Having spent the last three chapters on materials handling, and having selected the equipment to be used, it is now time to return to step 6 of our over-all plant layout procedure. As indicated in Chapter 3, this next step is "Operation and Work Area Planning." Until now, the major concern has been with the broad, general phases of flow patterns, larger area relationships, and plantwide movement of materials. Attention must now be focussed on the individual operations or work areas which must be carefully positioned within the framework of the over-all flow pattern.

The subject of work area planning is properly the concern of the field of motion study. Books on that subject will cover much more detail than is contained in this chapter and should be referred to for additional information.

What Is a Work Area? In general, a work area is that space which is occupied by:

1. A machine or work bench
2. Auxiliary equipment, such as materials handling equipment, stock containers, smaller benches or tables, inspection equipment, etc.
3. The operator

The work area may, of course, vary somewhat from the above. It may contain a group of smaller or a group of similar machines. It may require more than one operator. Or it may be merely a "piece" of floor space where an operator works alongside a conveyor—as in an assembly operation. Figure 14–1 shows a "typical" work area.

Guides to Work Area Planning. No presentation of work area planning would be complete without a consideration of the principles of motion economy and work place design. As in the case of the principles of materials handling, these concern items which have been found to be good practice in the experience of practitioners in this field. The more common and applicable principles of motion economy are as follows:

1. Plan for the work of the two hands to be simultaneous and symmetrical.
2. Plan for tools, gages, materials, and machine controls to be located close to and in front of the operator.
3. Plan a definite location for tools, gages, and materials.
4. Plan to use gravity feed bins and stock containers to deliver the materials to a convenient location for the operator.
5. Plan to preposition tools and materials.
6. Plan for the original delivery of materials or stock containers to a position convenient to the operator.
7. Plan for the removal of materials from the workplace.
8. Plan to relieve the hands of all work which can be done more advantageously with the feet, power tools, or holding devices.
9. Plan the location of items in the workplace to permit the best sequence of motions.
10. Plan for the proper height of the workplace.
11. Plan to combine two or more tools when practical.

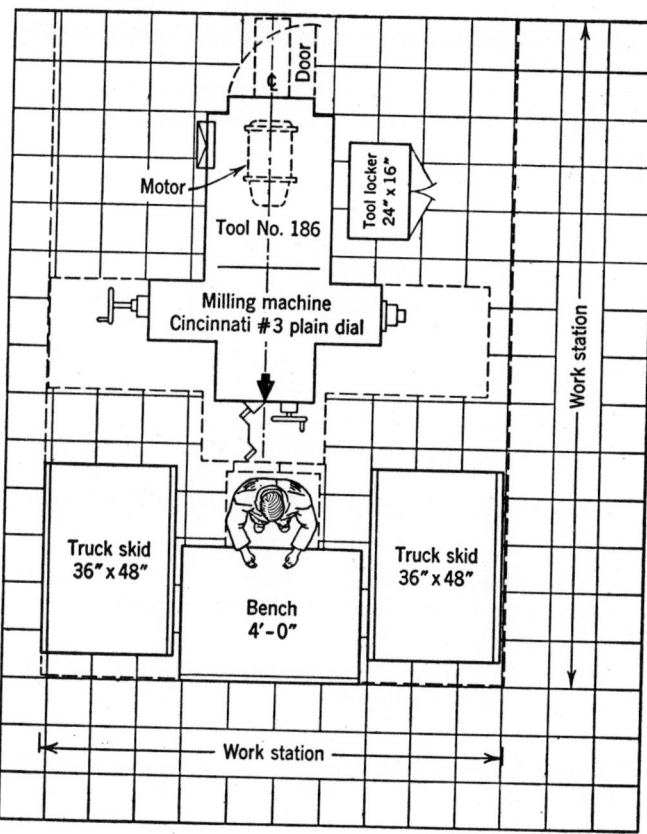

Fig. 14–1. A typical work area.

These principles are discussed in considerable detail in any of the many books on motion economy.

In addition to the above principles, there are other factors to be considered in work area planning. These factors, guides, or principles of work area planning are as follows:

1. In planning each individual operation, keep in mind its necessary relationships with preceding and succeeding operation or work areas.
2. Provide adequate space for the operator to work in, remembering that he should be neither crowded in, nor allowed so much space he must do excessive walking, or make excessive movements.
3. Allow for the overtravel of machine parts such as milling machine tables, etc.
4. Allow for the projection of work, such as the bars of stock fed through a turret lathe.
5. Leave enough room for delivery and removal of parts that are large or are handled on skids, pallets, or in tote boxes.
6. Include floor conveyors, chutes, stock tables, etc., in the plan.
7. Allow enough space to permit placing parts in machines and removing them with ease.
8. Provide area for the storage of the maximum amount of work to be on hand and for the work completed and awaiting removal from the work area.
9. Do not place machines or auxiliary equipment so that access to parts requiring adjustment, lubrication, frequent repair, etc., is difficult or impossible.
10. Assure quick access to safety stops.
11. Be sure that handling equipment selected for one operation ties into the over-all process, both as to type and to capacity.
12. Plan for storage of a minimum of material in the work area.
13. Arrange automatic or semiautomatic machines so that one operator can operate more than one machine.
14. Consider the location of columns, aisles, and elevators.

In reference to number 2, above, the following rules-of-thumb should be used as guides:

1. For machines placed end-to-end
   —allow at least 1 foot between machines for access
2. For machines placed back-to-back
   —allow at least 1 foot between machines for access
3. For machines placed front-to-back
   —allow at least 3 feet for the operator
4. For machines placed front-to-front
   —allow at least 3 feet for one operator
   —allow at least 5 feet for two operators

These relationships are shown in Figure 14–2.

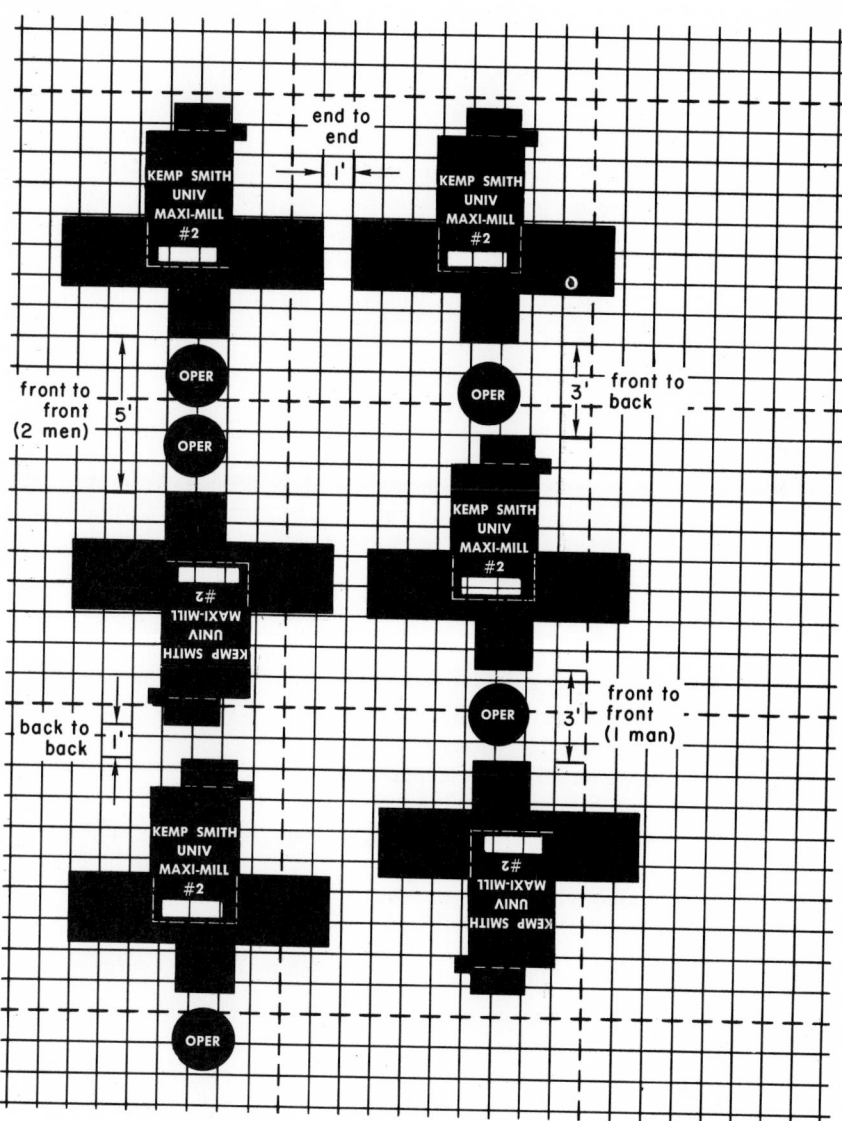

Fig. 14–2. Adequate spacing of equipment permits access for both operator and service personnel.

Materials Handling at the Work Area. Even though the individual work area may be relatively small, and the materials handling problems associated with it seem insignificant, it should be remembered that there are *many* (possibly thousands) work areas within a plant. Any oversights or errors in materials handling planning in the work areas may be multiplied many, many times over and may therefore become major causes of lost effort, labor, efficiency, and money. The plant layout engineer should be particularly careful in his planning activities in this regard. By all means, he should seek the aid of the methods or motion economy personnel in his plant because of their great concern for the efficiency of individual operations.

Materials handling problems at the work area divide themselves into three major categories, as follows:

1. Supplying materials *to* the work area
2. Handling materials *in* the work area
3. Removing materials *from* the work area

None can be overlooked during the planning process.

The delivery of materials to and removal of materials from the work areas may have been planned for in the over-all materials handling planning (Chapter 13). However, there are some further aspects beyond the transportation aspect which should be emphasized at this point.

When planning for the delivery of materials *to* the work area:

1. Plan for the material or container to be positioned at the point of use, directly upon delivery from its previous location, whenever possible. This will eliminate rehandling it later.
2. Plan for mechanical delivery if practical. This will assure a uniform, constant, regulated uninterrupted flow.
3. If not mechanical, plan some alternate means for delivery at the proper intervals.
4. Be sure to allow sufficient space at or near the work area for an adequate supply of material ahead of the operation.

When planning for materials handling *within* the work area:

1. Review the principles of motion economy and work area planning previously stated.
2. Make use of mechanical feeders whenever practical, for individual pieces, sheets, coils, bars, etc. These devices will increase both efficiency and safety in loading machines, etc.
3. Make use of mechanical unloading devices for the same reasons given above.
4. Make use of "convenience" devices in the work area, such as magnetic sheet separators, lift tables, vibratory feeders and hoppers, and containers with counterbalanced bottoms, which maintain material at work level, etc.
5. Make use of special racks to permit ease of picking up and disposing of materials.

When planning for materials handling *from* the work area:

1. Be sure to allow space for a normal amount of finished material.
2. Plan for removal at proper intervals to avoid congestion at the work area.
3. Arrange for mechanical removal if practical.
4. Plan for the normal accumulation and prompt removal of chips, turnings, trimmings, etc., from the work area.

Materials handling equipment particularly useful within the work area might include the following:

1. Short lengths of roller, wheel, or belt conveyors
2. Metal or wood chutes or slides
3. Specially designed racks or tables
4. Standard commercial stock pans
5. Larger stock containers on pallets, skids, or on special "stands" to keep material at work level.

Figures 14–3 through 14–8 illustrate some of the items discussed above.

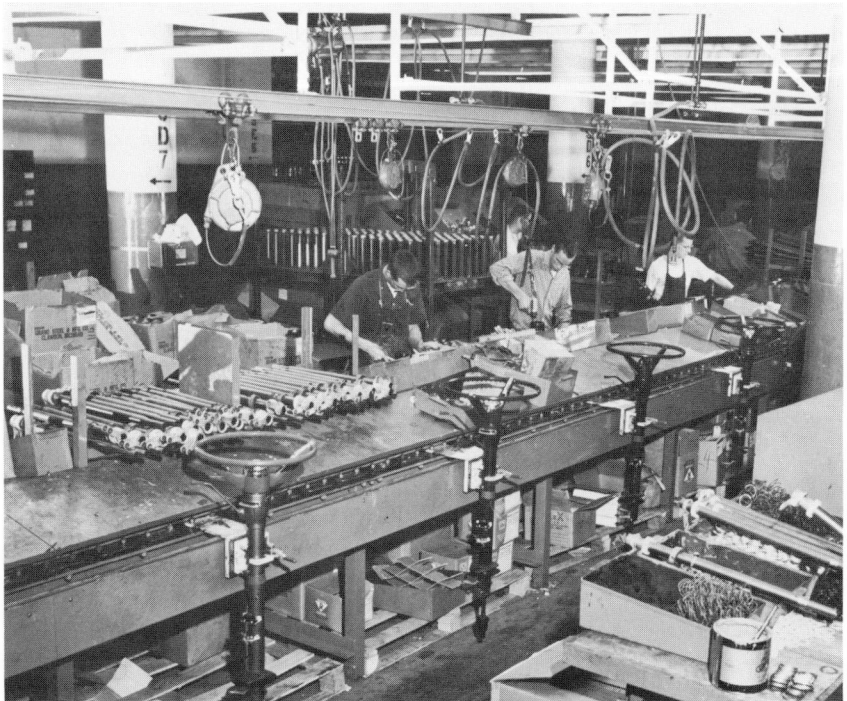

Fig. 14–3. Assembly of steering wheels and columns. Note conveyor, clamps for holding columns, and tools overhead. (By permission of Oldsmobile Division, General Motors Corp.)

Fig. 14–4. Typical workplace layout using commercial small parts bins. (By permission of Bathey Mfg. Co.)

Fig. 14–5. Typical assembly line work station using portable tray trucks for parts from sub-assemblies made in bays at rear. (By permission of Clarke Floor Machine Co.)

Fig. 14–6. Typical work place layout using small parts bins, shop boxes in rack, and served by overhead trolley conveyor. (By permission of Bathey Mfg. Co.)

Fig. 14–7. Typical workplace layout using a revolving table containing several work stations (note also shop boxes on rack, gravity chutes, and suspended power tools.) (By permission of General Electric.)

Fig. 14–8. Unique "ferris-wheel arrangement to furnish small parts for a group of related small assemblies. (By permission of General Electric.)

General Procedure in Planning a Work Area. It must always be remembered that each work space is a "miniature" factory with its own receiving, production, and shipping areas. The one big problem in planning the many work areas is that of tying each one into the over-all flow pattern. To aid in reaching this objective, the following general procedure will serve as a guide:

1. Determine direction of general flow of material or activity through the department or plant from the over-all flow pattern.
2. Based on the above, determine the desired direction of flow through the work area., i.e., left to right, right to left, front to back, or back to front.
3. Determine items required to be contained in the work area, such as machine type, bench, stock containers, conveyors, etc.
4. Make a rough sketch of the major pieces of equipment in the work area in their approximate desired positions and indicate direction of materials flow (from No. 2 above) by an arrow.
5. Indicate source of material for the area and the direction from which it comes.
6. Indicate destination of material from the area and the direction to which it must go.
7. If applicable, indicate method of waste or scrap disposal and direction to which it must go.
8. Sketch in any materials handling equipment serving the area.
9. Check the principles of motion economy and work area planning against the sketch to assure consideration of necessary factors.

10. Indicate distance between items in the area on the sketch.
11. Record work area plan to scale and in detail on an Operation Planning and Analysis Sheet or similar form.
12. If practical at this point, indicate desired method operator should follow in performing the operation.

The above procedure is illustrated in Figures 14–9, 14–10, and 14–11.

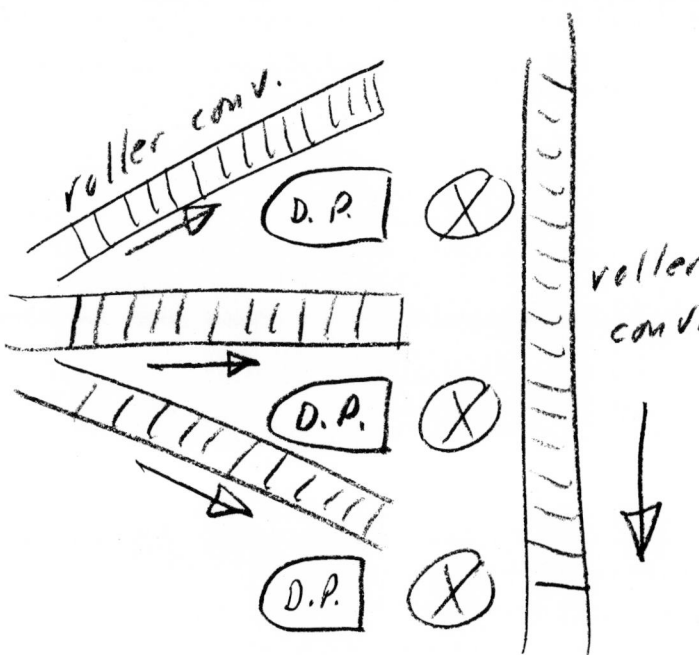

Fig. 14–9. Preliminary sketch of a work area plan.

Line Production. The problem of making full use of equipment and man-power is one of balancing schedules with facilities. In plants where schedules are large enough to permit it, line production is a technique which can aid the full utilization of men and machines.

Line production is a manufacturing technique whereby work areas are so planned and arranged that the material moves continuously, at a uniform rate. Operations are performed simultaneously at all work stations; each area turns out the same number of pieces per unit of time, and the material flows in a reasonably direct path.

Line production of this sort is usually attained by pacing production. This means maintaining the production rate by establishing a pace, in

OPERATION PLANNING AND ANALYSIS SHEET

PART NAME Brace   PART NO._____

OPERATION DESCR. Drill 4 holes   OPER. NO. 30

OPERATOR_____ CLOCK NO._____

ANNUAL PROD'N 100,000 **PCS./HR.**_____ STD. TIME_____

☐ PRESENT METHOD SOURCE OF MATERIALS Conveyor from oper. 20

☐ PROPOSED METHOD DESTIN. OR MATERIALS Conveyor to oper. 40

ITEMS IN WORK AREA 3 Delta drill press 17-211 1 SPDL

     1' wide roller conveyor

RECORDED BY J. L. Heard   DATE May 14, 1962

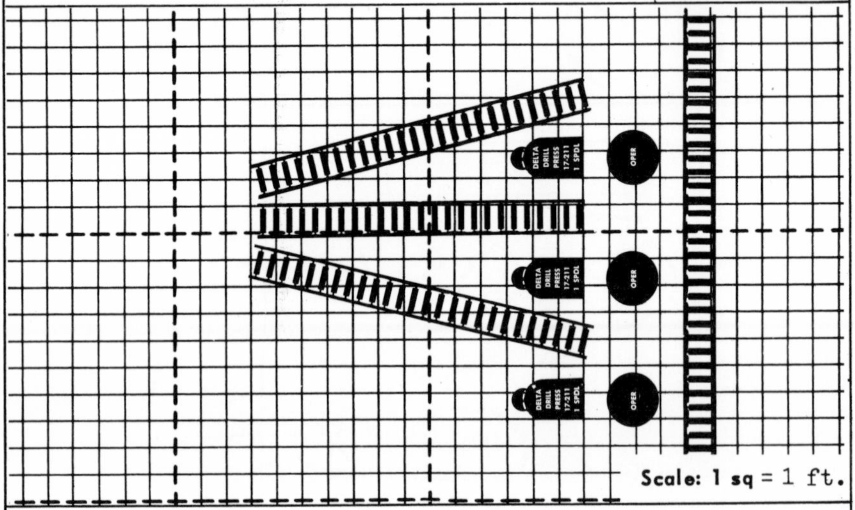

Scale: 1 sq = 1 ft.

	LEFT				RIGHT		
explanation	ob-ject	time	motion symbol	motion symbol	time	ob-ject	explanation
from conveyor	pc.		Get	Dis-pose		pc.	to conveyor
in fixture	pc.		Place	Get		d.p. hdle.	
in fixture	pc.		HOLD	Place		hdle.	down
			D R I L L				
WAIT			—	Get		pc.	from fixture

Fig. 14–10. Final layout of a proposed work area.

terms of units per hour. This pace may be governed by the speed of a conveyor, or the output of a certain machine or work area, by the stimulus of incentive pay, or by the slowest man. In practice, perfect pacing is most closely realized with the transfer-type machine, as was discussed in Chapter 5.

However, this concept is probably best known by the type of assembly line commonly associated with the production or assembly of such items as automobiles, refrigerators, radios, and similar mass-produced items.

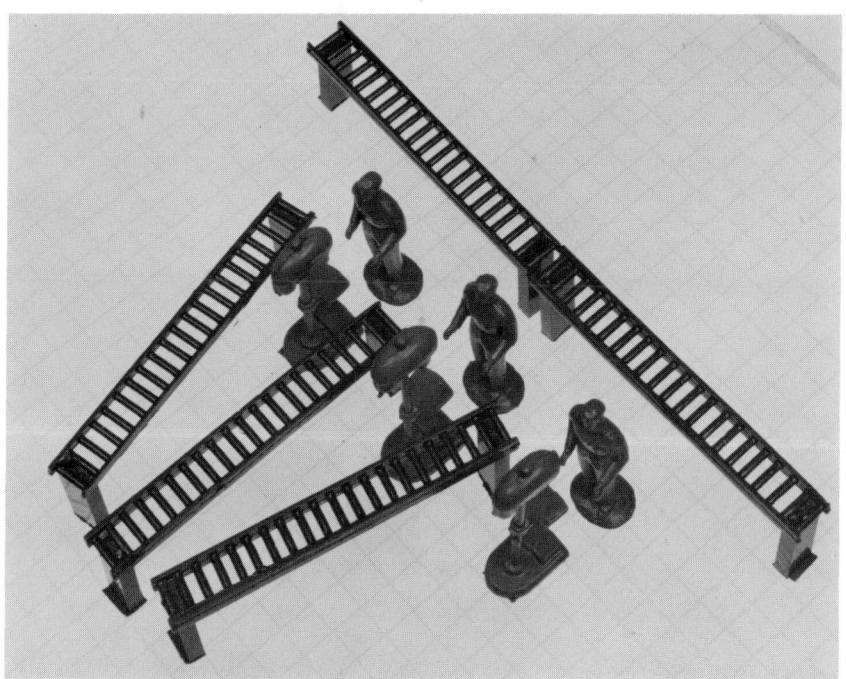

Fig. 14–11. Same work area as in 14–10, but in scale models.

The technique is applied equally as well to the production of unit parts such as machined castings, sheet-metal stampings, wood parts, etc.

In order for line production to be at all successful, each work station must feed material to the next station at a fixed rate in terms of units per hour. That is, if 60 units per hour are wanted at the end of the line, then each work station must turn out 60 units per hour, regardless of the actual time required to perform its own operation. This means that if a certain work station turns out only 30 pieces per hour, two stations will be required. If it turns out 15 pieces per hour, four will be required; and if a machine or operator turns out 120 pieces per hour, he will be busy only one-half the time. The balancing of operations in the line is the biggest problem in line production. It should be the concern of all to see that the major factors—men, machines, and materials—are furnished in balanced quantities at each work station. The work should be so planned that each operator's share of the over-all job is a multiple of the cycle time set for the line. That is, if the cycle time is set at 1 minute, then an operator's share should be 1 minute or a multiple thereof. This concept will be illustrated later in this chapter.

Although line production may appear to be the best way to produce any item, it most certainly should not be attempted in every case. There are many times when line production would not be the answer to the production problem. The following are some of the prerequisites necessary to the successful application of the production-line plan of manufacturing:

1. There must be sufficient quantity to justify the product-type machine arrangement.
2. The product must be of such a nature that the operations to be performed on the line are broken down into units sufficiently small:
    a) To permit each to be learned in a relatively short time by a relatively unskilled operator, thus facilitating the shifting of personnel necessitated when production increases or decreases.
    b) To permit the elements of work to be recombined into time units of about equal length for each operator in the line.
3. Jigs and fixtures must be used to make sure that each operation is performed in exactly the same manner on each part or assembly.
4. The line, after it is set up, must not be so inflexible as to prevent minor alterations which might result from design, model, or methods changes on the part or product. In spite of the application of the production-line technique to the nth degree to automobile assembly lines, one manufacturer turns out 20,000 variations of his product on one line. At the General Motors Corporation, Buick-Olds-Pontiac Divisions, all three cars are turned out on one line!
5. Materials must be continuously supplied to the line at the required places in order that a materials shortage will not cause the line to be shut down. Production control and materials control must be properly worked out and must function well.
6. There must be enough operations to be done on the part or product to warrant the "line."
7. The production of each kind of unit must extend over a sufficient period of time. A line cannot be set up if a month's supply can be turned out in a few hours, as on an automatic screw machine.
8. The line must run a sufficient portion of the working time to be economical.
9. The job must last long enough to justify setting up the line.
10. The design must be fairly well "frozen" or standardized so that changes will not disrupt the line too often.
11. Parts must be interchangeable.

It would seem that if all these prerequisites are necessary, line production would be next to impossible. However, a glimpse into almost any plant will show the line production principle in use to some degree. It is in the plants which make items in large quantities that the line production principle really finds its most efficient applications.

Conveyorized Lines. A production line as discussed above may or may not be conveyorized. If it is conveyorized there will be certain advantages, such as:

1. Uniform rate of production
2. Simpler cost keeping
3. Pacing of operators
4. Less handling
5. Shorter time cycle for work-in-process
6. More effective use of labor
7. Easier production control
8. Easier supervision
9. Less congested work areas

Balancing Line Production. Stated briefly, the problem to be solved is one of planning the work to be done so that each work station will carry an equal work load and turn out the same number of pieces in a unit of time. Because situations within individual lines cause each problem to be different, various ways have been developed to aid in attaining balance. These are:

1. Banks of materials
2. Moving or shifting operators
3. Grouping and/or subdividing work elements
4. Improving the operation
5. Improving operator performance
6. Having the operator work on subassemblies during idle time

Probably the easiest, but not at all the best, method of balancing a line is to build up "banks" of materials ahead of the slower work areas. These areas must then work overtime or take on additional personnel. This is not an equitable solution and usually results in a large "float" of materials in the line, with accompanying bottlenecks, wasted space, and idle time.

The second method is to have an operator move along the line so that he covers more than one operation when his work assignment is shorter than the others; or if it is longer than the others, he may be instructed to work on only every other unit. Then a second operator takes the alternate unit.

The third method is probably the most common. It involves subdividing the work to be done into elements, and then recombining the elements into tasks of equal length. This method is widely used and is reasonably successful. However, there are places where it is not applicable; for instance, when the work is of such a nature that it cannot be subdivided, or if it requires a particular skill, or if it would be too costly to work out the methods and equipment for accomplishing the work in subdivisions of the whole.

A fourth method, and one which should always be tried, is improving the operations. This method is especially useful if the line is already set up and several operations appear to be slower than the others. Studying the method should nearly always result in discovery of a better way to do the work and thereby reduce the time required so that it will be in line with the others.

The fifth method is very closely related, and concerns itself with improving operator performance. This can be accomplished in many cases by additional training of the person doing the work or, in some cases, by substituting an operator better fitted for the task at hand.

The sixth method is to have those operators with idle time making up subassemblies when not occupied on the line. This is more successful on slowly moving lines, with long cycle times, than it is on rapidly moving lines with short cycle times.

It can be readily imagined that in many cases, several of these methods are used together to attain balance on a particular line. It should also be pointed out that some types of lines are relatively easy to set up and balance, while others are obstinately complex. For instance, the problem of balance becomes more serious when the number of variations of the product increase, and when the size of the object increases.

Figures 14–12 and 14–13 illustrate the third method described above—that of combining work elements into uniform tasks of equal length.

Coordinating the Individual Work Areas. At this point in the planning process, a sizable amount of detailed work has been done which may appear to be unrelated. Actually it is all very closely related. The need is for some means of tying it all together; and for this reason, the Layout Planning Chart was developed.

The Layout Planning Chart. The Layout Planning Chart is somewhat of a combination of a Flow Process Chart and a Production Routing with other pertinent data added to aid in the planning of the layout. Many plants use a form similar to the Layout Planning Chart, although it may vary somewhat in detail. It is frequently found that certain processes or kinds of work are better recorded if the form is designed specifically for use in a given plant or department. Columns can be changed, omitted, or

Operations from Routing	Operation Elements from Time Study	Task Assignments at 100% Production (elements combined to make tasks of approximately equal duration)	Task Assignments at 50% Production
1	.14 min. / .26 } .80 / .08 / .11 / .21	.48 min. = Task No. 1 } = .98 = Task No. 1
		.50 min. = Task No. 2	
2	.06 / .12 } .46 / .28		
		.46 min. = Task No. 3	
3	.18 / .25 } .91 / .10 / .16	.51 min. = Task No. 4 } = .97 = Task No. 2
4	.09 / .13 } .25 / .09 / .16	.47 min. = Task No. 5	.... etc.

Fig. 14–12. Theory of assembly line balancing.

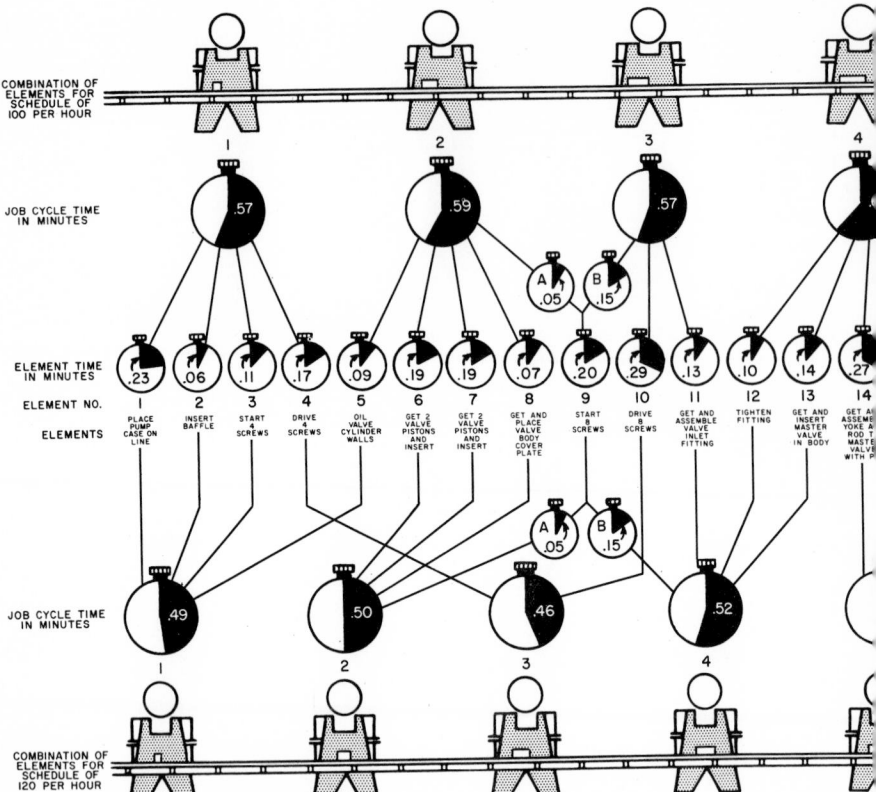

Fig. 14–13. Illustration of equitable distribution of work on conveyorized assembly line for

added to suit the particular needs of the type of problem under consideration. A typical Layout Planning Chart is shown in Figure 14–14. Items
other than those shown which might be desirable on the chart are:

1. Machine or equipment number
2. Tool names and numbers
3. Floor space requirements
4. Utilities needed, etc.

It will be seen that the left-hand side of the chart is the commonly
known Flow Process Chart. It is included here as a check on previous
planning to be sure that each and every step in the process has been given
proper consideration, and that a method of performing each step has been
determined. A Flow Process Chart cannot be properly made without recording plans for each step, so at this point a check is made. If such plans
have not been made during the operation planning phase, then they must
be made here. This is actually a method of forcing the planner to con-

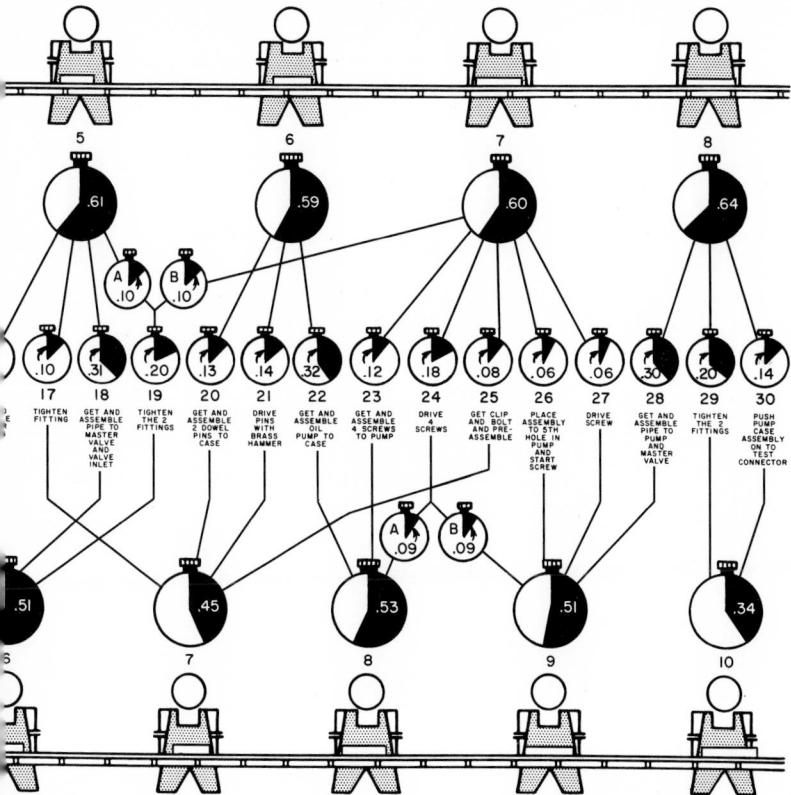

each of two production schedules. (By permission of General Motors Institute.)

sider the steps or activities in the process which occur between the operations as listed on the Production Routing. Here the interrelationship of operations must be considered, and "non-productive" as well as productive activity must be planned.

To make out a Layout Planning Chart, the following steps are suggested:

1. Fill in the heading from information on the Production Routing or available from some other source.
2. Referring to the operation planning sketch previously made, decide which process symbol represents the first step in the operation. It will probably be "Storage" because the object must be picked up from where it has been stored, awaiting the process. (Detailed instructions for making the Flow Process Chart are presented in Chapter 9.)
3. In the first column, insert step number.
4. In the description column, enter just enough information to indicate what is not told by the other columns on the chart. In this case, the infor-

LAYOUT PLANNING CHART

Part No. 1
Assy. No.
Material Aluminum alloy
Part Name Powrarm Base
Assy. Name
Size 6" x 6" x 3-5/8"

PCS./ASSY. 1
ASSY./JOB
PCS./DAY
PCS./HR. REQ.
PROD. HRS./DAY
MODEL M-2

SHEET 1 OF 2
PREPARED BY F. J. Wenkkes
DATE 7/11

ST. NO.	O T I D S	DESCRIPTION	OPER. NO.	DEPT. NO.	T.S. REG. NO.	TIME PER PC.	PCS. PER HOUR	TOTAL LOAD HRS.	OPER. PER MACH.	TOTAL MAN-POWER	MACHINE OR EQUIPMENT	NO. MACH. REQ'D.	DIST. MOVED	HOW MOVED	TYPE OF CONT'R	REMARKS
1		gondola													Gon	
2		to Operation 1											6'	Hand		
3		face bottom	1	2		.016	60		1	1	14" LeBlond engine lathe	1				
4		to table or roller conveyor											4'	Hand		
5		on table									Table & roller conveyor					
6		to Operation 2											3'	Hand		
7		face top, turn O.D., neck, drill and ream 5/8" hole	2	2		.042	23.8		1	3	3 – Warner & Swasey turret lathes	3				
8		to roller conveyor											3'	Hand		
9		change of carrier														
10		along roller conveyor									Roller conveyor		10'	Mech.		
11		on table														
12		to Operation 3									Table		4'	Hand		
13		drill 3 bolt holes	3	2		.012	83.4		1	1	21" Cleveman drill press	1				
14		to table											4'	Hand		
15		on table									Table					
16		to Operation 4											3'	Hand		
17		drill pin hole	4	2		.0042	238.0		1	1	Delta drill press	1				
18		to table											2'	Hand		
19		on table									Table					
20		to operation 5											2'	Hand		
21		drill & ream 3/4" eccentric hole	5	2		.0153	65.4		2	2	#4 Fosdick 2-spindle drill press	1				
22		to table											3'	Hand		

Fig. 14-14. Layout planning chart for Powrarm base.

mation would probably be merely an indication of where the part had been stored, such as "in gondola."

5. Fill in any other columns pertaining to the step just recorded. In this case, probably the only one of importance is the "Machine or Equipment" column, where "gondola" and its specifications could be entered.

Other columns are explained as follows:

Operation Number. Pertains only to "operation" or "inspect" steps and should show same number as on the Routing or Operation Process Chart.

Department Number. Identification of department, plant, or area performing the operation.

Time Study Register Number. Serial number of time study from which time per piece is taken.

Time per Piece. Standard time in minutes or hours per piece.

Pieces per Hour. Number of pieces to be expected per hour at 100 per cent performance, according to standard time in previous column.

Total Load Hours. Number of hours required to produce the pieces per day indicated in the heading of the chart.

Operators per Machine. Number of operators required for each machine.

Total Manpower. Number of operators to man the machines required to produce the daily requirements.

Machine or Equipment. Brief description, name, or number of machine or equipment necessary.

Number of Machines Required. Number of machines or pieces of equipment needed to handle the daily production.

Distance Moved. Estimated distance the average part will move from one step to the next.

Type of Container. Designation of container to be used in handling the object.

Remarks. Any other pertinent data.

6. Repeat steps 2, 3, 4, 5 until every step of each operation in the planned process has been recorded.

7. Repeat steps 1 through 6 for each part to be processed.

It will be seen from the completed Layout Planning Chart that many of the loose ends of the planning process have been tied together. At this point a check has been made, by means of the chart, on the completeness and accuracy of the planning. This is where any errors or omissions in the planning should be corrected.

The Flow Diagram. Closely related to the Flow Process Chart is the Flow Diagram, which was first presented in Chapter 9 as an analytical technique (see Figure 9-8). In the *planning* process, it becomes the next step in the coordination of the individual work areas—however, in this instance, the Flow Diagram must be synthesized. Actually, the Flow Diagram, in this case, is merely a consolidation or integration of the individual operation charts previously made. This concept is indicated in Figure 14–15, in which are shown the seven operations on the Powrarm

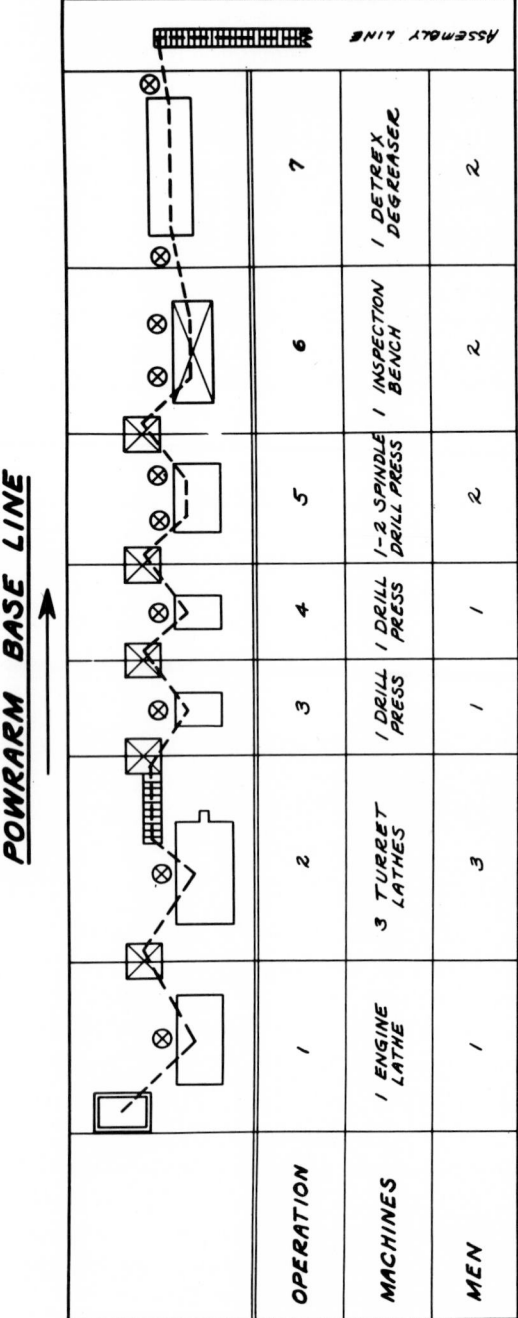

Fig. 14–15. Preliminary production line planning showing relationships of individual operations to each other.

base, which were "coordinated" on the Layout Planning Chart in Figure 14–14.

The completed Flow Diagram shown in Figure 14–16 is adjusted to suit the more specific nature of the actual space allocated. In performing this step, either templates or scale models of the equipment and facilities may be used—or the diagram may be roughly sketched as in Figure 14–16. Figures 14–17 and 14–18 show the same arrangement in commercial templates and in scale models.

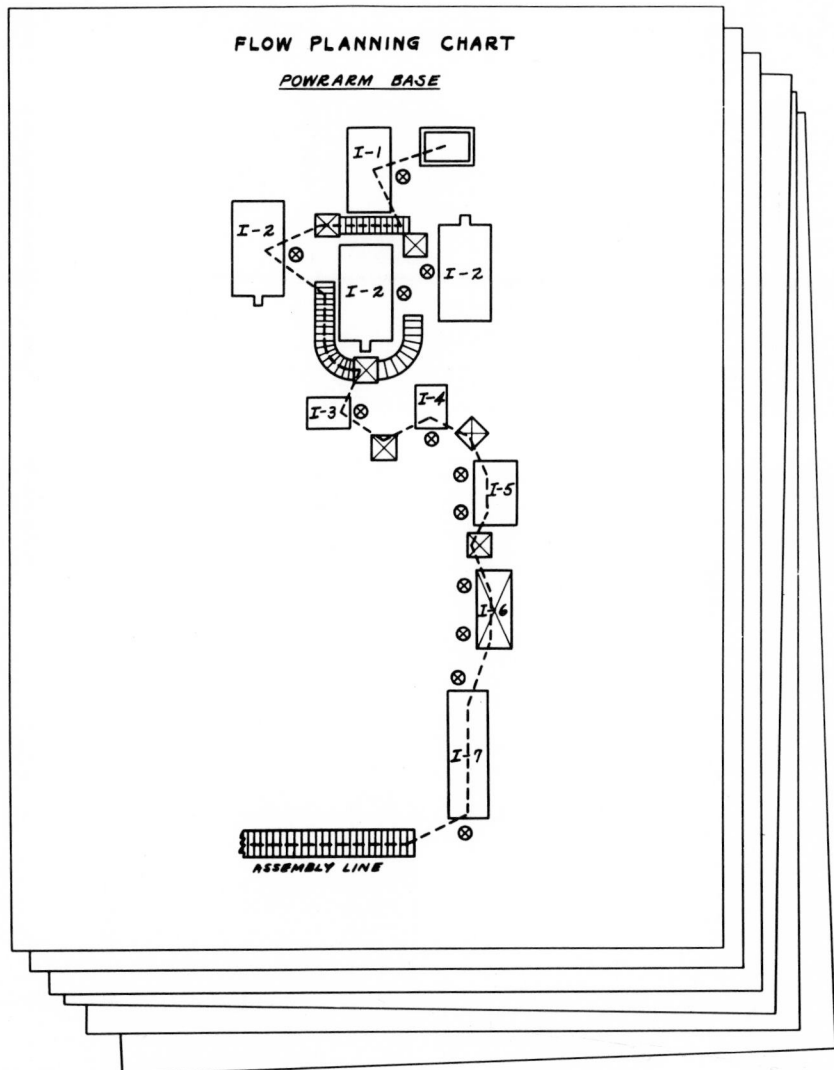

Fig. 14–16. Flow planning chart, or flow diagram, for Powrarm base; sheets behind indicate one such chart for each machine group, department, or area.

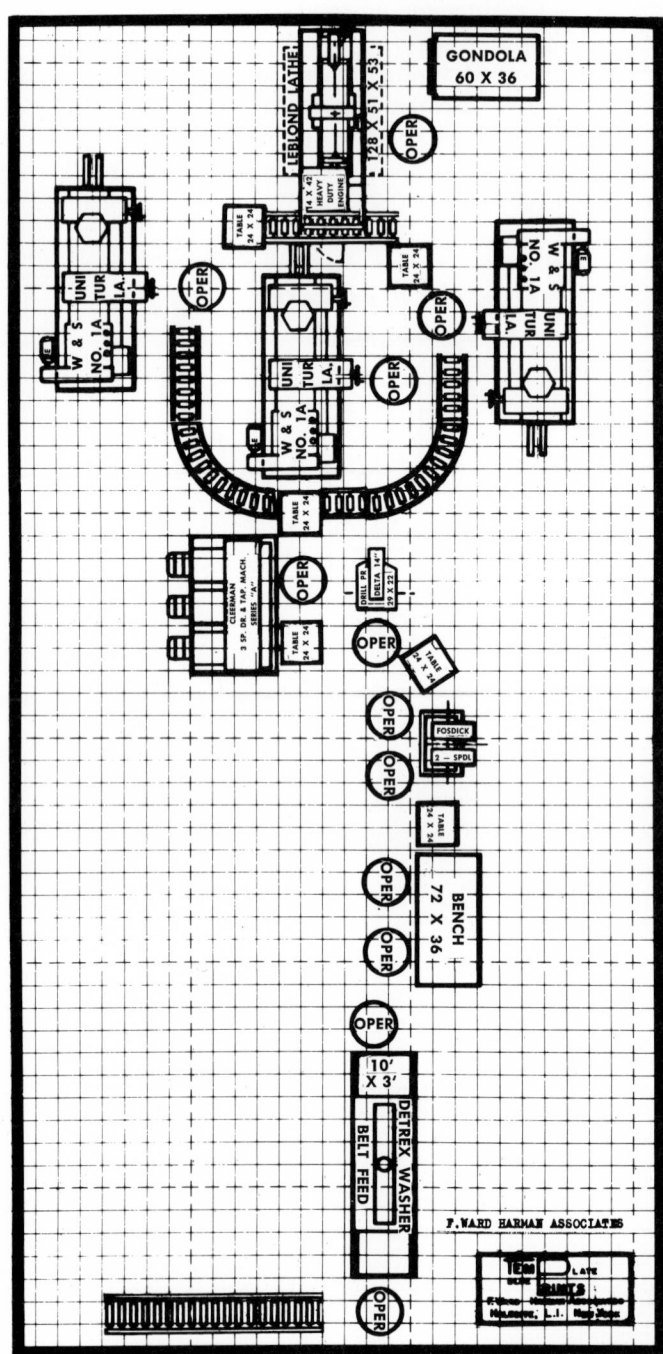

Fig. 14–17. Flow diagram using commercial templates. (By permission of F. Ward Harman Associates.)

Fig. 14–18. Flow diagram using commercial models (same area as in Fig. 14–16). (By permission of Visual Plant Layouts, Inc.)

CONCLUSION

Planning of the individual work areas is one of the most important phases of plant layout work. Any small error or extra cost inherent in a single work area is multiplied over and over in the operation of the plant.

This chapter has presented an approach to work area planning and coordination that should be extremely helpful in the development of the final layout, as discussed in Chapter 15.

QUESTIONS

1. What is meant by the term "work area"? What does a work area usually include?
2. State some principles of motion economy applicable to work area planning.
3. What are some of the other factors or guides for consideration in work area planning?
4. What are the three major phases of materials handling activity at the work area?
5. What are some of the factors to be remembered in each phase?
6. Show by a sketch how the flow of materials through a work area is related to the over-all flow pattern.
7. What is meant by line production?
8. What are some prerequisites of line production?
9. What are some advantages of conveyorized line production? Disadvantages?
10. What is meant by line balance?
11. What are some of the ways in which line balance can be achieved?
12. Show a few calculations to indicate how tasks are realigned to achieve line balance.
13. How is the Layout Planning Chart "related" to the Flow Process Chart?
14. How does it aid in coordinating the individual work areas?
15. What purpose does the Flow Diagram serve in the coordination?

15

Making the Plant Layout

Introduction. After fourteen chapters describing preliminary planning and related details, the time has finally arrived for the actual construction of the plant layout. Because of the careful preplanning which has been done in previous steps, the actual layout construction should be a relatively easier task. However, the plant layout engineer should be warned that there still remain many important decisions to be made and details to be worked out.

The general objective, at this point, is the coordination of all previous planning activities and the transfer of plans made in previous steps to a master plant layout. Before beginning the layout construction, there are still a few important factors to be considered—upon which decisions must be made—prior to the final layout.

Relationships Between Layout and Land Area. Before the actual plant layout is constructed, there are several relationships which should be considered between the layout proper and the piece of land upon which it will be placed. The first of these is the size of the piece of property. One leading industrial contractor suggests that the plot should be about eight times the size of the presently proposed building. That is, for a 20,000–square foot building (½ acre), a plot of 4 acres would be required. While this may seem like a high ratio, it must be remembered that land area is required for access of public·transportation (shipping and receiving); employee parking; landscaping; employee recreation area; and last but not least, expansion, as was discussed in Chapter 10. Common experience is that the average plant will expand its physical facilities to about four times the original building size—leaving a ratio of only two to one!

Transportation facilities, particularly for incoming material and outgoing product, should also be reviewed at this point, since they will affect the orientation of the building and layout on the property. This subject was covered in Chapter 7, in the general discussion on shipping and receiving. Refer to Figure 7–1.

Space required by the layout, as well as its tentative shape, should be considered in relationship to the proposed plot of land. These two factors will be important in deciding on the orientation of the building on the property. In general, the building should be near one corner of the property or centered along one side. This will depend, of course, on the plans for expansion and the proposed directions of the planned expansion (see Figure 10–4). The direction which the building faces on the property is also of great importance. This may be dictated by other factors, such as existing roads, railroad tracks, etc.

The building orientation with reference to the points of the compass may also be influenced by the desired (or undesired) light, heat, or prevailing winds. Some authorities claim the main axis of the building should run east and west to permit maximum use of the north, or steadiest all-day light—and to minimize glare from the low sun in the west. However, the heat will be at a maximum on the south side. If it is desired to take advantage of the heat, or to avoid it, the main axis of the building should be appropriately located.

Aisles. Another important consideration, prior to constructing the layout, is the proposed size and location of aisles. The following passage, quoted from Sidney Reibel, Materials Handling Consultant for the Jervis B. Webb Co., presents an excellent picture of the important part played by aisles in the layout of a plant.[1]

In the average industrial plant, aisles are the highways and byways, the roads, on which almost all movement of workers and materials takes place—with the exception of course of the work accomplished by conveyors and cranes. Aisles take up a lot of space, sometimes so much that plant efficiency is affected. Therefore, careful consideration of the location and arrangement of aisles is not only advisable but is likely to be profitable as well.

Two types of such passageways are found in most plants—main aisles and department aisles. Main aisles, as distinguished from department aisles, are utilized for movement between departments and into or out of a plant. Ordinarily a department will have a main aisle on at least one border line.

In the layout of a new plant one of the first procedures is to locate the main aisles. Once the positions of the main aisles are fixed, they are seldom changed. Moreover, after plant facilities—such as elevators, toilets, locker and wash rooms, cafeteria and first aid—are located, they are not easily movable and, of course, they must be installed on aisles or have aisles leading to them. Thus, the placing of aisles is given preference in planning the layout of a new plant or building; that is, main passageways are located first, and then the facilities.

In general the larger the plant, the farther apart the main aisles can be, and the less space (in percentage) they will occupy. A building 20 ft. wide may have one 5 or 6 ft. aisle which represents 25 to 30% of the floor space. But a building 600 ft. wide may require three main aisles—one down the center, and one on

[1] Reibel, Sidney, "Aisles Can Affect Efficiency of Handling and Storage Methods," *Industry and Power,* Oct., 1949, p. 78.

each side—three hundred feet apart. If these aisles are 10 ft. wide, only 5% of the space is taken up by them.

However, the comparison is not between 25% in one case and 5% in the other. Naturally the narrow building will have department aisles, as well as the main passageways, and the total area of all aisles may be 12 to 20% or more of the floor area.

Common practice calls for one "backbone" main aisle located at or near the center of the building. This is the principal thoroughfare and usually the widest. Side aisles are parallel to the backbone, and cross aisles are provided wherever required.

A main aisle should start at an outside entrance and run as straight as possible. Sharp offsets are undesirable, and if jogs are unavoidable, offset angles should be held to the minimum. On the first floor, aisles should terminate at a building entrance or at main cross aisles; aisles on upper floors of multistory buildings may dead-end.

Interior aisles are used to provide room for:

1. Movement of workers and materials
2. Moving supplies, and removal of trimmings, chips, and scrap
3. Servicing and removal of machines for repairs
4. Fire department access to the area

All departments do not necessarily need interior aisles. Sometimes working spaces around the machines are sufficient for movement of workers and materials. Nevertheless the majority of departments will have aisles bordered by machines, and in such cases the layout is the determining factor in aisle location. Interior aisles are often offset, may dead-end, and may be quite narrow.

If aisles are needed for passage of machines to repair shops, clearance for the largest machines determines the aisle width. However, if space is at a premium, narrower aisles can be employed; but, if they are, several machines, or a whole row of them, may have to make way for moving the crippled machine out of the department. This makes a lot of extra work at times, but if it does not occur often, the savings in floor space due to narrower interior aisles may be worthwhile. Factors to consider are the expected frequency of machine overhaul or breakdown, whether or not moving the machines is a long and difficult task, and how serious is the interference with production.

Fire and other hazards must be anticipated when laying out the aisles. If hazardous conditions exist, interior aisles must allow quick, easy access of fire-fighting and first-aid equipment to points where fire and accidents can happen. Aisles must be made wide enough and kept clear for this purpose at all times, without exception, and the layout checked for prevention of disastrous panic conditions.

If aisles are made wide enough at the start, are allowed to stay that way, and are kept clear and free from obstructions, the best results in movement of materials and workers will follow. Unfortunately few plants keep their aisles wide enough for proper, smooth, unimpeded flow of traffic. All too often the remedy for a shortage of space is to cut down on aisle width.

In large plants the backbone aisle may be 12 to 20 ft. wide. A 10 ft. passageway constitutes a good, wide aisle and in a majority of cases will accommodate two loaded lift trucks passing in opposite directions, plus clearance for a pedestrian. Eight foot aisles may be crowded, especially if truck loads are more than 40 in. wide. Man-passage and interior aisles may be as narrow as 2½ to 3 ft., but movement in them will be very constricted.

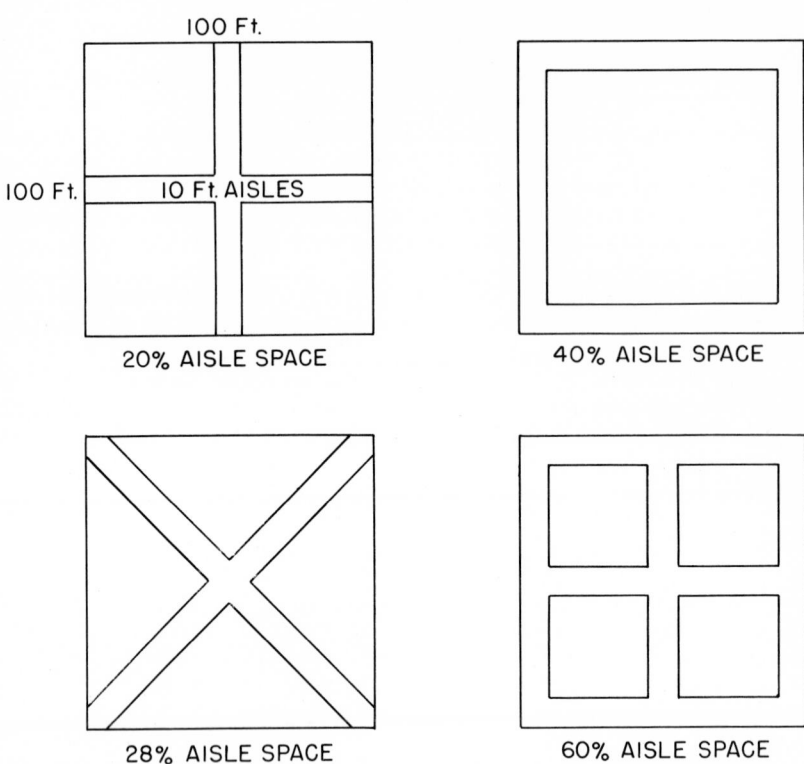

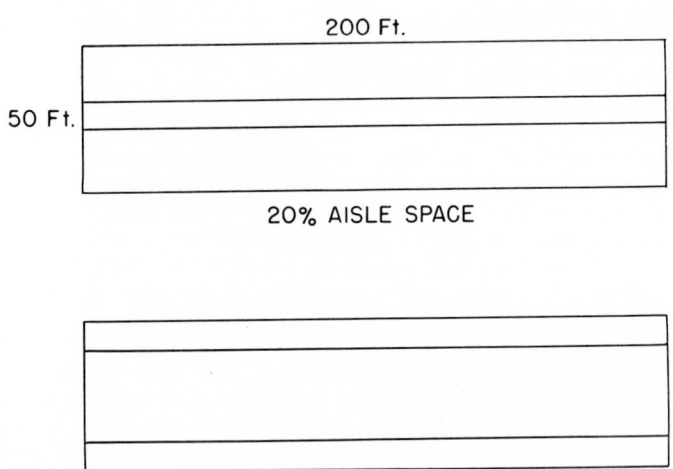

Fig. 15-1A. Ratio of aisle space to total plant area.

One of the principal factors in setting minimum width for interior trucking aisles is the space necessary for maneuvering power lift trucks. Turning radius, end—as well as side—clearances, and size of loads of the specific equipment must be checked by clearance diagrams to help determine the width of aisles.

Widespread use of unit loads has made it desirable to restrict width of loads to not more than 48 in. But this limitation is not always feasible, and in any case the width of aisles must be enough for free passage of the widest loads. When wide loads are of infrequent occurrence, the aisles need accommodate only one such load going in one direction. But, if wide loads occur often enough to interfere to an appreciable extent with other traffic, set-backs can be provided at intervals; then one load can wait (like a train on a side-track) until the other has passed. In effect, this calls for aisles of varying widths, a condition encountered quite often, although it slows traffic.

Main aisles should be so located as to allow a short set-back to freight elevators. This arrangement prevents interference with main aisle traffic while loading or unloading the elevator. Then, too, a space is provided for temporary storage of goods, which have just been unloaded and are ready to be hauled away, or for goods being held until the elevator arrives at the floor. Set-backs must be short, if space is to be conserved and excessive travel prevented.

Figure 15–1 indicates some of the relationships discussed above. Even though the suggestions are theoretical, it can be seen that the proper width and placement of aisles calls for careful study.

Aisle Widths

For personnel only (2 persons to pass)	30 inches minimum
For two-wheel hand truck (no passing or turning with load)	30 inches minimum
For stock truck (where trucker must pass around it)	20 inches plus width of truck
For stock truck (where other trucks and workers must pass)	36 inches plus twice the width of trucks
For stackers hand-operated fork truck, pallet transporter, semilive skid and jack	5 to 8 feet, depending on nature of load
For narrow aisle industrial trucks	5 to 6 feet depending on load
For 2,000-pound fork truck	8 to 10 feet
For 4,000-pound fork truck	10 to 12 feet
For 6,000-pound fork truck	12 to 14 feet
For Fork Trucks—angle storage	5 to 7 feet

Aisle Width Depends Upon:

Use of the aisle—material, personnel, handling equipment, machinery, and other equipment
Frequency of use—volume of traffic (at peak loads)
Speed of travel permitted or desired
One-way or two-way traffic

Fig. 15–1B. Aisle widths commonly used in industry. (By permission of Paul T. Eaton, Georgia Institute of Technology.)

Column Spacing. Most buildings, to be economical, require columns or posts to hold up the roof and/or provide necessary supports for overhead equipment. In the larger plants, bay sizes are increasing in the new structures over those in plants built prior to 1940. This construction requires wider spacing of columns than was common some years ago. One authority states that, previous to World War II, the average plant had 150 interior columns for 100,000 square feet of floor space. This average has been reduced to about 40 columns per 100,000 square feet by using bay sizes up to 100 feet in one direction. Here again there are exceptions, particularly in some of the large aircraft plants where 300–foot spans are not unusual. Some wide spans, of course, are necessary because of the nature of the product but are more costly due to the expensive structural work necessary for construction. In general, wide column spacing is desirable for maximum efficiency in handling materials, arranging equipment, and in providing flexibility for the future. In today's plants, common spacing of columns varies from 24 to 50 feet, with some up to 100 feet or over. Most common spacing would be about 30 feet by 40 feet, 40 feet by 40 feet, 40 feet by 60 feet, etc. Actual distances are best determined by consulting contractors and checking "standard" sizes of structural members in the locality.

One authority has discussed column spacing, or spans, as follows: [2]

> Far too many plants are still being built with spans of 30 by 40 feet or 50 by 20 feet. That some recognition of the importance of long spans has been realized is indicated by the increasing number of plants with 60 by 40 foot column spacing. But there have been too few built with 100 by 40, and 120 by 60 foot column spacing. Such spans add slightly to the first cost but pay handsome returns in long useful occupancy and the lower cost of future improvements and changes in production equipment, plant layout and material handling methods.

Methods of Constructing the Layout. There are four common methods of constructing or representing the final layout. They are:

1. Drawn in the conventional drafting manner on drawing or tracing paper.
2. Constructed with two-dimensional templates ("cutouts," to scale, representing the shape and size of each piece of equipment), mounted on a suitable base or grid.
3. Constructed with three-dimensional scale models in place of templates.
4. Constructed with scale models *and* templates—for ease of reproduction.

Figures 15–2, 3, 4, and 5 illustrate the basic techniques listed above. It will be noted that Figures 15–4 and 15–5 are for the same area and "complement" each other. In general, the method selected for a spe-

[2] Waidelich, A. T., "Trends in Modern Industrial Buildings," *Mill and Factory*, May, 1958, pp. 3–4.

cific project should be based on the characteristics tabulated in Figure 15–6. The four methods compared are:

   I. Conventional two-dimensional templates, "homemade," as in Figure 15–3
  II. Reproducible two-dimensional templates, as in Figure 15–4
 III. Three-dimensional scale models as in Figure 15–5
 IV. A combination of scale models and reproducible templates.

The probable conclusion to be drawn is that number IV is preferable when its cost can be justified. This may not be as difficult as it may seem, when one calculates that the cost of a complete scale model and matching template layout amounts to about $.07/square foot of actual plant area for necessary materials. This is less than 1 per cent of the cost of construction! The architect's fee will range from 5 to 7 per cent. For example, on a 100,000–square foot building, the comparison might be somewhat as follows:

Building—100,000 square feet at $10/sq. ft.   = $1,000,000
Architect's fee—$1,000,000 × 6%   =   60,000
Scale model—100,000 square feet at 6¢/sq. ft. =   6,000
Template layout—100,000 square feet at 1¢/sq. ft. =   1,000

It should be recognized that the models and templates are as much a "tool" of the plant layout engineer as a screwdriver is to a production operator! Would management ask the operator to make his own screwdriver?

The "plain" drawing can be properly used:

1. For simple projects
2. For preliminary sketching
3. When "in a hurry"
4. When no reproduction equipment is available

Plant Layout Tools and Techniques. The basic materials used in plant layout work are described below.

1. Base material upon which the layout is constructed. Common materials for this purpose are:
   a) Plastic sheet (.0075–.0100 inch) with grid lines printed on back surface.
   b) Plastic "board" (¼ inch) with grid lines scribed on back surface.
   c) Metal faced plywood with appropriate finish on metal surface.
   d) Sheet metal, plywood, or composition board (Masonite or Celotex style) with appropriate finish.
   e) Drawing or tracing paper.

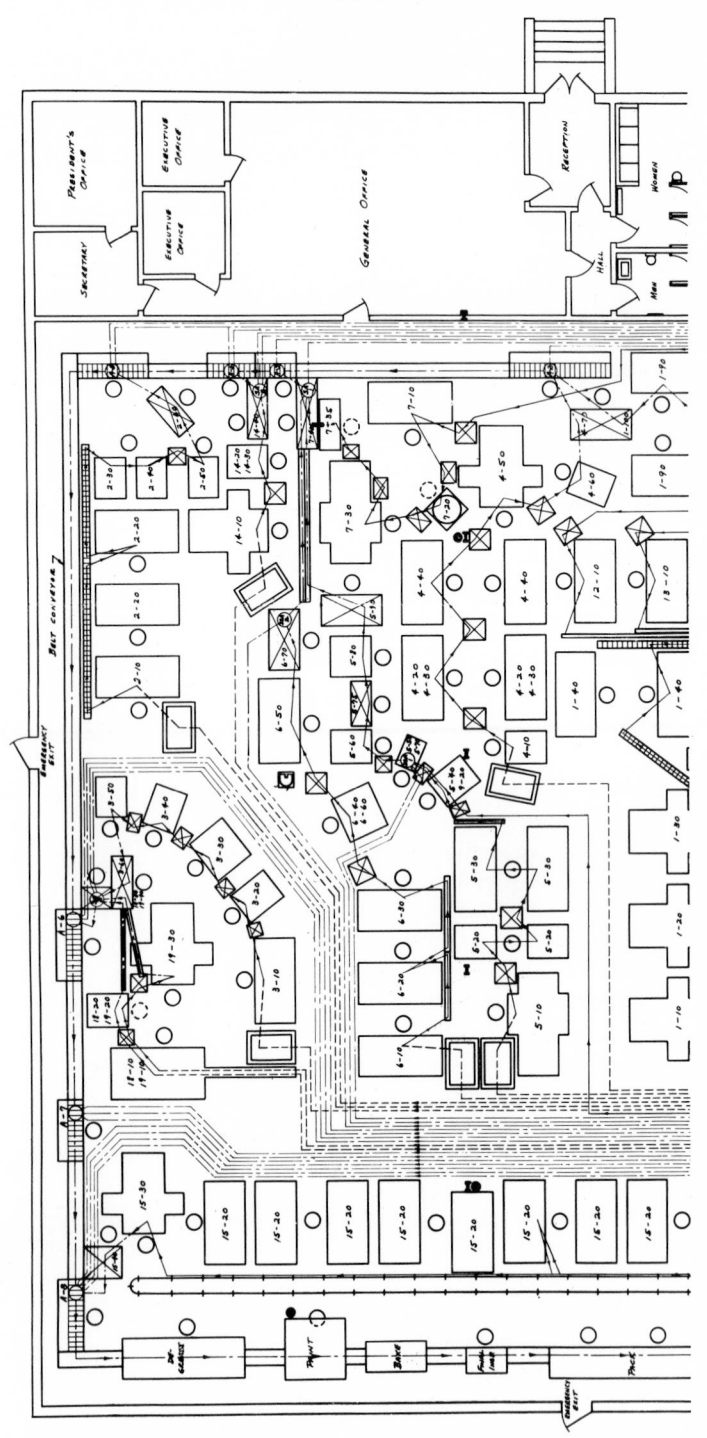

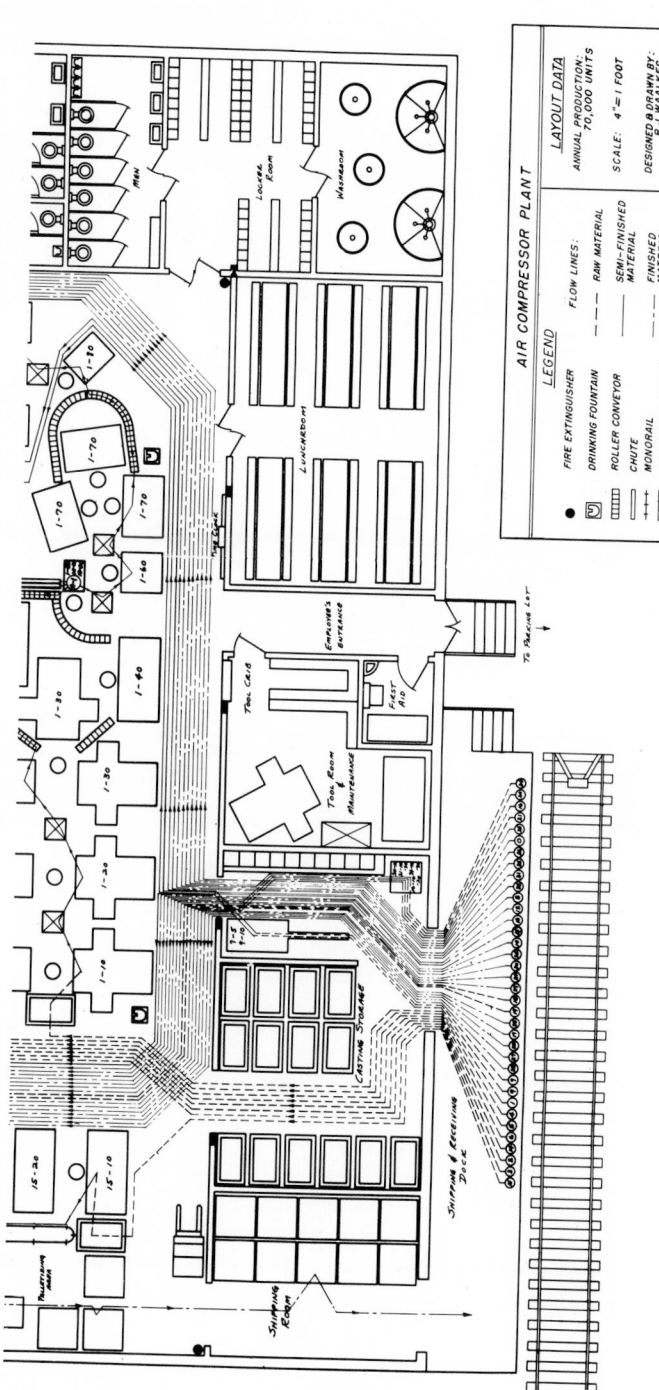

Fig. 15-2. Typical plant layout drawing.

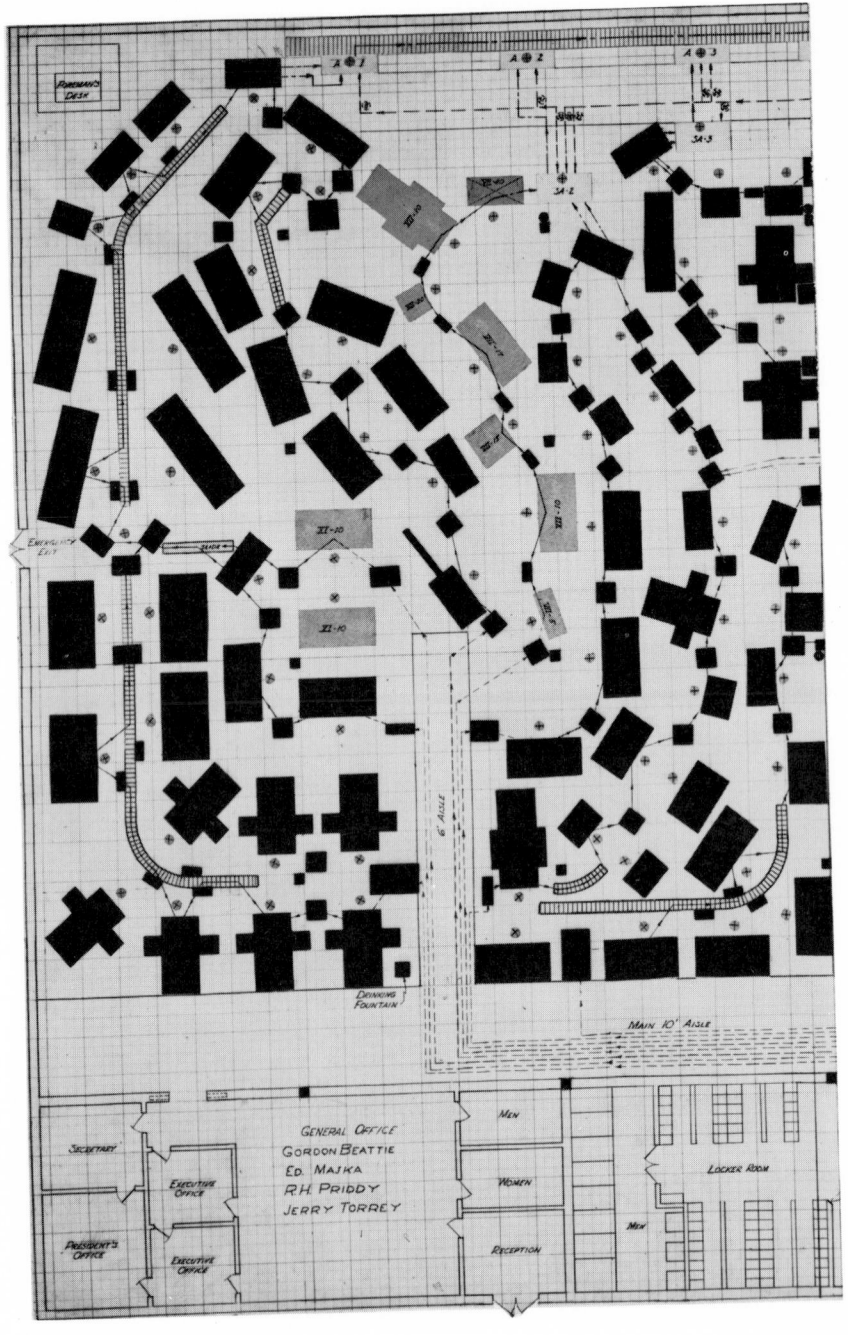

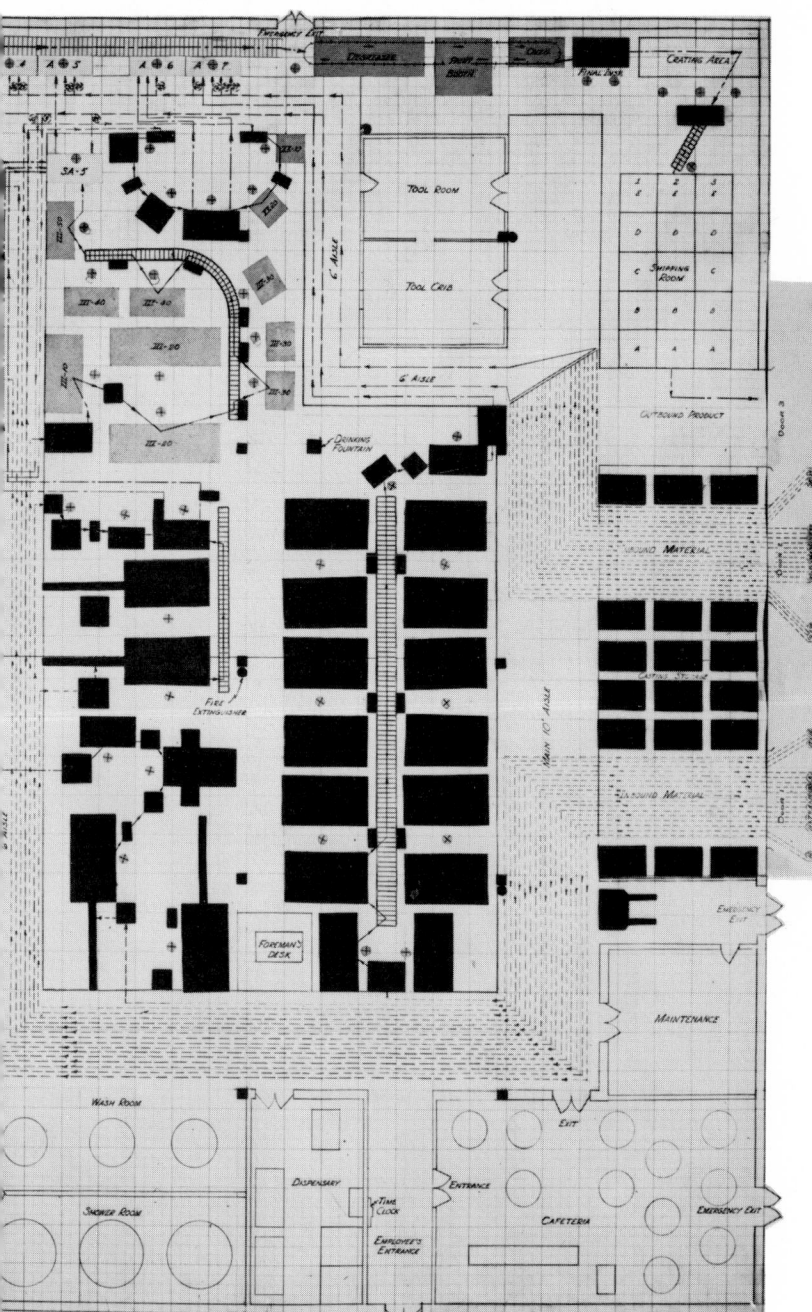

Fig. 15–3. Plant layout using "home-made" templates.

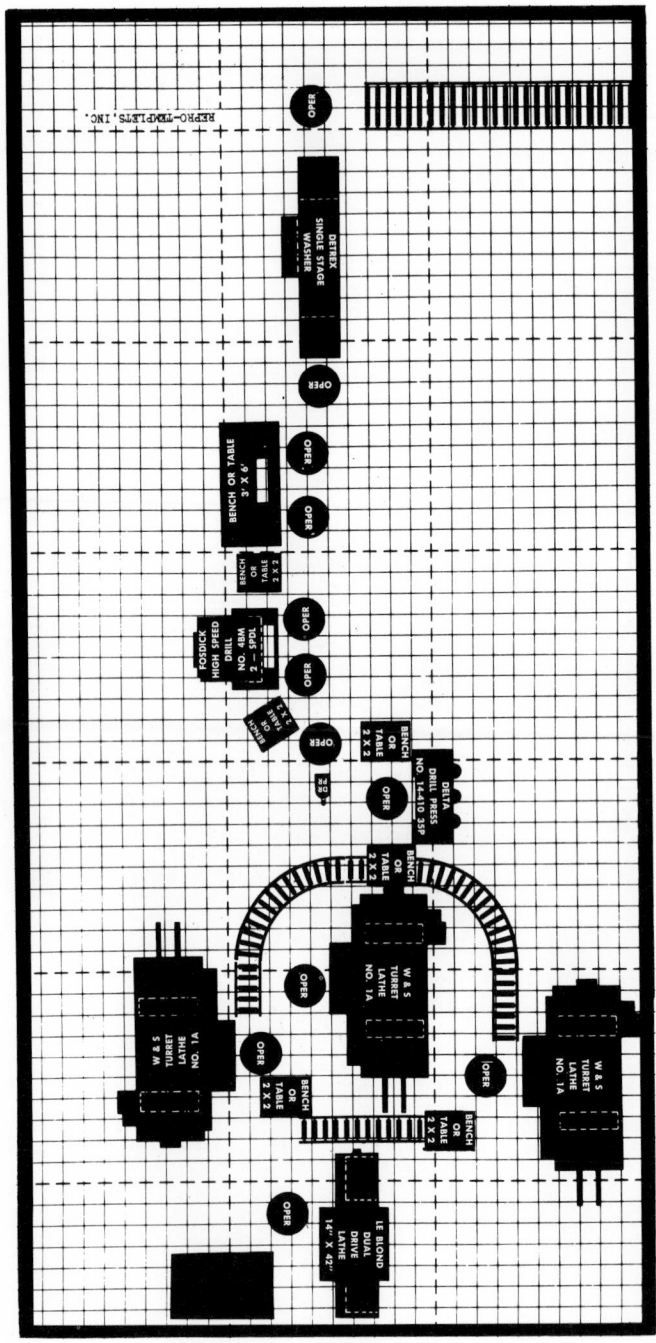

Fig. 15–4. Plant layout using commercial templates.

Fig. 15–5. Plant layout using commercial models. (By permission of Model Planning Co., Inc.)

Characteristic	I. Conventional 2-Dimensional Templates	II. Reproducible 2-Dimensional Templates	III. 3-Dimensional Scale Models	IV. Combination of Templates & Scale Models
Materials	Heavy paper or cardboard, pinned or glued to base material	Transparent grid sheets, templates, tapes, etc.	Exact scale models of all plant equipment and buildings	Combination of II and III
Design and Construction Characteristics	Roughly drawn and cut out from paper or cardboard	Carefully drawn to show exact physical dimensions, travel of machine components, and service area. Reproduced on transparent plastic.	Constructed to exact scale in three dimensions, and to actual height, to represent specific make and model accurately. Assembled from Lucite, cast in metal, or a combination of both.	Combination of II and III
Engineering Value	Practically none – due to probable inaccuracies	Good, for trained personnel and engineers: accurate and detailed.	Better, since third dimension adds note of realism and enables easy interpretation by persons inexperienced in plant layout work.	Best, because it combines the characteristics of both two and three dimensional methods.
Relative Cost	Engineer's time to measure and sketch: Draftsman's time to draw up and reproduce. Time required to cut out. Total estimated at one hour per template or about $5-$6 each. Probably most expensive of all four methods.	Commercially available at 2¢–18¢ each; average cost 9¢ each. Special items might go to $1.00 each. Would amount to about 1¢/actual square foot of building, on 40–50,000 sq.ft. order	Average cost about $2-$4/model for typical machine tool. Small items less, unusual or special items may be considerably more. Would amount to about 6¢ per square foot of actual building, including all plant equipment and building model on 40-50,-000 sq.ft. order	Combination of II and III, or about 7¢ per square foot of actual building.
Advantages	None	–Accurate detailed layout –Less time required to produce layout that no.I –Clearly indicates actual relationships in terms of floor space requirements –Serves as permanent record	–Enables non-technical personnel to study and evaluate the layout –Quickly rearranged to study alternative layout plans –Photos of alternate proposals can be studied –Shows overhead details and clearances –Assures more correct location of each piece of equipment –Saves expensive moving of equipment after installation. –Models last indefinitely –Invites participation in planning	

	—Minimum storage space required —Economical upkeep —Prints easily produced —Special templates easily made —Flexibility permits easy changes —Overlays and underlays easily made and used —Eliminates drafting —Trial layout can be printed; alternate arrangements worked out; compared with original; and remade into original form, using trial layout print as a record of the original layout.	—Aids in selling the project. —Exposes design errors —Shows up potential danger spots —Permits accurate study of manpower requirements —Speeds actual plant construction work, using model as a guide —Facilitates study of congested areas, especially where overhead conveyors, piping, etc., are involved —Easier to interpret than blueprints —More accurate visualizing of space utilization, thereby making it easier to plan proper use of building cube —Makes entire organization layout conscious —Useful in employee orientation and training —More nearly approaches the actual situation —Shows details unobtainable on drawings —Better depicts mass, depth, height and clearances —Leaves less planning to the imagination —Shows plans in all planes —Subject to less mis-interpretation —Reduces executive time required to study and approve —Shows up errors prior to installation —Aids cooperation from all concerned —Provides a better understanding of the problem	
Disadvantages	—Difficult to visualize —Alternate plans must be drawn and redrawn —Time consuming —Expensive —Requires tracing for reproduction —Inaccurate —Invites errors and discrepancies	—Vertical dimensions impossible to visualize —Planners must carry all vertical details "in their heads,"	—Difficult to obtain copies unless template reproduction is made —Does not include detailed information shown on templates —Costs more than template method, no. II	—Highest initial cost of the three modern methods (II, III, IV), but probably LESS than no. I, in the long run, if accurate costs are kept.

Fig. 15-6. Comparison of basic plant layout methods.

2. Tapes, etc., to represent architectural and other details, which are commercially available as follows:

   a) Lines—solid, broken, dotted, in various colors.
   b) Walls—in accurate architectural symbols.
   c) Aisles—cross-hatched and labeled, in various widths.
   d) Arrows—continuous, to represent flow lines.
   e) Building columns, posts, stairways.
   f) Operators—2-foot circles or sketches.
   g) Conveyors—roller, wheel, slat, belt, overhead, drag-chain.
   h) Railroad tracks.
   i) Symbols—numbers, letters, power and telephone outlets, telephones, hydraulic and pneumatic connections.
   j) Pallets, gondolas, drums, skids, tables, benches, etc.

3. Templates to represent physical facilities.

   a) Hand drawn and photographically reproduced on sheet plastic.
   b) Commercially available on sheet plastic:

   (1) Black and white outline style.
   (2) Black and white negative style (also in color).
       [(1) and (2) fastened to grid sheet with double-coated clear pressure sensitive tape, rubber cement, or have pressure sensitive adhesive preapplied and protected with "waxed" paper]
   (3) Color—with magnet attached.
   (4) ⅛-inch Lucite—with magnet inserted for use on metal surfaces.

4. Scale models commercially available or "homemade," to represent physical facilities, etc.

   a) Lucite—built up—some with die-cast components, etc.
   b) Cast metal.
   c) Wood.

Figures 15–7 and 15–8 illustrate some of the many types of templates and models in common use.

Model and Template Standards. In 1949, a subcommittee of the American Society of Mechanical Engineers drafted a standard for plant layout tools, which was subsequently adopted. (See Appendix V.) Basically, the standard outlines the characteristics of templates and models which have been used as guides by both commercial suppliers of such materials and by those companies that choose to construct their own. The scale recommended is ¼ inch = 1 foot, which has become the most commonly accepted scale. Occasionally, a larger scale is used to show greater detail; or a smaller scale is used for large areas, with little detail required, such as on plot plans or building outlines.

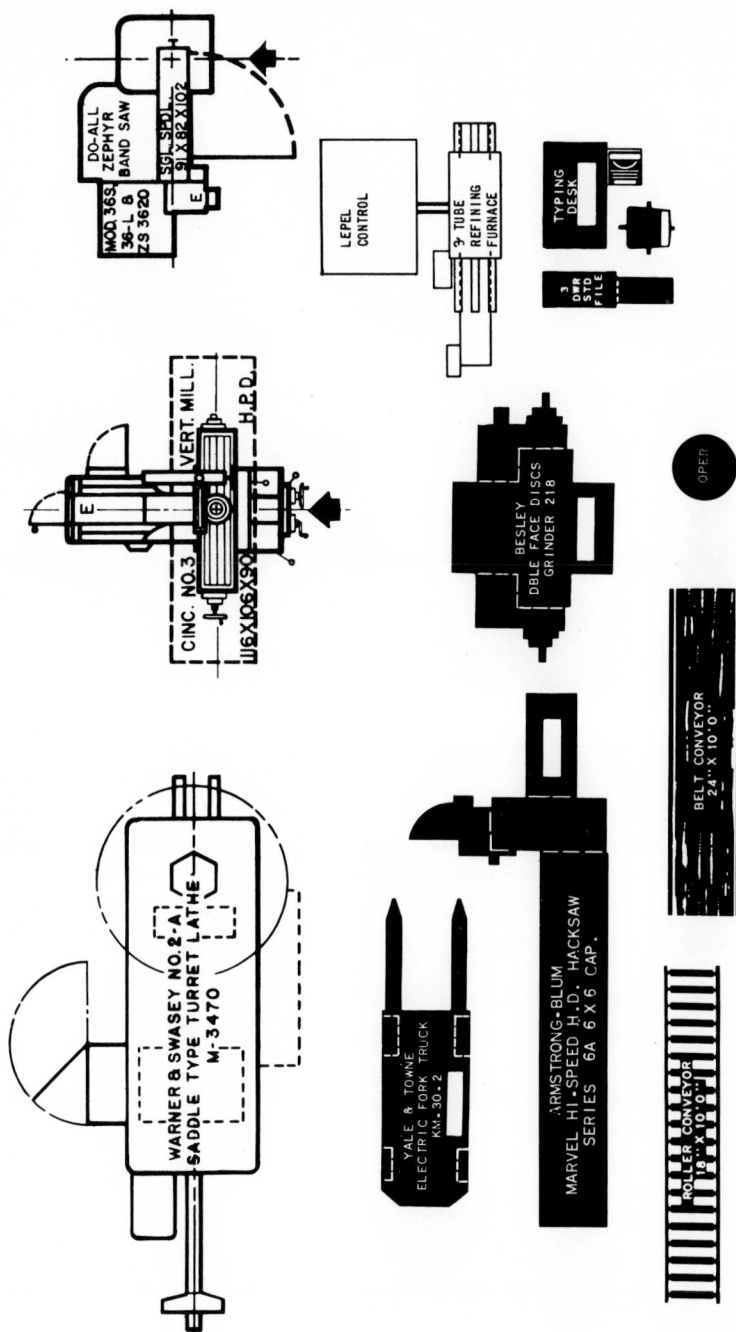

Fig. 15-7. Common templates used in plant layout work.

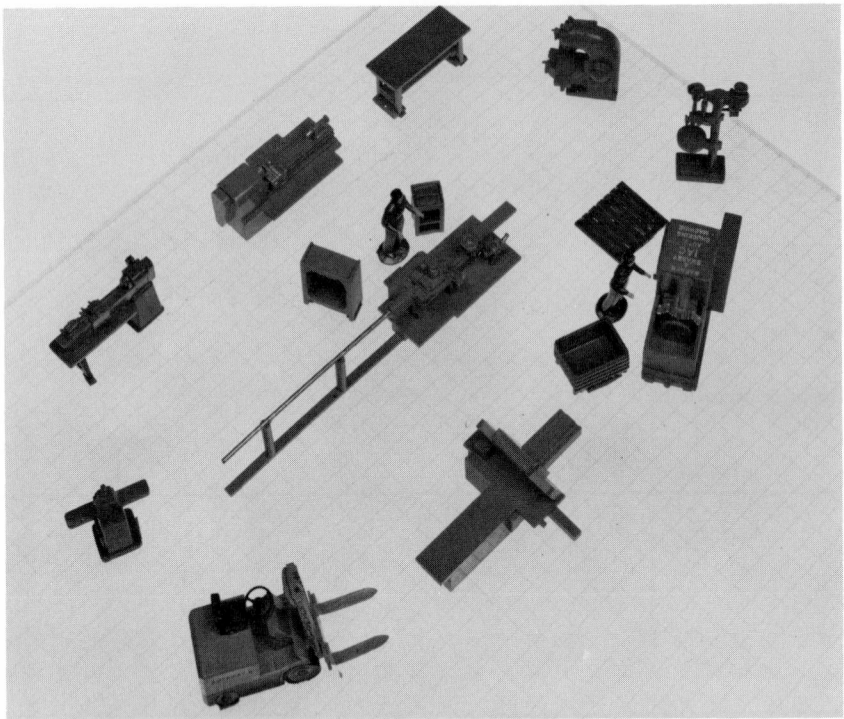

Fig. 15-8. Common models used in plant layout work.

Plant Layout Construction Procedure. The actual construction of the final plant layout requires that the many detailed plans and decisions previously worked out must now be resolved or integrated into one "master" plan or representation of the ideas developed. As a guide to the integration process, the following step-by-step procedure is suggested:

1. Gather together all planning data for easy reference. This will include:

   a) Parts Lists.
   b) Assembly Charts.
   c) Operation Process Charts.
   d) Production Routings.
   e) From–To Charts.
   f) Activity Relationship Diagrams.
   g) Area Allocation Diagrams.
   h) Operation Charts.
   i) Layout Planning Charts.
   j) Flow Diagrams.

2. Determine rough over-all size of layout from Area Allocation Diagram.

3. Decide on appropriate scale to be used.

4. Obtain grid sheet for "base" of layout. Work on *opposite* side from printed or scribed cross-section lines.
5. Obtain templates or models and related supplies.
6. Establish bay size or column spacing.
7. Estimate number of bays (width and length) and determine their "fit" on the grid sheet.
8. Locate a "fixed" corner or other location (such as shipping, receiving, office, etc.) and apply tapes (etc.) to locate this area on the grid sheet.
9. Locate columns on grid sheet (if not done in No. 7 above) and outline entire building, *if* possible, at this point.

   Note: If building or area in which layout is included already exists, omit steps 6, 7, 8, 9 and merely reproduce present walls, columns, etc., on grid sheet.

10. If possible, at this point, indicate probable locations of aisles on the floor plan. (Use "aisle" or 1/16-inch "line" tape.)
11. Working from the Area Allocation Diagram and individual Flow Diagrams, gradually transfer preliminary plans to the grid sheet with templates or models and necessary tapes, etc.
12. Continually adjust preliminary plans as they are transferred to allow for columns, aisles, or desirable changes that may become apparent as the layout progresses.
13. Work out final arrangements and details for service areas, such as:

    a) Locker rooms.   *g*) Storage areas.
    b) Lavatories.   *h*) Shipping and receiving.
    c) Offices.   *i*) Auxiliary equipment.
    d) Toolroom.   *j*) Materials handling
    e) Tool crib.   equipment and facilities.
    f) Maintenance.

14. If desired, erase cross-section lines from back of grid sheet, outside the building walls, with paint remover or recommended solvent.
15. Arrange for duplication, if desirable at this time—or wait until after evaluation, critique, and approvals.

Finishing Up. In spite of all the planning which has been done up to this point, the plant layout problem still resolves itself into an intricate game of chess—a moving, shifting, and rearranging of templates or models and areas until a satisfactory solution has been found. The solution will probably be a compromise between what has been planned in previous steps and what would be an ideal situation, if one were possible. While it is true that preliminary sketches and plans have been made, they must all be resolved into a workable and economical solution. The reason for the detailed planning beforehand has been to eliminate as much time and as many mistakes as possible in the preparation of the final layout. It is far easier to correct mistakes on "paper" than to attempt to correct them after the machinery and equipment have been installed. And this

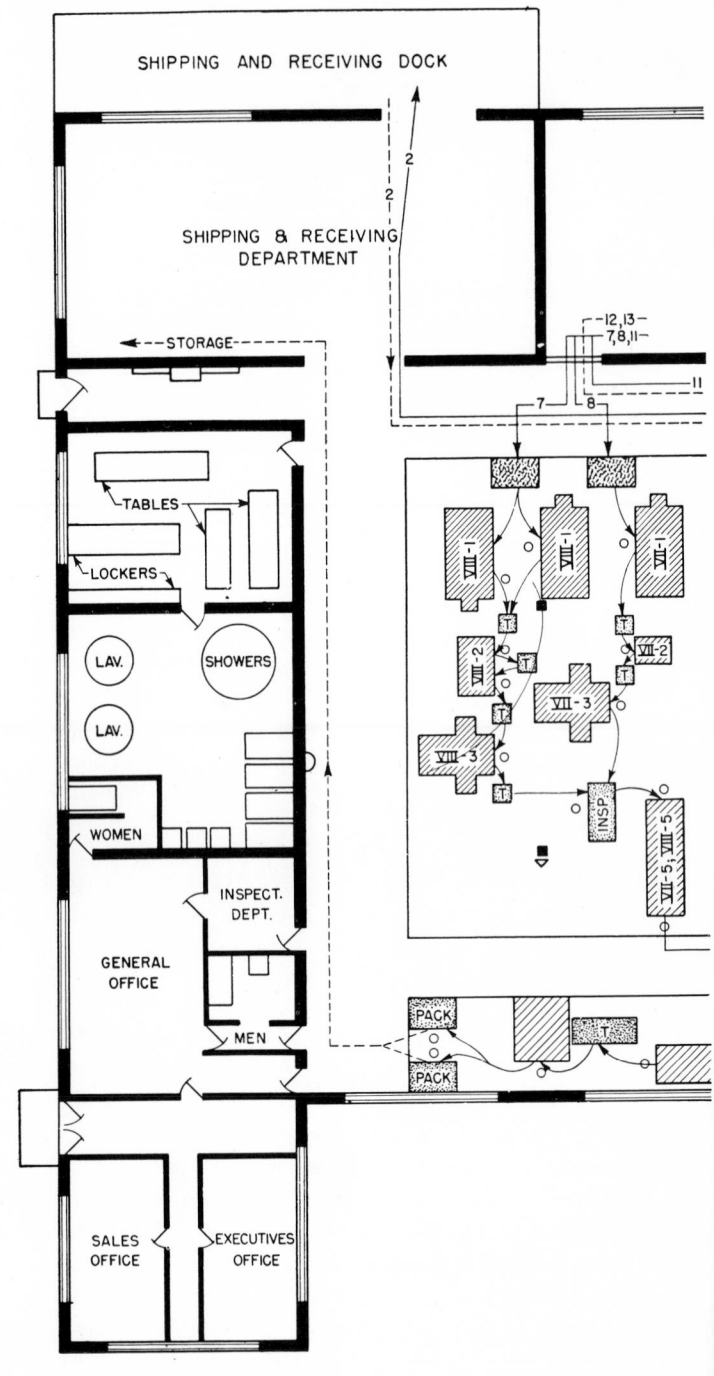

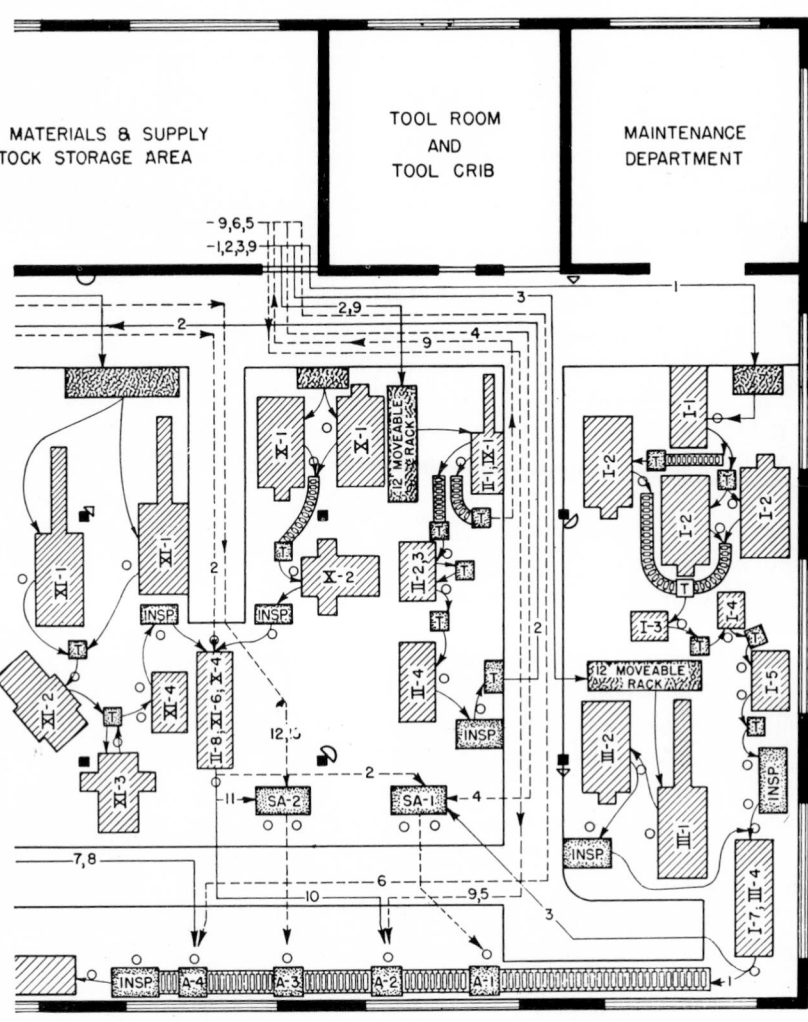

O EMPLOYEES
D DRINKING FOUNTAINS
▽ FIRE EXTINGUISHERS

▨ TABLES
▨ RAW MATERIAL HANDLING
▨ MACHINERY
▦ MECHANICAL HANDLING

Fig. 15–9A. Finished layout of Powrarm plant based on plans made throughout text.

certainly will happen if the layout is hurriedly thrown together without adequate preliminary planning. The work, as outlined above, should be continued until a satisfactory solution has been reached, and the layout is complete.

Figure 15–9A represents the final plant layout for the Powrarm plant, which has been used throughout the text. A reexamination of Figures 4–11, 9–2, 10–15A, 10–17, 10–19, 14–14, and 14–16 will show that the basic planned relationships have been carried through the various steps. As has been mentioned many times, compromises have been made along the way, as they became necessary. Nevertheless, the orderly procedure followed has greatly aided the development of the final layout shown here.

Flow Lines. As the layout progresses, or when it is complete, it is highly desirable to add flow lines to represent the actual paths to be traveled by major parts being processed. The flow lines should indicate the path each part will follow from the time it enters the plant as raw material until it becomes part of an assembly or leaves the plant as a finished product. The lines should follow as nearly as possible the exact path the part will follow in the plant. If several parts flow through a single machine or piece of equipment, a separate line should be shown for each, if practical.

These flow lines are an important part of the layout, as they help to indicate how well the principles of good plant layout have been followed, especially in regard to straight-line flow, backtracking, and congestion in aisles or specific areas. A large number of flow lines in a given aisle or area obviously represents heavy traffic and possible operating difficulties.

The flow lines may be added to the layout by several different methods. On the plastic grid sheets, they may be applied with narrow tapes or by means of arrow templates commercially available. Or it may be desirable to make a print of the layout and draw the flow line with colored pencils. Another alternative would be to make an intermediate ("brown" line or sepia) and apply the tape or drawn lines to the intermediate tracing and then make a print. A fourth method is to mount a print of the layout on a composition board, insert pins or tacks at appropriate locations, and represent the flow lines with colored strings. In this case, the strings can even be removed and measured to determine travel distance for a specific part. Figure 15–9B shows a layout with flow lines added.

Checking and Approving the Layout. After the plant layout has been completed (and before it is presented to others for review), the plant layout engineer should carefully check every detail. This will assure that he has not overlooked any important items that may cause difficulties or embarrassment later on. Figure 15–10 lists some of the many items to be checked.

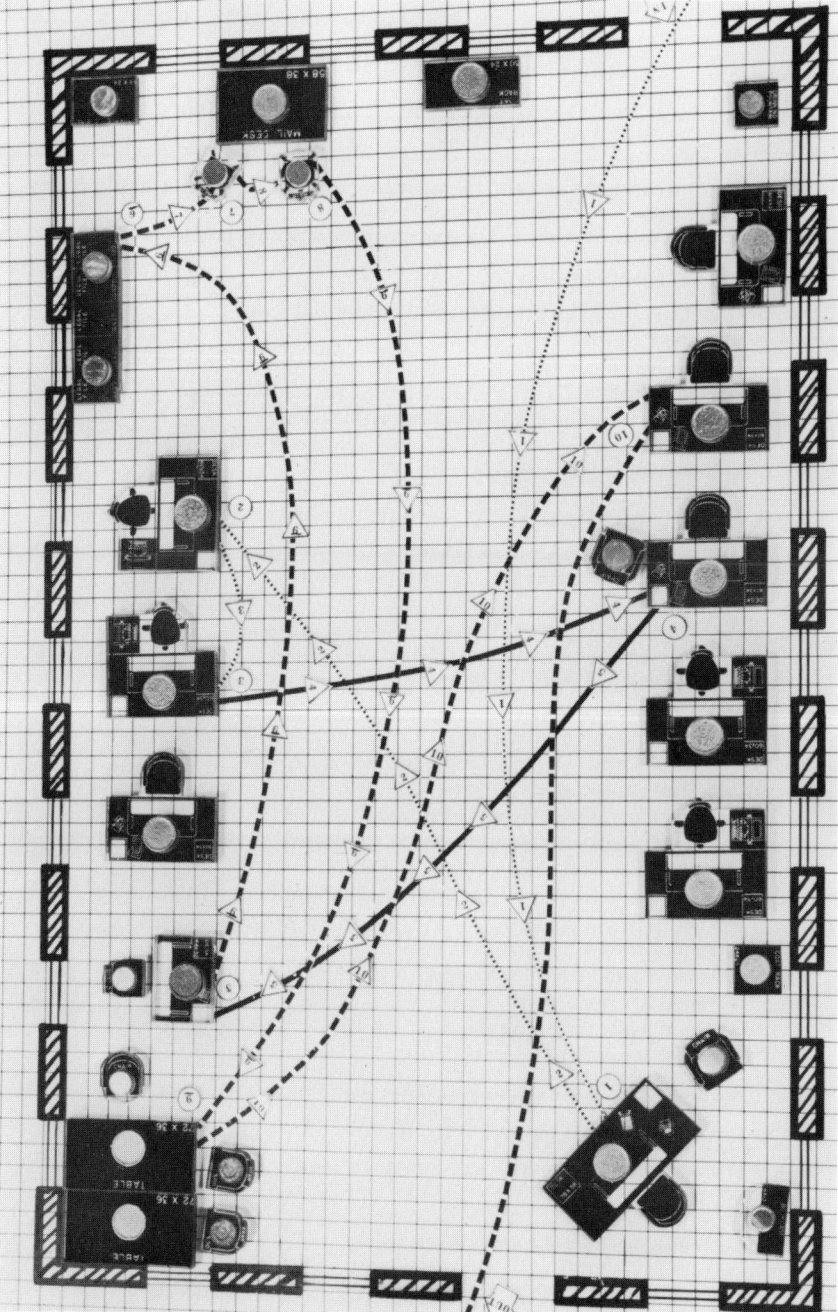

Fig. 15–9B. Flow lines on finished layout (note use of "magnetic" templates). (By permission of Magne-Plastic Corp.)

PLANT LAYOUT CHECK SHEET

Company _____ Plant _____

Checked By _____ Date _____

Before submitting the layout for official approvals, check against the following items

INDUSTRIAL ENGINEERING	not applic.	OK	remarks
1. Machinery and equipment arranged to make full use of capacity?			
2. Machinery and equipment accessible for material supply and removal?			
3. Machinery and equipment located for maximum operator efficiency?			
4. Line production used where practical?			
5. Proper use made of mechanical handling?			
6. Processing combined with transportation?			
7. Minimum walking required of operators?			
8. Finished work of one operator easily accessible to next?			
9. Machinery and equipment "block in" any operators?			
10. Machine overtravel extend into aisles or interfere with operator?			
11. Adequate storage space at work stations?			
12. Efficient work place layouts?			
13. Service areas conveniently located: (tool room, tool crib, maintenance, etc.)			
14. Easy for supervisor to oversee his area?			
15. Machine arrangement permit maximum flexibility in case of product change?			
16. Space allocated for foremen and production control records?			
17. Related activities located near each other?			
18. All required equipment included in layout?			
19. Floor area fully utilized?			
20. Provisions made for expansion?			
21. Provisions for scrap removal?			
22. Crowded conditions anywhere?			
MATERIAL HANDLING			
1. Incoming materials move directly to work area?			
2. Processes involving heavy or bulky materials close to receiving area?			
3. Sub-assemblies flow into final assembly?			
4. Plans for auxiliary material flow in case of tie-up?			
5. Minimum of backtracking?			
6. Obstacles in material flow?			

MATERIAL HANDLING (cont'd)	not applic.	OK	remarks
7. Excessively long moves?			
8. Conveyors "box in" anyone?			
9. Material handling equipment bring materials to operators?			
10. Material handling equipment remove materials from operators?			
11. Each material handling method integrated into overall system?			
12. Conveyors from receiving to processing areas?			
13. Conveyors from assembly to shipping area?			
14. Minimum of manual handling?			
15. Material handling equipment carry materials in a position to conserve space?			
16. Widely separated areas connected by suitable mechanical handling system?			
17. Aisles and doors wide enough for maximum loads and fire equipment?			
18. Ramps at lowest possible grade?			
19. Proper use of conveyors for efficient handling?			
20. Adequate storage space for containers and material handling equipment?			
21. Use of conveyors for floats and banks of material?			
22. Adequate storage for materials in process?			
23. Shipping and receiving docks covered?			
24. Proper dock heights and/or levelling devices?			
25. Maximum use made of building cube?			
26. Aisles straight and clearly marked?			
PERSONNEL AND SAFETY			
1. Exits, fire doors and fire escapes adequate and properly located? Free of obstruction?			
2. Easy exit from any location in building?			
3. Plans checked by local fire, police and safety officials?			
4. Plans approved by insurance companies?			
5. Lifts and hoists provided for loads over 50 lbs.?			
6. Adequate work area for each operator?			
7. Easy access to all safety devices?			
8. Hazardous and unpleasant operations isolated?			
9. Adequate storage for inflammable materials?			
10. Drinking fountains in enough locations?			
11. Maximum use made of natural light?			
12. Adequate artificial light provided for?			
13. Proper ventilation provided where required?			

Fig. 15–10. (continued)

	not applic.	OK	remarks
PERSONNEL AND SAFETY (cont'd)			

14. Employee service areas provided for and conveniently located:
    - a. first aid
    - b. toilets
    - c. locker rooms
    - d. smoking areas
    - e. coat racks
    - f. food service
    - g. time clocks
    - h. stretchers
15. Parking space provided for employees?

PLANT ENGINEERING

1. Floor loads within allowable limits?
2. Overhead clearances adequate?
3. Proposed overhead loading within limits?
4. Special foundations or equipment mountings required?
5. Floor and roof drains provided for?
6. Elevators required, located, specified?
7. All possible use made of under-floor, overhead, and on-the-roof space?
8. Layout make efficient use of building shape, size, cube?
9. Machinery and equipment accessible for maintenance?
10. Layout conducive to good housekeeping?
11. Provisions for rubbish collection, storage, and removal?
12. Utilities provided for and properly located:
    - a. air
    - b. gas
    - c. water
    - d. electricity
    - e. steam
    - f. telephone
    - g. sprinklers
    - h. sewers
    - i. air conditioning
    - j. heating
    - k. ventilation
    - l. lighting
13. Detailed drawings of special equipment or installations?
14. Fire extinguishers and fire protection equipment provided for?
15. Layout satisfy all safety codes?

PRODUCTION CONTROL

1. Inventory checking easy?
2. Adequate space and facilities for salvage operations?
3. Proper protection for material and finished goods storage?
4. Valuable materials protected from pilferage?
5. Adequate space for shipping and receiving?

PRODUCTION CONTROL (cont'd)	not applic.	OK	remarks
6. Adequate area for trucks waiting at shipping and receiving?			
7. Layout permit operations to be performed in logical sequence?			
8. Easy adjustment to changing schedules?			
9. Layout permit paced production?			
10. Will equipment breakdown shut down line or plant?			
11. Inspection points located at strategic points?			
12. Straight flow lines?			

OTHER COMMENTS OR SUGGESTIONS

Fig. 15–10. Plant layout check sheet.

After the plant layout engineer has carefully and thoroughly checked the entire layout, he should ask others to check for specific items of interest to them and their functions. Many persons will have to "live" with a new layout once it is put into effect. For this reason, as many as possible of those persons should be given a chance to participate in the planning of the layout, each to check for approval the area or areas which will particularly concern him. If the new layout is a revision of the former one, there are even more reasons for asking for advice. Persons who have lived and worked with the old layout are bound to have suggestions for a change as a result of their experiences. Then, too, there will be those who are pretty well satisfied with the present layout and who may be antagonistic toward any changes. Consulting with such persons and asking their advice is one of the best ways of gaining their acceptance of any necessary revisions.

Approval of the Layout. After the layout has been made and checked by all who might have interests in it, as indicated above, there remains the problem of having the layout approved. Persons who should approve the layout will vary from plant to plant depending on the procedures, size of the plant, etc. Some of those who probably will either want to, or will be required to, approve the finished layout before putting it into effect are:

1. Department foreman
2. General foreman
3. Factory manager
4. Production engineer
5. Methods engineer
6. Plant layout engineer
7. General manager and/or top executive

Each of these persons will, of course, have been consulted during the construction of the layout, as will many others. Some plants make it a practice to get the ideas of the employees who will be working in the area. Frequently the familiarity of the workers with the processes and operations to be performed will be of great value in planning the layout. One plant placed in its cafeteria a three-dimensional scale model of a proposed new layout of its manufacturing equipment and solicited suggestions on the spot from the workers. Needless to say, many valuable suggestions were received on points which might have been overlooked and thus have caused production difficulties after the layout was installed.

Frequently, the official approval or signatures will come as a result of a meeting at which the layout is presented in its final form and discussed by interested persons.

QUESTIONS

1. What are some of the important relationships between the building and the plot of land on which it will be located?
2. Suggest some factors to be considered in planning aisles.
3. What items should be considered in locating columns and establishing bay sizes?
4. What are the principal methods of making the master layout? Give some advantages and disadvantages of each.
5. What are the advantages of adding flow lines to the layout?
6. Who might be consulted in checking the layout—prior to presentation for approval? Why would each one be selected?
7. Who might be required to approve the final layout?

16

Evaluating and Installing the Layout

Introduction. Now that the layout has been completed, there remain the evaluation of the layout, its presentation to management, and the installation of the plans indicated by the layout. These are extremely important steps in the over-all procedure and deserve as much consideration as the construction of the layout itself—if the final project is to be successful.

Evaluating the Layout. The evaluation of a layout may arise from either of two possibilities:

1. An evaluation of an existing layout for the purpose of discovering improvement possibilities
2. An evaluation of alternative layouts under consideration for a single problem or project area

And the evaluation may be either qualitative or quantitative. That is, it can consist of a relatively simple balancing of advantages versus disadvantages; or it can consist of some quantitative means of "measuring" the value of the layout or layouts. If the problem is a relatively simple one, or if there are no alternatives at this point, then the evaluation might involve no more than the use of the check sheet in Figure 15–10. For a more complex project, or for comparing several alternatives, the techniques should be more formal or sophisticated.

Qualitative Evaluation Techniques. The most common and simplest approach to layout evaluation is the listing of advantages and disadvantages of the layout at hand or the alternatives being considered. Such a tabulation might appear as in Figure 16–1.

A more complete qualitative evaluation, more useful as an "audit" of an existing operational layout, can be made with the aid of the charts [1]

[1] Apple, James M., "How To Spot Your Plant Layout Problems . . . ," *Factory Magazine,* Jan., 1959.

PLANT LAYOUT EVALUATION GUIDE

Plant or Area _____ Date_____

Alternative No. _____ Sq. Ft. Involved _____ Approx. Cost _____

Brief Description of Project or Alternative _____

_____ Evaluation by _____
(refer to attached layout or sketch)

Advantages	Weight or Value	Disadvantages	Weight or Value

Fig. 16–1. Plant layout evaluation guide.

CHART 1 – How to Recognize Plant Layout and

Indicators of Layout and Related Problems \ Possible Causes of Problems	GENERAL						MATERIALS HANDLING											PLANT LAYOUT															
	1. Poor housekeeping	2. Crowded conditions	3. No over-all plan	4. No alternatives	5. Excess mtls. on hand	6. Poor schedule, dispatch	7. Bldg. cube unused	8. Delayed mtl. movement	9. Unsuitable containers	10. Non-use of mech. equip.	11. Manual hndlg., rehndlg.	12. Loads not unitized	13. Long hauls	14. Wrong move, first time	15. Mtls. piled on floor	16. Poor storage equip.	17. Poor flow pattern	18. Unbalanced oprns. seq.	19. No flexibility	20. No space	21. Inadequate equip., fac.	22. Bad space allocation	23. Poor plant layout	24. Poor process methods	25. No aisle markings	26. Poor placing, spacing	27. Poor loc., source or dest.	28. Poor loc. related activ.	29. Employees waiting	30. Material-flow blocks	31. Scattered buildings	32. Rel. areas partitioned
GENERAL a. Crowded aisles	✓	✓		✓	✓	✓	✓	✓					✓	✓	✓	✓		✓			✓	✓	✓	✓		✓			✓			
b. Hazardous areas	✓	✓						✓	✓	✓	✓							✓			✓	✓		✓		✓	✓		✓			
c. High accident rate	✓	✓						✓	✓	✓								✓			✓	✓		✓	✓	✓	✓		✓	✓	✓	✓
d. High overhead	✓	✓		✓	✓	✓	✓	✓	✓	✓	✓	✓	✓	✓	✓	✓	✓	✓	✓	✓	✓	✓	✓	✓		✓	✓	✓	✓	✓		
e. Crowded conditions	✓			✓	✓	✓	✓	✓	✓				✓			✓	✓	✓			✓	✓			✓	✓			✓			
f. Poor housekeeping		✓			✓		✓	✓	✓				✓			✓	✓				✓	✓	✓			✓	✓					✓
PRODUCTION a. High indir. labor				✓				✓	✓	✓	✓	✓			✓			✓			✓	✓		✓		✓				✓		✓
b. Unexplainable delays	✓	✓	✓		✓	✓		✓	✓	✓	✓	✓		✓			✓	✓	✓	✓	✓	✓		✓		✓			✓	✓	✓	✓
c. Scheduling trouble	✓	✓	✓	✓	✓	✓		✓			✓						✓	✓	✓		✓			✓		✓			✓	✓	✓	✓
d. High in-process mtl.				✓	✓	✓	✓		✓									✓	✓	✓		✓		✓		✓			✓			
e. Too many men collecting scrap, waste								✓	✓	✓	✓		✓			✓		✓			✓			✓		✓			✓		✓	✓
f. Material-flow blocks	✓	✓		✓	✓		✓	✓	✓	✓			✓		✓			✓			✓		✓	✓	✓	✓	✓		✓	✓		
g. Equipment moved often		✓	✓														✓				✓	✓	✓	✓		✓			✓		✓	✓
h. Related work scattered		✓	✓			✓											✓				✓	✓	✓	✓		✓			✓	✓	✓	✓
i. Uneven flow rate	✓	✓		✓		✓		✓	✓	✓		✓		✓		✓		✓	✓	✓	✓			✓		✓			✓	✓		
j. Scattered buildings		✓	✓			✓															✓	✓	✓			✓			✓	✓		
k. Vanishing aisles	✓	✓	✓		✓		✓	✓					✓			✓	✓				✓		✓			✓	✓	✓		✓		
l. Walls, partitions, betw. related areas		✓																✓			✓		✓			✓			✓			
m. Blocked doorways	✓	✓		✓	✓			✓	✓							✓	✓				✓		✓			✓			✓			
n. No flexibility	✓	✓	✓	✓				✓	✓	✓								✓			✓	✓	✓	✓	✓	✓				✓	✓	✓
o. Makeshifts perpetuated		✓	✓																		✓		✓	✓	✓		✓	✓		✓		
p. Working in aisles		✓		✓	✓	✓												✓			✓		✓	✓		✓	✓	✓		✓		✓
q. Mtnce. hard to perform	✓	✓	✓			✓										✓					✓		✓			✓			✓			✓
r. Mfg. cycle too long	✓	✓			✓	✓		✓							✓		✓	✓	✓			✓		✓		✓			✓	✓	✓	✓
s. Idle production equip.				✓	✓	✓		✓	✓									✓	✓	✓	✓					✓				✓	✓	✓
t. Overloaded prod. equip.				✓	✓	✓												✓	✓	✓						✓				✓		
u. Low production density	✓	✓	✓	✓	✓	✓		✓		✓	✓	✓						✓	✓	✓	✓	✓		✓		✓				✓	✓	✓
v. Vacant floor space				✓	✓																✓	✓	✓			✓			✓			
w. Poor quality	✓	✓	✓	✓					✓	✓		✓		✓	✓	✓					✓		✓			✓						
x. Line-machine breakdowns		✓	✓	✓		✓													✓		✓		✓			✓						
y. Inaccessible machines	✓	✓	✓		✓		✓	✓	✓									✓			✓		✓			✓	✓		✓		✓	✓
z. Bottleneck operations		✓	✓	✓		✓						✓		✓				✓	✓	✓	✓			✓		✓					✓	✓
aa. Crooked aisles		✓	✓	✓				✓											✓			✓			✓	✓		✓		✓		
MANPOWER UTILIZATION a. Too many men moving materials			✓	✓	✓			✓	✓	✓	✓	✓	✓	✓	✓	✓	✓	✓	✓			✓				✓		✓	✓	✓	✓	✓
b. Handling by skilled men			✓	✓	✓			✓	✓	✓	✓	✓	✓			✓	✓		✓					✓					✓	✓		✓
c. Excess manual handling			✓	✓	✓			✓		✓	✓	✓	✓			✓	✓							✓					✓			
d. High labor turnover	✓	✓	✓																										✓			
e. Walking for tools, mtls.					✓		✓			✓	✓	✓	✓	✓			✓	✓	✓	✓	✓					✓		✓	✓	✓	✓	✓

Fig. 16-2. Indicators and causes of plant layout and related problems. (By permission of

---

shown in Figures 16–2 and 16–3. These charts have been designed to simplify the tasks of:

1. Spotting indicators of plant layout problems
2. Identifying causes of the problems indicated
3. Finding areas for possible elimination of the problems.

Related Problems – and How to Spot the Causes

Possible Causes of Problems (columns) — GENERAL (1–7), MATERIALS HANDLING (8–16), PLANT LAYOUT (17–33)

Indicators of Layout and Related Problems	1. Poor housekeeping	2. Crowded conditions	3. No over-all plan	4. No alternatives	5. Excess mtls. on hand	6. Poor schedule, dispatch	7. Bldg. cube unused	8. Delayed mtl. movement	9. Unsuitable containers	10. Non-use of mech. equip.	11. Manual hndlg., rehndlg.	12. Loads not utilized	13. Long hauls	14. Wrong move, first time	15. Mtls. piled on floor	16. Poor storage equip.	17. Poor flow pattern	18. Unbalanced oprns. seq.	19. No flexibility	20. No space	21. Inadequate equip., fac.	22. Bad space allocation	23. Poor plant layout	24. Poor process methods	25. No aisle markings	26. Poor placing, spacing	27. Poor loc., source or dest.	28. Poor loc. related activ.	29. Employees waiting	30. Material-flow blocks	31. Scattered buildings	32. Rel. areas partitioned	33. Crooked aisles
MANPOWER UTILIZATION																																	
f. High load, unload time				✓					✓					✓																			
g. Cramped work quarters	✓	✓		✓	✓	✓	✓	✓	✓		✓						✓			✓		✓	✓	✓		✓			✓		✓	✓	✓
h. Idle personnel			✓		✓		✓		✓									✓	✓		✓		✓	✓				✓					
i. Awkward work cycle.	✓	✓		✓	✓			✓	✓	✓							✓			✓	✓	✓	✓	✓			✓			✓			
j. Difficult handling	✓	✓						✓	✓	✓	✓	✓	✓	✓			✓				✓		✓			✓		✓	✓	✓	✓	✓	✓
k. Waiting for mach. cycle			✓															✓			✓		✓			✓							
l. Waiting for materials			✓		✓		✓	✓	✓		✓	✓	✓				✓	✓					✓				✓	✓	✓	✓			
m. Waiting for help			✓				✓	✓			✓				✓		✓												✓				
n. Unsafe conditions	✓	✓	✓					✓										✓	✓				✓	✓	✓								
o. Operator away from work			✓		✓			✓			✓							✓	✓											✓			
MATERIALS HANDLING																																	
a. Backtracking		✓	✓	✓		✓		✓			✓						✓	✓			✓		✓	✓		✓			✓	✓	✓	✓	
b. Zig-zag flow lines		✓	✓	✓		✓		✓			✓		✓	✓			✓	✓			✓		✓	✓		✓			✓	✓	✓	✓	✓
c. Traffic jams	✓	✓		✓	✓	✓		✓	✓	✓	✓	✓	✓				✓				✓		✓	✓		✓	✓	✓	✓	✓			✓
d. Long hauls			✓	✓		✓		✓					✓				✓				✓		✓	✓		✓					✓	✓	✓
e. Overloaded hndlg. equip.			✓	✓	✓			✓			✓	✓	✓	✓			✓				✓		✓			✓					✓		✓
f. Underloaded hndlg. equip.			✓					✓		✓			✓				✓				✓		✓			✓				✓		✓	✓
g. Rehndlg. and transfer		✓	✓	✓	✓	✓		✓	✓	✓	✓	✓	✓	✓	✓		✓				✓	✓	✓	✓		✓		✓	✓	✓	✓		
h. Two-man hndlg. tasks			✓					✓	✓		✓	✓					✓				✓		✓			✓							
i. Idle hndlg. equipment	✓	✓			✓			✓							✓	✓			✓				✓			✓							
j. Manual handling		✓		✓				✓	✓	✓	✓	✓		✓	✓	✓	✓				✓		✓			✓	✓	✓	✓		✓		
k. Piece-at-a-time hndlg.			✓					✓	✓	✓	✓	✓	✓		✓		✓				✓		✓			✓	✓	✓	✓	✓			✓
l. Mtls. damaged, pilfered	✓	✓		✓		✓		✓	✓	✓	✓	✓	✓				✓				✓		✓					✓				✓	
m. Slow mtls. movement	✓	✓	✓	✓	✓	✓		✓	✓	✓	✓	✓	✓	✓	✓	✓	✓				✓		✓					✓		✓	✓	✓	✓
n. Much hndlg. betw. oprns.		✓			✓				✓		✓	✓		✓	✓		✓				✓		✓	✓		✓	✓	✓			✓	✓	✓
o. High equip. mtnce.			✓							✓											✓		✓										
p. Obsolete hndlg. equip.			✓						✓																								
(STORAGE / SHIPPING-RECEIVING)																																	
a. Transfer betw. containers			✓		✓			✓			✓			✓			✓				✓		✓						✓				
b. Excess temp. storage				✓	✓	✓	✓	✓			✓						✓				✓								✓				✓
c. Manual loading, hndlg.			✓	✓				✓	✓		✓						✓				✓		✓							✓			
d. Mtls. piled on floor				✓	✓	✓		✓	✓		✓						✓				✓		✓							✓			
e. Disorderly storage area	✓	✓		✓	✓	✓	✓	✓			✓				✓	✓					✓	✓	✓			✓				✓			
f. Unused overhead space								✓							✓	✓					✓		✓										
g. Poor storage equip.																					✓												
h. Misplaced materials	✓	✓		✓	✓			✓			✓			✓	✓	✓	✓				✓		✓							✓	✓	✓	✓
i. Waiting carriers				✓				✓	✓	✓	✓	✓	✓								✓		✓			✓			✓		✓	✓	✓
j. Shipping delays				✓	✓			✓	✓		✓	✓	✓				✓				✓		✓							✓	✓	✓	✓
k. Demurrage charges				✓	✓	✓	✓	✓			✓						✓				✓		✓							✓	✓	✓	✓
l. Unstandardized containers			✓								✓						✓						✓										

Factory Magazine.)

On the two charts, there will be found:

76 indicators —or symptoms of the basic difficulties of the inefficient plant layout

33 causes —typically found in a plant and which produce the indicators or symptoms observed

73 "solutions"—or areas for investigation in hopes of removing the causes

Observing the chart in Figure 16–2, it will be seen that there are check marks *opposite* each indicator and *under* probable or possible causes of

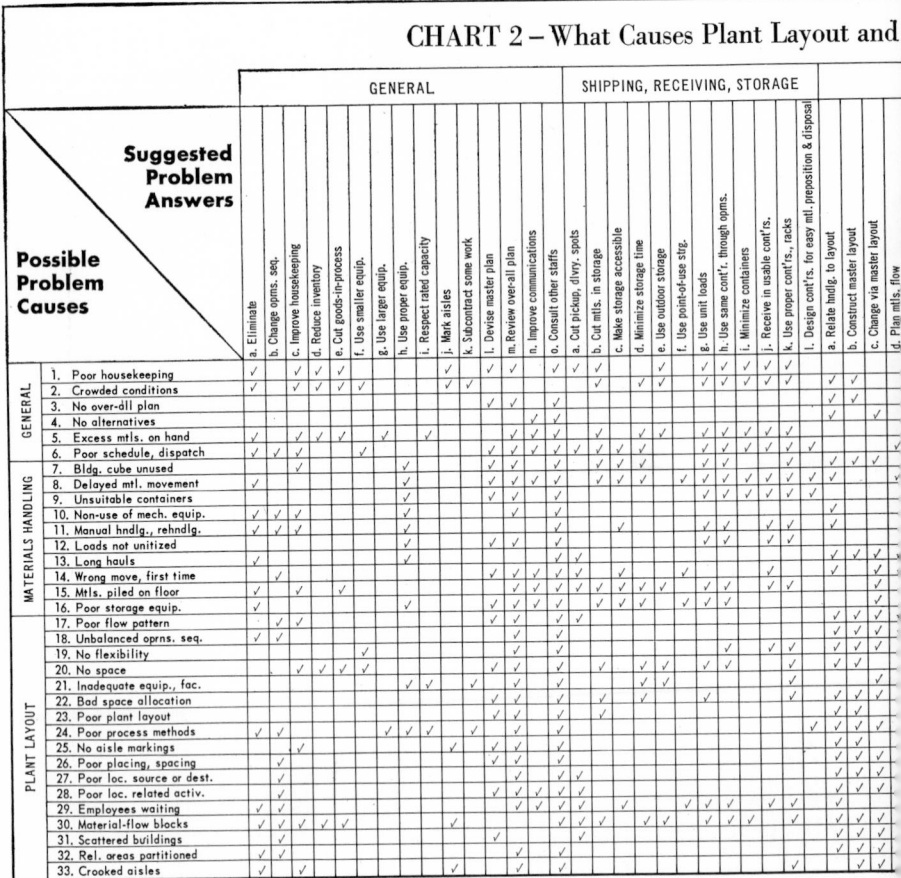

Fig. 16–3. Causes and suggested answers to plant layout and

the basic problem or difficulty. The chart attempts to relate the appropriate causes to the indicators spotted in the plant. Figure 16–3 uses the same format to relate suggestions for improvement to the problems identified in Figure 16–2. The *same* causes are listed on the left of the chart as were found at the top of Figure 16–2. In the case of the second chart, the "remedies" are listed along the top. In using the charts, it will be found helpful to:

1. Systematically review activities in each plant area with the aid of the chart in Figure 16–2.
2. List indicators in the first column of the worksheet in Figure 16–4.
3. Select causes of indicators from top of chart in Figure 16–2 and list (by code number) in column 2 of worksheet.
4. Opposite each "cause," list (by code letters) the suggested solutions from the top of the chart in Figure 16–3.

₄ted Problems – and What to Do About Them

	PLANT LAYOUT		MATERIALS HANDLING		WORKPLACE LAYOUT

Column headers:

PLANT LAYOUT: g. Minimize backtracking; h. Plan for flexibility; i. Plan controlled flow; j. Plan for line prodn.; k. Bring related jobs close; l. Use heavy mt. near rcvg.; m. Provide aux. flow lines; n. Plan growth, shrinkage; o. Make aisles adequate

MATERIALS HANDLING: a. Larger unitized lds.; b. Don't pile on floor; c. Use mech. hndlg. equip.; d. Design built-in. hndlg.; e. Take direct to use point; f. Schedule, dispatch for min. hndlg.; g. Use gravity; h. Combine proc. & transp.; i. Utilize bldg. cube; j. Mechanize scrap removal; k. Use flexible hndlg. equip.; l. Use low-cost hndlg. equip.; m. Use space-saving equip.; n. Use movable equipment; o. Use var.-spd. cnvrs.; p. Floats, banks on cnvrs.

WORKPLACE LAYOUT: a. Supply and remove mtls. at proper rate; b. Automate processing; c. Plan opns. sequentially; d. Keep workers on prodn.; e. Plan nec. manual hndlg. meth.; f. Make work space adequate; g. Scan man-machine rel'ships; h. Integrate hndlg. & process; i. Search for improvements; j. Store min. mtl. at place; k. Use multi-opm. equip.; l. Minimize walking; m. Reduce manual hndlg.; n. Plan equip. arrang't.; o. L-O for motion econ.

related problems. (By permission of Factory Magazine.)

5. Eliminate duplication by circling each cause the *first* time it appears in a subcolumn or column of the worksheet.

6. Using Plant Layout Audit Assignment Sheet in Figure 16–5 for each major indicator, enter all appropriate solutions in the proper column.

7. Indicate departments or individuals to whom responsibility is to be assigned for further investigation and analysis of possible causes of each problem indicated.

8. Plan for a follow-up to assure that:

   a) Proper causes have been identified.

   b) Best possible solutions have been devised.

   c) Solutions have been installed.

   d) Solutions are solving the indicated problem(s).

   e) Solutions are *not* creating additional problems.

WORKSHEET FOR SPOTTING AND ANALYZING LAYOUT PROBLEMS

PLANT AREA __Acme Mfg Co__   OBSERVER __T. L. Foster__   DATE __Oct. 24__

Indicators from Audit Check Sheet	Possible Causes of Problems Indicated	Preliminary Tabulation of Suggested Solutions or Areas for Investigation				
		General	Shipping Receiving, Storage	Plant Layout	Materials Handling	Workplace Layout
j. scattered buildings	3 lack of planning	(l), (m), o	—	(a), (b), (h), (n)	(b), (f)	(i), (n)
	4 lack of alternatives	(n), o	—	a, (c), h, n, (m)	—	i
	7 failure to use bldg. cube	(c), (h), l, m, o	(b), (c), (d), (g), (h), (k)	a, b, c, n	b, (c), (d), (l), (m), (n), (i)	i
	22 improper space allocation	l, m, o	b, d, g, k	a, b, c, (d), (l), n, (o)	i, m, n	(f), i, (j), n
	23 poor plant layout	l, m, o	b	a, b, d, (e), (g), h, (j), (f), (k), l, m, n, o	h	c, i, n
	27 poor location of source or destination	b, m, o	(a)	a, b, c, d, f, g, h, k, l, n	(e), f, l	(a), c, i, (l), (m), n, (o)
	28 poor location of related activities	(b), l, m, n, o	a	a, b, c, d, f, g, h, j, k, n	l	a, (b), (c), (h), i, l, m, n, o

Fig. 16-4. Worksheet for spotting and analyzing layout problems.

PLANT LAYOUT AUDIT ASSIGNMENT SHEET

Indicator ___ j. Scattered Buildings _____

Causes	Suggested Solutions or Areas for Investigation	Assigned for Investigation to:
3. lack of planning 4. lack of alternatives	Change oprns. seq. Improve housekeeping Use proper equipment Devise master plan Review overall plan Improve communications Consult other staffs	R.T.S.
7. Failure to use building cube 22. improper space allocation	Cut pick-up delivery spots Cut materials in storage Make storage accessible Minimize storage time Use unit loads Use same cont'r, through oprns. Use proper cont'rs., racks	N.F.B
23. poor plant layout 27. poor location of source of destination	Relate hndlg. to layout Construct master layout Change via master layout Plan mtls. flow Plan direct mtls. flow Plan for best flow rate Minimize backtracking Plan for flexibility Plan for line prodn. Bring related jobs close Use heavy mtl. near rcvg. Provide aux. flow lines Plan growth, shrinkage Make aisles adequate	J.T.J.
28. poor location of related activities	Don't pile on floor Use mech. hndlg. equip. Design built-in hndlg. Take direct to use point Schedule, dispatch for min. hndlg. Utilize bldg. cube Use low-cost hndlg. equip. Use space-saving equip. Use movable equipment	D.R.G.
	Supply and remove mtls. at proper rate Automate processing Plan oprns. sequentially Make work space adequate Integrate hndlg. and process Search for improvements Store min. mtl. at place Minimize walking Reduce manual hndlg. Plan equip. arrang't. L-O for motion econ.	G.L.K.

Fig. 16–5. Plant layout audit assignment sheet.

While such a procedure may appear rather complicated, it will be seen that it *does* provide an orderly method of suggesting any one, or a combination, of 73 possible solutions or areas for investigation in improving plant layout difficulties. It is probable that the analyst would be aware of many of the suggestions indicated, but the proper solution may lie in one of the areas he was not cognizant of.

Quantitative Evaluation Techniques. If the layout project calls for a more quantitative evaluation, there are several techniques which might be used. They can be briefly described as follows:

1. Rating the advantages and disadvantages
2. Evaluation of layout objectives or criteria
3. Calculation of mathematical indices
4. Use of From-To charts
5. Cost evaluation or comparison

In the first method, numerical values may be placed in the appropriate columns on the form shown in Figure 16–1. Values might be assigned as follows:

Perfect	10
Ideal	9
Excellent	8
Very Good	7
Good	6
Fair	5
Average	4
Poor	3
Unsatisfactory	2
Unacceptable	1

Each advantage or disadvantage should be assigned a value relative to the importance of the item to the over-all results of the proposed solution.

Evaluation of Layout Criteria. Somewhat more accurate would be the actual weighting of desired criteria, plus a rating of each for the proposed alternatives. The Plant Layout Evaluation Sheet in Figure 16–6 is composed of selected items from previous check sheets, principles, objectives, etc., and contains those which it is felt there is a reasonable chance of observing, and evaluating "on paper." For a specific layout, the form might be adapted or rewritten to match the project at hand.

In using the Plant Layout Evaluation Sheet, it is necessary to:

1. Identify the project.
2. Establish the relative weight of each major criterion, i.e., items 1–10. This should be based on company policies, aims, or objectives and should be done by appropriate management personnel. The weights should be allocated to equal 1, 10, 100, etc. If desired, the subitems might even be weighted within each major group. If this much detail is not desired, the

subitems can be used as guides in observing and rating the major factors. Enter weights in column two.

3. Evaluate each factor or subfactor on a basis of 1–10, as indicated in the previous tabulation. If more than one layout is being evaluated, rate all layouts on a specific item at one time to aid in comparison. Enter ratings in appropriate columns.
4. Multiply factor weight by rating to obtain weighted rating for each and enter result in appropriate column.
5. Add each "weighted rating" column to determine "score" for each layout.

It should be remembered in using any such evaluation technique, that it is necessary to apply quantitative measures to factors that are usually considered qualitative. Nevertheless, such a technique will force better thinking from those involved in the evaluation process than could be obtained by purely qualitative or subjective means.

Efficiency Indices. A still more "mathematical" approach are the indices developed by Gantz and Pettit.[2] There are ten of these indices, as reproduced here for consideration or adaptation to a specific problem.

1. Index of Indirect Materials Handling $= \dfrac{a}{b}$

    $a =$ the sum of the distances that a part moves automatically from machine to machine, without external materials handling. ("External materials handling" means manual movement of production materials from one location to another, in boxes, tote pans, and the like.)

    $b =$ the total actual distance that a part travels on the production route from raw stores to finished stores. This can be rephrased to read "distance from the layout area entrance to the exit from the layout area," for the purpose of dealing with smaller organizational units.

    This index has been found to be consistent and accurate and is recommended as a good measure of the efficiency of the production route with respect to the mechanized handling of materials.

2. Index of Direct Materials Handling $= b$

    This value represents the exact distance a part or piece is required to travel during production. It is not an index, properly speaking, but simply a number of feet. It is a good measure of the efficiency with which the production route is laid out and can be used to compare plants or areas manufacturing the same type of product. It was found to be more accurate than any ratio investigated.

3. Index of Gravity Utilization $= \dfrac{d}{e}$

    $d =$ the sum of the vertical distance that gravity feed is used in a multistory plant. (It gives peculiar and unreasonable results when applied to single story operations.)

[2] *Plant Layout Efficiency,* Modern Materials Handling, Jan. 1953.

PLANT LAYOUT EVALUATION SHEET

Plant or Project ——————————————————— Date ——————

Brief Description of Project ———————————————————

Evaluated by: ——————

Criteria, Factor, Characteristics	Weight	Alternate		Alternate		Alternate		Comments and Notes
		Rating	Weight. Rating	Rating	Weight. Rating	Rating	Weight. Rating	
1. GENERAL								
a. overall appearance								
b. crowded conditions								
c. excess or duplicate equipment								
d. ease of supervision								
e. ease of production control								
f. provisions for inspection								
g. access for repairs								
h. adequate exits								
2. FLOW OF MATERIALS								
a. planned								
b. "straight" line								
c. good equipment arrangement								
d. good equipment utilization								
e. adequate aisle space								
f. straight aisles								
g. straight flow lines								

h. minimum back-tracking
i. related operations close together
j. obstacles in material flow
k. no apparent bottlenecks
l. line production where practical

3. FLEXIBILITY TO MEET CHANGING CONDITIONS

4. EXPANDABILITY WITHOUT MAJOR DISRUPTION

5. SPACE UTILIZATION
a. fully utilized
b. effective use of space available
c. effective use of "cube"

6. MATERIALS HANDLING
a. materials handling planned for
—to production
—through production
—to assembly
—through assembly
—to shipping
b. minimum handling
c. short hauls
d. mechanized where practical
e. integrated system
f. use of unit loads
g. provisions for scrap handling

Fig. 16-6. (continued)

PLANT LAYOUT EVALUATION SHEET (Continued)

Criteria, Factor, Characteristics	Weight	Alternate		Alternate		Alternate		Comments and Notes
		Rating	Weight. Rating	Rating	Weight. Rating	Rating	Weight. Rating	
6. MATERIALS HANDLING (Continued)								
h. operations during transit								
i. materials used from vendor's cont'rs.								
j. effective use of gravity								
7. STORAGE ARRANGEMENTS								
a. rough or raw materials								
b. in-process materials								
c. finished parts or components								
d. finished products or assemblies								
8. SHIPPING AND RECEIVING								
a. provisions for common carriers								
b. docks covered								
c. receiving close to first operations								
d. provisions for receiving inspection								
e. mechanical handling where practical								
f. shipping close to last operations								
g. provisions for packing								

9. SERVICE ACTIVITIES
   a. convenience of location
   b. adequate coverage
      —first aid
      —toilet & wash facilities
      —smoking areas
      —drinking fountains
      —lockers or coat racks
      —food service
      —parking
      —tool room
      —tool crib
      —maintenance
      —offices adequate and convenient
      —rubbish collection
      —fire extinguishers, sprinklers

10. BUILDING AND UTILITIES
   a. size adequate, reasonable
   b. shape practical
   c. bay size reasonable
   d. clear height sufficient
   e. entrances, exits adequate & convenient
   f. necessary utilities provided for
      —light
      —heat
      —water
      —sewage
      —drains
      —gas
      —air
      —electricity
      —telephone

Fig. 16-6. Plant layout evaluation sheet.

e = the total vertical distance up or down that a part moves, involving either machine or human effort, from the layout area entrance to the layout area exit of a multistory plant.

Although this index has not been fully evaluated, it can be considered a good indication of the extent to which gravity is used in moving parts up and down.

4. Prime Index of Automatic Machinery Loading $= \dfrac{f}{100g}$

f = the sum of the percentages of machine down time from all cases where the individual percentages of down time are equal to or less than 50% of the individual work cycles. ("Down time" is that portion of the work cycle in which the machine is loaded and unloaded.)

g = total number of operators on these machines.

This index is an accurate indicator of the efficiency obtained by grouping machines for multimachine operation. It should be noted that it is used only when the machine time portion of the over-all work cycle is automatic and machines may be left unattended while in operation.

5. Secondary Index of Automatic Machinery Loading $= \dfrac{h}{100g}$

h = the sum of the percentages of machine down time from all cases where the individual percentages of down time are greater than 50% of the individual work cycles.

This criterion is similar to Index No. 4, except that it is used only for odd groupings of machines that might not be adapted to Index No. 4.

6a. Index of Production Line Flexibility $= \dfrac{j_1}{k_1}$

j_1 = the number of machines or work stations performing operations on the part under consideration, so designed that they can be moved to a new location in the same production line in one working shift.

k_1 = the total number of machines or work stations performing operations on the part under consideration, in the production line.

Definitions

Machine: A nonportable device with a separate or individual power source.

Work Station: The area covered by the tools, equipment, machines, and in-process material necessary to the performance of a given operation.

6b. Index of Work Station Flexibility $= \dfrac{j_2}{k_2}$

j_2 = the number of machines or work stations within the area under consideration so designed that they can be moved to any other location in one working shift.

k_2 = the total number of machines or work stations within the area under consideration.

Index 6a is satisfactorily used as a measure of machine flexibility in the production line in relation to the flow of the part. Index 6b is a successful measure of machine and work station arrangements in terms of utilization of men and machinery.

7. Index of Floor Area Loading Density $= \dfrac{(m + 2)(n + 2) + p}{q - (r + u)}$

$m =$ extreme machine length

$n =$ extreme machine width

$p =$ the total work area normally required by an operator in the performance of his job

$q =$ total layout floor area

$r =$ total aisle area

$u =$ total floor area occupied by temporary or controlled storage of materials, or tools and equipment required to modify this material

This index is an accurate indication of the efficiency with which plant floor space is utilized. "Machine" here means all production machinery, including conveyors resting on or near the floor, but excluding overhead conveyors that pass over and clear other machinery. It should be emphasized that the areas occupied by the machines, work stations, and operators may be totally independent of each other; that is, a productive work area may consist of machines or work stations operated by workers, or of machines operating independently, or of workers operating independently.

8. Index of Aisle Space $= \dfrac{r}{q}$

$r =$ total aisle area

$q =$ total layout floor area

This index gives a true indication of the over-all utilization of layout floor area for aisles. An increase or decrease in aisle area is readily reflected by an increase or decrease in this index value—the particular manufacturing conditions encountered will determine whether a high or low value is desirable.

9. Index of Storage Space $= \dfrac{q - u}{q}$

$q =$ total layout floor area

$u =$ total floor area occupied by temporary or controlled storage of material, or tools and equipment required to modify this material.

This index is an adjunct to the Index of Floor Area Loading Density, where u retains the same meaning. It gives a true indication of the over-all utilization of layout floor area for storage of in-process materials or the tools and equipment required to modify this material. It readily reflects an increase or decrease in storage area.

10. Index of Storage Volume Utilization $= \dfrac{v}{w}$

$v =$ volume occupied by raw materials or finished goods at the normal maximum level of storage.

w = total volume available for storage of raw materials or finished good

This criterion has not been thoroughly tested but shows promise of beir an excellent measurement of the cubic utilization of storage or warehou spaces, such as receiving and shipping. It is also a good potential measur of proper packaging, palletizing, or materials handling, as applied t storage systems.

The above indices might be calculated for several alternative layou and tabulated to determine which layout is best.

Layout Evaluation by From–To Charts. The From–To Chart, as describe and discussed in Chapter 9, is an ideal technique for comparing alte native layouts. Figures 9–11 and 9–13 illustrate this approach, with tl comparison shown by the tables in Figures 9–12 and 9–14.

Cost Evaluation of Layouts. Probably the ultimate and most desirabl evaluation of a layout is in terms of dollars. While this is more difficu to accomplish, certain costs can be determined and compared. Amon those costs which can be readily determined or estimated are the following

TYPICAL EXPENSE SCHEDULES

Investment Schedule	Operating Cost Schedule
Land	Direct Labor
Building	Direct Materials
Structure	Factory Overhead (selected items)
Lighting	Indirect labor
Heating	Indirect materials
Sprinkler	Supplies
Air conditioning	Maintenance
Plumbing	Utilities
Road	Taxes
Drives and parking	Insurance
Fence and gates	Depreciation
Sidewalk	Administrative Overhead
Landscaping	Wages and salaries
Power panel	Selling expenses
Equipment	Advertising expenses
Machinery	Supplies
Materials handling	Depreciation
Office	Employee benefits
Auxiliary equipment	Community gifts
Working Capital	Interest
Salaries	Insurance
Wages	Fire
Inventories	Workmen's compensation
Other Expenses	Liability
	Property damage
	Taxes
	Building, etc.
	Machinery and equipment
	Inventory

The above costs should be worked up into a form to suit the project or projects being evaluated and compared. The project showing the lowest total would then have to be studied in light of other facts—advantages, disadvantages, etc.—in coming to the final decision.

Any or all of the above evaluation techniques might be used on a given layout project. The engineer must study each individual problem and determine which technique(s) would be most useful and applicable to the situation at hand.

Presenting the Layout to Management. Nearly the last step in the plant layout project is the presentation and selling of the layout to the management. Needless to say, the first consideration is the accumulation of all pertinent data and exhibits for supporting the presentation and for examination by management. These items would include the following:

Final layout(s)
Flow diagrams (or other simplified versions to more easily present over-all flow pattern in simpler terms)
Evaluation forms or tabulations
Cost comparison sheets
Summary of intangible benefits

The actual presentation itself should be well planned and rehearsed, and sufficient supplementary data should be at hand for reference or display if called for. The oral report might follow the pattern outlined below: [3]

Step 1. Make Ready	State objectives, prepare for contemplated questions, size up management group.
Step 2. Approach with Benefits	Induce an affirmative reaction as you describe potential gains, over-all advantages and/or savings.
Step 3. Stimulate Desire and Induce Belief	Demonstrate through use of simple visual aids, compare with existing methods, induce management participation, present as a common goal of plant layout and management.
Step 4. State the Facts	Simply prove it workable and beneficial by utilization of devices to convince: comparison, cause and effect, contrast.
Step 5. Eliminate Retardants	Encourage objections to details not to principle and eliminate by presentation of counterbenefits.
Step 6. Provide Conclusions	Restate, or recapitulate, the reasons for belief; summarize main points.
Step 7. Request Approval	Clear statement of action desired.

[3] Air Materiel Command, *Plant Layout Engineering Manual* No. 66–9, 1957, Wright-Patterson Air Force Base, Ohio.

Where a formal report is desirable or required, the contents might include: [4]

1. The presentation of the problem.
2. A condensed statement of proposals.
3. A statement of the costs of installing the proposals.
4. A statement of the expected savings in operating expenses.
5. A statement of the expected increases in operating expenses.
6. A cost analysis and engineering economy study summarizing the effects of the proposals and comparing the proposals with present conditions.
7. Recommendations for other improvements in related areas, schedules of installations, and procedures for the relayout or rearrangement of the plant areas.

8. Appendix:

   a) Drawings and blueprints of the present and the proposed plans.
   b) Detailed calculations supporting the findings listed in parts 2, 3, 4, 5, and 6, above.
   c) Specifications for all equipment, supplies, tools and other items which must be purchased or made.
   d) An explanation of any proposed plans that may need amplification (cross-referenced with the referred-to item in the main body of report or in the Appendix).
   e) A summary of plans or proposals that were studied and discarded, together with the reasons for their discard.

It should be remembered that the more complete the picture presented to top management, the better the chance of gaining approval.

In this connection it may be well to re-emphasize the value of scale models in selling the layout. Even though the models may not be too fancy or exact, they add immeasurably to the ability of a person, not familiar with the details, to evaluate the planned layout.

A Michigan automobile manufacturer spent $200,000 making a full size mock-up of a portion of a new assembly line which was to introduce a radical idea in progressive assembly. This full size "model" helped in many ways. It sold the management on the general idea, as well as pointing out to the methods engineers that they had a few kinks to iron out.

If scale or full-size models are impractical, then good use can be made of elevation drawings, or even perspective drawings, to help explain complicated set-ups or to prove or disprove whether a group of machines will fit in a given space. This is especially true when ceiling height, rafters, girders, or trusses are likely to interfere.

No step is more important to the plant layout engineer than the presentation of his final work to management for approval. No effort should be

[4] Ireson, W. G., *Factory Planning and Plant Layout* (Prentice-Hall, Inc., 1952), Chap. 13.

spared in the preparation of any necessary visual aids or supplementary data. Certainly it would be disastrous to "lose the battle" at this crucial point in a long and arduous project. The presentation deserves top effort in preparation—as well as whatever time must be spent in "practice" presentations or rehearsals.

Installing the Layout. The last, but by no means least, task of the plant layout engineer is the actual "installation" of the completed layout. All of the preceding detailed planning is of little avail if the installation of the layout project is not in exact accordance with the carefully made plans. It is of utmost importance that the plant layout engineer oversee or supervise the necessary work in connection with the culmination of the project.

If the final layout is turned over to the architects or contractors, the plant layout engineer must carefully observe all subsequent planning to assure that *his* work is properly incorporated into the building drawings. Often, much of the value of the plant layout work can be nullified by small changes in such details as building shape, column spacing, truss height, orientation on the property, interior partitions, window and door location, floor drains, down spouts, etc. Each step in the building design should be followed closely in order to catch any such changes as may be inadvertently made by the building designer or contractor—or purposely made to suit *his* objectives or cost relationships.

Before actual construction and installation can begin, much additional work must be carried out to complete the detail plans for equipment procurement and installation or the actual move itself. Among the more important items of work yet to be done are:

1. Detail drawings of certain phases
2. Exact specification of production equipment
3. Exact specification of materials handling equipment
4. Detailed listing of all equipment involved in the utility requirements
5. Actual plans and schedule for the building construction and/or the move into the proposed space

Detailed drawings should be made (possibly by plant engineering, the architect, or the contractor) of any unusual features of the layout to assure compliance with the original plans. This might include such features as mezzanines, balconies, docks, pits, equipment overhead or on the roof, foundations for certain equipment, etc.

Exact production equipment specifications should be on hand now, from the planning work. If not, complete details must be worked up for use as purchase specifications or as an aid to installation. For actual use during installation, the necessary data are recapped on a form similar to that in Figure 16–7. In the actual building process and installation

PRESS EQUIPMENT	ELECTRICAL MOTORS	ELECTRIC DRIERS/HEATERS	NATURAL GAS	WATER	SANITARY SEWER	COMPRESSED AIR	PROCESS STEAM	EXHAUST
Web Offset Multi-Press	50 HP 440V 3φ Main Drive 25 HP 440V 3φ Auxiliaries 75 HP	----	1,200 cu ft/hr	19,200 gals/24 hrs at 50° F	2 floor drains & Traps	20 CFM	----	5,000 CFM
22¾" Web Offset	50 HP 440V 3φ Main Drive 25 HP 440V 3φ Auxiliaries 75 HP	----	1,200 cu ft/hr	19,200 gals/24 hrs at 50° F	2 floor drains & Traps	20 CFM	----	5,000 CFM
Variable Multi-Press (Web Offset)	50 HP 440V 3φ Main Drive 25 HP 440V 3φ Auxiliaries 75 HP	----	1,200 cu ft/hr	19,200 gals/24 hrs at 50° F	2 floor drains & Traps	20 CFM	----	5,000 CFM
Press No. 28	60 HP 440V 3φ Main Drive 40 HP 440V 3φ Auxiliaries 100 HP Main Drive has Thymatrol DC Converter (450V DC)	1-40 kw luker temp. control	1¼" Line Pressure 6" WC. average 900 cu ft/hr Max Demand 2000 cu ft/hr (1000 BTU/CF)	19,200 gals/24 hrs at 50° F	2 floor drains & Traps	Note 4 For supplying entire Lord St. Plant: Presses 1,2,3, 4,5,7,8,9,10, 15,16,19,20, 21,22,23,24, 25,26,27,28 Foundry Misc. All Bindery Eq. except Binders 1 & 2 Foundry Composing Maintenance Laboratory Misc. 10-2 S CFM	Note 5: For supplying entire Lord St. Plant: Presses 21, 28, 27 Foundry Misc. 4,500 gals/month No. 6 oil, for process steam (Press 21 uses 40% 27 & 28 use 10% Foundry uses 50%	Note 6: For entire Lord St. Plant: Presses 1,2,3,4, 5,7,8,9,10,19, 20,21,22,23,24, 25,26,27,28 All Bindery Equipment except Binders 1 & 2 Foundry Composing Maintenance Lab - Misc
Press No. 27	50 HP 440V 3φ Main Drive 28 HP 220/440V 3φ Auxiliary Main Drive has Thymatrol DC Converter (450V DC)	----	1¼" Line 6" w.c. average 900 cu ft/hr. Max Demand 2000 cu ft/hr (1000 BTU/CF)	19,200 gals/24 hrs	Required	10-20 CFM		
Press No. 25	25 HP 115V DC Main Drive 14 HP 440V 3φ Auxiliaries	----	½" Line 6" w.c. Pressure Requirement is small	----	----	Laboratory Misc. 2 Air Compressors are used: 1) 12x11 75 HP 220V 3φ - 304 CFM 2) 9x9 30 HP 220V 3φ 25C Total 457 CFM (90 P.S.I.) 10 CFM	27 & 28 use 50%	Process Exhaust ist Pressroom Exh. 50,000 CFM Foundry Exh. 15,000 CFM Balance of Bldg. 25,000 CFM Total 90,000 CFM
Press No. 26	25 HP 115V DC Main Drive 6.5 HP 440V 3φ Auxiliaries	----	3/8" Line, 6" w.c. Pressure Requirement is small	----	----	----	See Note 5 above	

Provide Steam for fire Prof. in Exh. hoods.

Fig. 16-7. Typical equipment and facilities requirement schedule. (By permission of The Austin Company.)

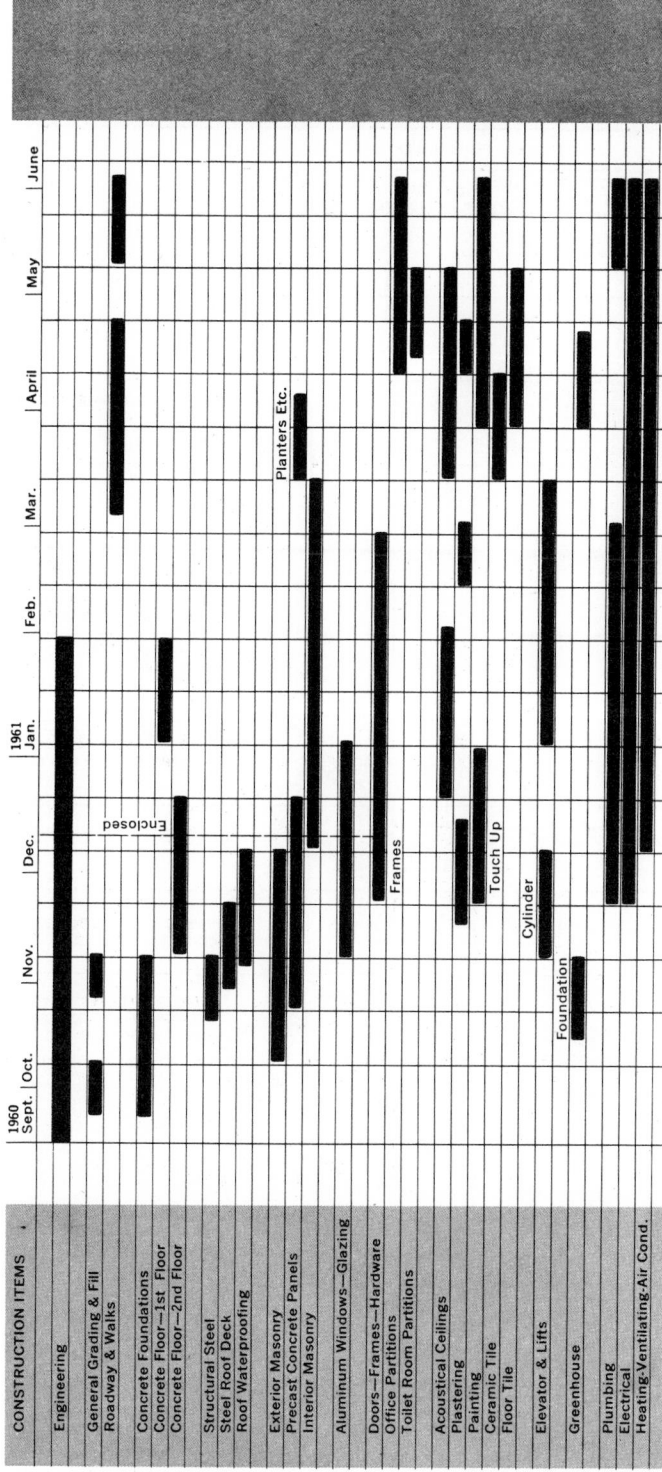

Fig. 16-8. Typical construction progress schedule. (By permission of The Austin Company.)

MOVE CONTROL PROCEDURE

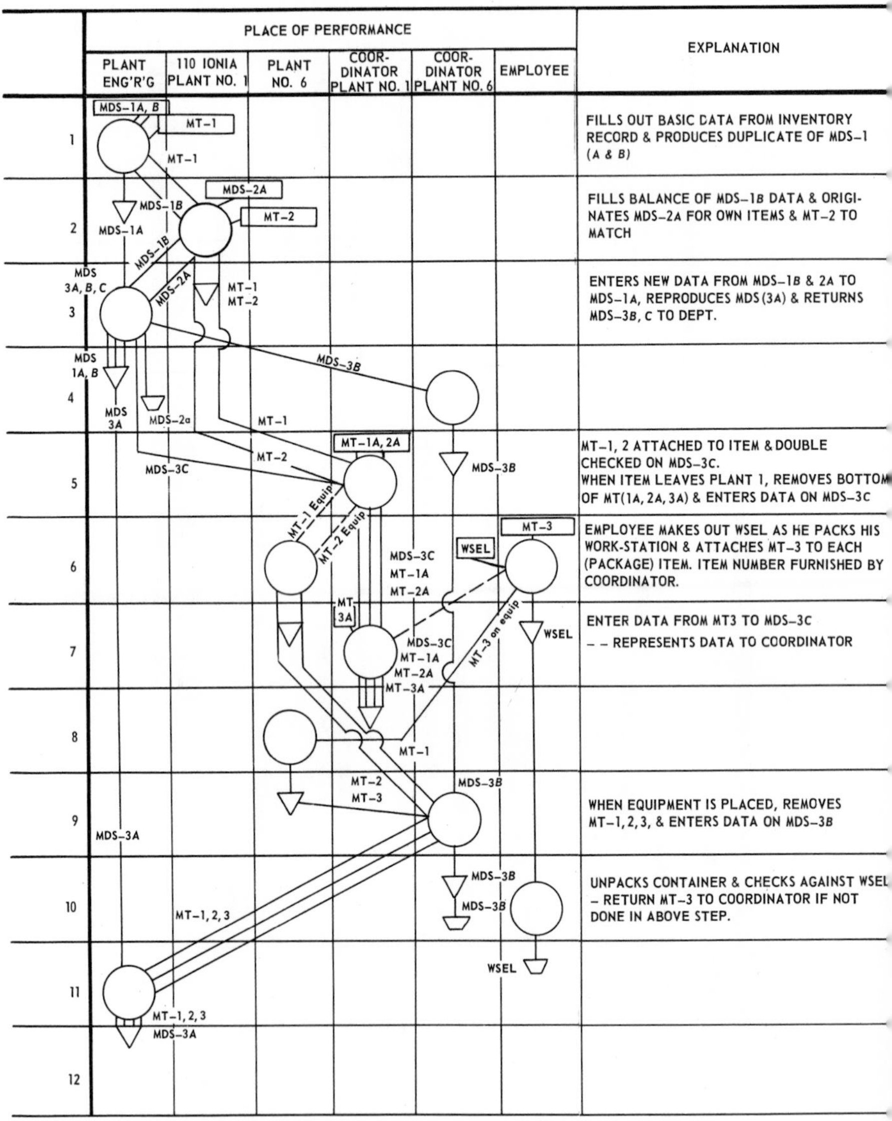

Fig. 16–9. Plant move control procedure. (By permission of Lear, Inc.)

PLANT MOVE MASTER DATA SHEET

MASTER SHEET NO. 22   OF 90
DEPT. SHEET NO. 1   OF 4
DEPT. NO. H 500

DEPT. NAME Sheet Metal Fabrication

ITEM NO.	ASSET TOOL PART OR JOB NO.	DESCRIPTION NAME	UTILITIES REQUIRED SERVICE	UTILITIES READY AT NEW LOCATION	TRADE DISCONNECT OLD LOCATION	TRADE CONNECT AT NEW LOCATION	NOTIFIED	LOCATION PRESENT FL/BAY	LOCATION NEW FL/BAY	LOCATION FL MARKED	LOCATION LINE STA	MOVE DATE SCHED	MOVE DATE LEFT	MOVE DATE CPLTD	REMARKS ADDITION DATA OR INFORMATION
760	19876	SPOT WELDER	440V 3PH 60 Cyc 150 KVA	Yes	Plumber Elect'	Plumber Elect'	White	4/6	14A	X	A/1	8-4	8-4	8-5	
761	7959	SPOT WELDER	440 V 3 PH 60 Cyc 100 KVA	Yes	Plumber Elect'	Plumber Elect'	White	4/6	14A	X	A/2	8-4	8-4	8-5	Power Supply Interlock Required
762	20101	SPOT WELDER	440 V 3 PH 60 Cyc 100 KVA	Yes	Plumber Elect'	Plumber Elect'	White	4/6	14A	X	A/3	8-4	8-4	8-5	
781	6954	RIVETER	None	--	None	None	White	4/7	14B	X	C/1	8-5	8-5	8-5	
782	7458	RIVETER	None	--	None	None	White	4/7	14B	X	C/2	8-5	8-5	8-5	
740	3828	100-Ton PUNCH PRESS	440 V 3 PH 60 Cyc	Yes	Plumber Elect'	Plumber Elect'	White	4/8	15C	X	A/1	8-4	8-5	8-5	
741	3925	100-Ton PUNCH PRESS	"	"	"	"	"	"	"	"	A/2	"	"	"	
742	22012	20-Ton PUNCH PRESS	440 V 3 PH 60 Cyc	Yes	New Equip.	Plumber Elect'	"	--	15C	X	A/3	8-4	--	8-4	Vendor delivers to new site 8-4
743	22013	20-Ton PUNCH PRESS	"	"	"	"	"	--	15C	X	A/4	8-4	--	8-4	"
744	7389	BUFFING JACK	440V 3 PH 60 Cyc	Yes	Elect'	Elect'	"	4/2	15A	X	B/6	8-4	8-4	8-4	"
745	9656	BELT SANDER	440 V 3 PH 60 Cyc	Yes	Elect'	Elect'	"	4/2	15A	X	B/7	8-4	8-4	8-4	
746	10202	POWER BRAKE	440 V 3 PH 60 Cyc	Yes	Elect'	Elect'	"	4/3	15C	X	B/1	8-4	8-4	8-4	
747	10301	HAND BRAKE	None	Yes	None	None	"	4/2	15A	X	B/5	8-4	8-4	8-4	
748	10703	CIRCULAR SHEAR	440 V 3 PH 60 Cyc	Yes	Elect'	Elect'	"	4/3	15C	X	B/2	8-4	8-4	8-4	
749	16780	FOOT SHEAR	None	Yes	None	None	"	4/3	15A	X	B/5	8-4	8-4	8-4	
750	10760	BAND SAW	440 V 3 PH 60 Cyc	Yes	Elect'	Elect'	"	4/3	15C	X	B/3	8-4	8-4	8-4	

LEAR 62.1-21

Fig. 16-10. Plant move master data sheet for accumulation of all data pertinent to a plant move. (By permission of Lear, Inc.)

procedure, this form is followed closely to assure proper utility connections at each machine location.

The entire construction and installation procedure is best planned and coordinated with a worksheet or schedule as shown in Figure 16–8. This helps to assure that no item is overlooked, that each is planned for, and that every step is on schedule.

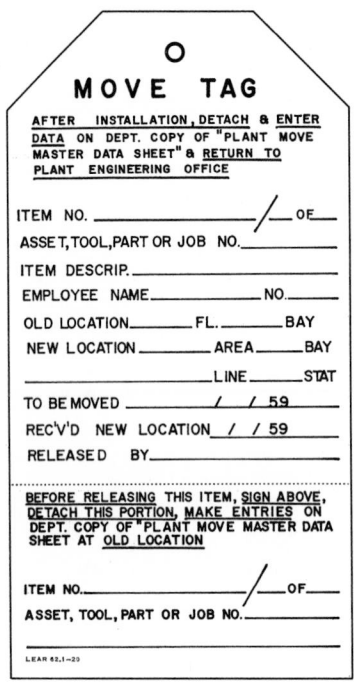

Fig. 16–11. Move tag, attached to every item in a plant move. (By permission of Lear, Inc.)

Making the Move. When the time has finally arrived to make the move into the new area or building, a very carefully worked out plan must be made to be sure all goes along smoothly. This will go beyond the Progress Chart shown in Figure 16–8 and should detail the activities involved in the actual movement of equipment into the building and its installation. One such procedure is shown in Figure 16–9. The related forms are shown in Figures 16–10 through 16–13, as developed by the writer for

LEAR, INCORPORATED
GRAND RAPIDS, MICHIGAN

Sheet No. ___ of _____

WORK STATION EQUIPMENT LIST

Department _____ Scheduled Moving Date _____

Work Station Designation _____
(line no., station no., operation name and/or no., etc.)

Work Station Location _____
(Dept., area, bay, line, station, etc.)

Operator(s) Name(s) _____

In order that you can start work at your new location, you must have on hand everything you need. To help you in this task, it is requested that you:

1. List all items in your work area on this sheet (a day or two before your scheduled move).
2. See that all items are on hand the day your work area is scheduled to move.
3. Check off each item as you pack it for moving.
4. Attach Move Tag to each item and/or container to be moved. Be sure tag has item number and that it is entered on Plant Move Master Data Sheet.
5. Attach "Do Not Move" labels to all items NOT to be moved.
6. Return this Work Station Equipment list to your Coordinator when you are through packing. It will be returned to you (or your counterpart on the next shift) at your new location.
7. Check off each item as you unpack it in Plant #6.

ITEM NO. (to be assigned)	DESCRIPTION	QUANTITY	ON HAND BEFORE MOVE	PACKED	ON HAND AFTER MOVE
			Enter check mark in space at proper time		
	EQUIPMENT – jigs, fixtures, meters, test equipment, etc.				
	AUXILIARY ITEMS – hand tools, etc.				
	MATERIALS, WORK-IN-PROCESS, & STOCK – for first day at new location				

Fig. 16–12. Work station equipment list for recording all items in a work station at time of plant move. (By permission of Lear, Inc.)

DEPARTMENTAL MOVE **PROCEDURE AND CHECK SHEET**	
1. Complete housecleaning	
2. Attach "Move Tag" to each <u>item</u> and container to be moved. Make sure each tag has item number and that it is entered on Plant Move Master Data Sheet.	
3. Attach "Do Not Move" labels to all items to remain in Plant 1.	
4. <u>Remove</u> all other "portable" items and materials.	
5. Assign 2 persons to coordinate the actual move (one for the Ionia Plant, one for the Eastern Ave. Plant).	
6. Coordinators check floor markings for location of equipment in Plant #6. Layout prints will be available.	
7. Be sure enough containers are on hand for packing all auxiliary items and materials.	
8. Plan for collection and packing of auxiliary items and materials.	
9. Plan to "disconnect" each piece of equipment.	

10. Prepare all equipment for moving
   a. Remove and pack "extensions"_____
   b. Secure all loose parts (handles, levers, cords, etc.)_____
   c. Fasten all drawers, doors, typewriter carriages, etc. (use
      glass reinforced tape where applicable). _____
   d. Pack all auxiliary equipment and related items._____	

11. Brief all employees on move
   a. Move in general _____
   b. His part in preparation_____
   c. Making out Work Station Equipment list_____
   d. His part in setting up new area _____
   e. The date of his move _____
   f. Where to report. _____	

12. Check <u>your</u> move <u>schedule.</u>	
13. Coordinators personally supervise removing, loading, and unload- ing of items.	

14. Remove proper portion of move tag and enter appropriate data on
copy of Plant Move Master Data Sheet.
   a. At Ionia Plant—remove bottom portion, enter data on Master
      Data Sheet. _____
   b. At Eastern Ave. Plant—Remove balance of tag, enter data on
      Master Data Sheet, and <u>return</u> tag to Plant Engineering. ____	

Fig. 16–13. Departmental procedure and check list for use in a plant move. (By permission of Lear, Inc.)

Lear, Inc., for use in a move of several departments from the original building to a new one several miles away. Over 10,000 items were moved, from one location to the other, including all work-in-process which was sealed in plastic film covers to prevent the accumulation of dust in the precision assemblies.

Reproducing, Displaying, and Storing the Layout. Obviously a plant layout is made to be used. Some of the persons who will want to use, or at least refer to, the layout are the millwrights, the plant engineer, electricians, building contractors, architects, plumbing contractors, methods engineers, and plant executives.

Since it is usually desired to keep the original layout intact, some method must be devised to make reproductions for the use of the people mentioned above. The layout(s) at this stage might consist of:

1. Grid sheet and template masters
2. "Blue" prints of grid sheets
3. Scale models
4. Photos of scale models
5. Drawings or tracings
6. Any combination of the above

Any or all of these forms are commonly used by the persons who must refer to them. Probably the "blue" print is the most common type of reproduction, but when scale models are used, it is possible to make photographs for reference purposes. One point should be mentioned here about the photographing of scale model layouts. It is best to photograph only a small section at one time. The small sections are then fastened together to reconstruct the layout. If too large a section is taken there will be distortion due to the angle between the camera lens and the models near the edge of the area. This distortion makes the print difficult to use in determining the proper location of facilities. It is for this reason that many plants using models for layout planning also make template layouts of the final arrangement.

In some cases, the model itself has been strategically located for reference use by the contractors. In this case it must be covered with sheet plastic and sealed from dust and dirt. In one case, the contractor specified in his bid that the model must be available at the site for use by his personnel and subcontractors.

It is usually desired also to have the layout on display for the purpose of study, discussion, or publicity. If this is the case, the same type of prints can be used; but they should be mounted in some convenient way for easy reference to either the whole layout or sections of the layout. Probably the most common method of displaying prints is by mounting them on boards which are then placed either on the wall or on tables. The method used depends somewhat on personal choice and on space available.

Some plants mount the boards on swinging panels fastened to the wall, so that they can be folded flat against the wall or swung out as desired.

A technique used by many plants having multistory buildings is to build a frame, representing in scale and shape the building itself. Layout boards are then inserted as "floors" in their respective positions.

Frequently the original layout is kept intact both for display and study purposes, and for making revisions and changes. If this is done, precautions must be taken to protect the layout from dust and dirt and also from tampering or unauthorized changes. This protection is frequently accomplished by keeping a cover over the layout. The cover may be of cloth, canvas, or transparent plastic. Protection is especially important if scale models are used, because they are excellent "dust-catchers" and are also easily moved or removed. One plant does not keep the scale models set up after the desired arrangement has been arrived at. Reproductions of the layout are made and the models are taken up and filed away for future use.

Many variations and combinations of these methods of presentation are in use, and only the ingenuity of the layout engineer limits the extent to which one may go. Figures 16–14 through 16–19 illustrate some of the points discussed above.

Follow-Up. Even though the plant layout project may be assumed to be complete with the filing of the prints or the display of the model, this is not entirely true. Like almost everything else in industry a plant layout must be kept up-to-date and must be continually studied for further improvement possibilities.

A planned procedure should be established to assure that any and all changes made in the plant are also made on the layout, so that it is current at all times. This is especially important immediately after completion of the installation when many minor changes may have been made as the project progressed. All layouts, drawings, and models should be corrected to reflect "as installed" conditions before they are filed away.

Needless to say, even the final, revised layout is seldom—if ever—perfect. Continuous study of plant operations will reveal the need for periodic changes—as will the several situations described in Chapter 1 (under Plant Layout Problems).

The alert plant layout engineer should always be on the lookout for improvement possibilities and the adaptation of the layout to keep abreast of the latest developments in methods and processing.

Fig. 16–14. A plant layout model serves as an excellent basis for study and discussion. (By permission of Fisher Body Div., General Motors Corp.)

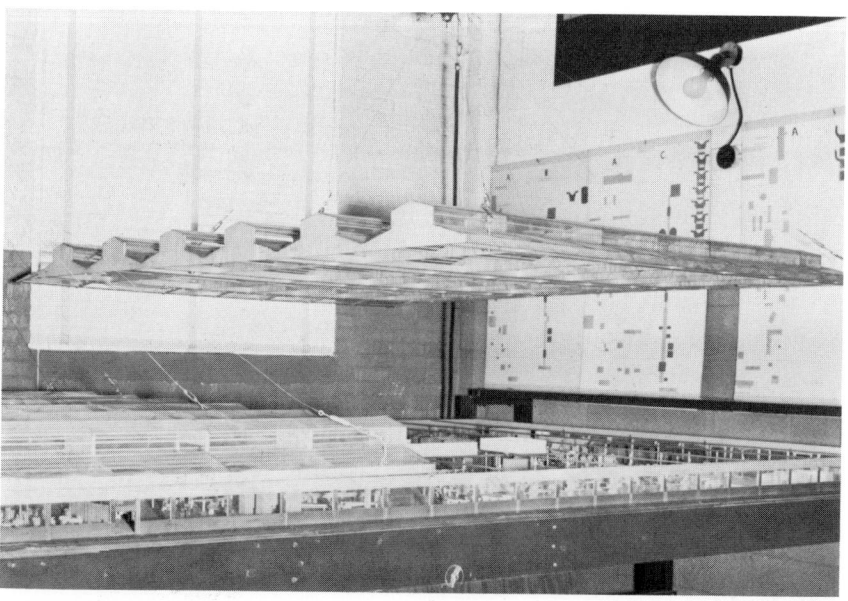

Fig. 16–15. Plant scale model showing use of a roof to protect it from dust. (By permission of Borg-Warner Corp.)

Fig. 16–16. "Filing" of completed layouts on overhead trolleys. (By permission of Industrial Photo Products, Inc., and Pontiac Motor Division, General Motors Corp.)

Fig. 16–17. Cabinets for storing template layouts. (By permission of Marathon Corp.)

Fig. 16–18. Unusual arrangement for storing scale model of multi-story plant; each "floor" is supported by counterweights. (By permission of Alderman & Alderman, Architects.)

Fig. 16–19. Plant model display table. (By permission of A. O. Smith Co.)

QUESTIONS

1. What are the purposes of evaluating a plant layout?
2. Differentiate between qualitative and quantitative evaluations. Which is preferable? Why?
3. In addition to the final layout, what else is necessary for the presentation to management?
4. Why must the plant layout engineer become involved in the installation of the layout?
5. What further work is necessary after the final layout is made—to supplement the layout print or model—to aid in the installation?
6. How would one keep track of the layout installation—to make sure everything is done, and done on time?
7. What important things must be done in preparing for and carrying out the move to a new area or plant?
8. What are some of the ways in which the "master" layout can be stored and protected for future use and reference? Prints? Grid master? Models?
9. What important task remains for the plant layout engineer after the entire layout project is complete, installed, and operating?

Bibliography

PLANT LAYOUT, GENERAL

Immer, J. R. *Layout Planning Techniques.* McGraw-Hill Book Co., Inc., 1950.
Ireson, W. Grant. *Factory Planning and Plant Layout.* Prentice-Hall, Inc., 1952.
Mallick, Randolph W., and Gaudreau, A. T. *Plant Layout Planning and Practice.* John Wiley & Sons, Inc., 1951.
Moore, J. M. *Plant Layout Design.* The Macmillan Co., 1962.
Muther, R. *Practical Plant Layout.* McGraw-Hill Book Co., Inc., 1955.
————. *Systematic Plant Layout.* Industrial Education Institute, 1961.
Reed, Ruddell, Jr. *Plant Layout.* Richard D. Irwin, Inc., 1961.
Shubin, John A., and Madeheim, H. *Plant Layout.* Prentice-Hall, Inc., 1951.

PRODUCTION PLANNING

Carson, G. B. *Production Handbook.* The Ronald Press Co., 1958.
Doyle, L. E. *Tool Engineering.* Prentice-Hall, Inc., 1950.
Ireson, W. G., and Grant, E. L. *Handbook of Industrial Engineering and Management.* Prentice-Hall, Inc., 1955.
Maynard, H. B. *Industrial Engineering Handbook.* McGraw-Hill Book Co., Inc., 1956.
Moore, F. G. *Production Control.* McGraw-Hill Book Co., Inc., 1959.

AUTOMATION

Bright, James R. *Automation and Management.* Harvard University Press, 1958.
Grabbe, E. M. *Automation in Business and Industry.* John Wiley & Sons, Inc., 1957.

STORAGE, WAREHOUSING, PACKAGING, ETC.

American Management Association. *A Basic Guide to Preparing Packaging Specifications.*
Briggs, A. J. *Warehouse Operations, Planning and Management.* John Wiley & Sons, Inc., 1960.
Brown, K. *Package Design Engineering.* John Wiley & Sons, Inc., 1959.
Friedman, W. F., and Kipnees, J. J. *Industrial Packaging.* John Wiley & Sons, Inc., 1960.
Larsen, S. A. *Packaging Research: An Inventory.* American Management Association.
Modern Materials Handling. *The Palletizer.* Boston Publishing Company, 1951.
Stern, W. *Package Engineering Handbook.* Chicago Board Products Publishing Co., 1954.
U.S. Department of Defense, Department of the Army. *Storage and Material Handling.* U.S. Government Printing Office, 1955. (TM743-200).
U.S. General Services Administration. *Warehouse Operations Handbook.* U.S. Government Printing Office, 1953.

MATERIALS HANDLING, GENERAL

American Materials Handling Society. *Materials Handling Bibliography.*
Apple, James M. *Lesson Guide Outline on Material Handling Education.* Material Handling Institute, 1961.
Barker, C. H., Footlik, I. M., Yarham, C. F., and Carle, J. F. *Industrial Materials Handling.* Lincoln Extension Institute, 1950.
Bolz, H. A., and Hagemann, G. E. *Materials Handling Handbook.* The Ronald Press Co., 1958.
Harrington, C. C. *Material Handling Manual.* Chilton Company, 1952.
Immer, J. R. *Material Handling.* McGraw-Hill Book Co., Inc., 1953.
Laughner, V. H. *Material Handling Manual No. 1—Principles.* 1955.
———. *Material Handling Manual No. 2—Equipment Selection and Application.* 1957.
———. *Material Handling Manual No. 3—Mechanization and Automation.* 1958.
———. *Material Handling Manual No. 4—Cost and Engineering Guide.* 1959.
Material Handling Institute, Inc. *Library of Material Handling Know-How: No. 1 Basic Concepts; No. 2 General Rules, Analysis and Cost Data; No. 3 Plant Layout, Maintenance, etc.; No. 4 Orgnization and Training.* The Material Handling Institute, Inc.
Stocker, Harry E. *Materials Handling* (2nd ed.). Prentice-Hall, Inc., 1951.
Urquhart, L. F., and Boyce, C. W. *Materials Handling Case Book.* McGraw-Hill Book Co., Inc., 1951.

MATERIALS HANDLING, ANALYSIS

Barnes, R. M. *Work Sampling.* John Wiley & Sons, Inc., 1957.
Heiland, R. E., and Richardson, W. J. *Work Sampling.* McGraw-Hill Book Co., Inc., 1957.
Morris, W. T. *Analysis for Materials Handling Management.* Richard D. Irwin, Inc., 1962.

MATERIALS HANDLING, EQUIPMENT

Apple, James M. *Lesson Guide Outline on Material Handling Education.* Material Handling Institute, 1961.
Caster and Floor Truck Manufacturers Association. *Handbook of Manual Materials Handling Equipment.* 1953.
Conveyor Equipment Manufacturer's Association. *Conveyor Terms and Definitions.* Washington, D.C., 1952.
Haynes, D. O. *Material Handling Equipment.* Chilton Company, 1957.
Haynes, D. O. *Material Handling Applications,* Chilton Co., 1958.
Hetzel, F. V., and Albright, R. K. *Belt Conveyors and Belt Elevators.* John Wiley & Sons, Inc., 1941.
Hudson, W. G. *Conveyors and Related Equipment.* John Wiley & Sons., Inc., 1944.
Industrial Publishing Company. *Material Handling Engineering Directory.* (biennial)
Industrial Truck Association. *Handbook of Powered Industrial Trucks.* Washington, D.C., 1958.

OPERATION AND WORK AREA PLANNING

Barnes, R. M. *Motion and Time Study* (4th ed.). John Wiley & Sons, Inc., 1958.
Mundel, M. E. *Motion and Time Study.* Prentice-Hall, Inc., 1955.
Muther, R. *Production-Line Technique.* McGraw-Hill Book Co., Inc., 1944.
Nadler, G. *Motion and Time Study.* McGraw-Hill Book Co., Inc., 1955.
Niebel, B. *Motion and Time Study.* Richard D. Irwin, Inc., 1958 (rev. ed.).

PERIODICALS

Automation, Cleveland 13, Ohio.
Distribution Age, Philadelphia 5, Pa.
Factory, New York 36, N. Y.
Fordern und Heben, Wiesbaden, Germany.
Materials Handling in Canadian Industry, Toronto 5, Ontario, Canada.
Material Handling Engineering, Cleveland 15, Ohio.
Mechanical Handling, London S.E. 1, England.
Mill and Factory, New York 17, N. Y.
Modern Materials Handling, Boston 16, Mass.
Production, Birmingham, Michigan.
Western Materials Handling, Los Angeles 4, Calif.

ARTICLES

Apple, J. M., "How to Spot Your Plant Layout Problems," *Factory Magazine,* Jan. 1959.

Baird, D. G., "Scale Models; How Kaiser Frazer Saves Time in Production Planning," *American Business,* Vol. 21, Aug. 1951, pp. 16–17.

Bannester, E. M., "How to Know Which Machine Goes Where," *Mill & Factory,* Vol. 57, Aug. 1955, pp. 85–86.

Bowen, H. J., "Scale Models," *Chemical Engineer,* Vol. 61, Aug. 1954, pp. 176–82.

Bowens, A. M., "Pentagonal Layout Table Saves Office Space," *American Machinist,* Vol. 92, No. 18, 1948, p. 99.

Boyce, C. W., "Adopt the Best in Plant Layout; Three-Dimensional Scale Models," *Factory Management and Maintenance,* Vol. 107, Sept. 1949, pp. 72–74.

———, "Scale Model Guides Four-Step Plant Building Replacement," *Factory Management and Maintenance,* Vol. 107, Sept. 1949, pp. 72–74.

Brinkerhoff, H. W., "Three-Dimensional Drawings Aid Plant Layout Visualization," *Chemical Industry,* Vol. 56, Mar. 1945, pp. 410–411.

Buffa, Elwood S., "Sequence Analysis for Functional Layout," *Journal of Industrial Engineering,* Mar.–Apr. 1955, p. 12.

Bunce, J. P., "Now, the Three Stage Layout," *Factory Management and Maintenance,* Vol. 113, Nov. 1955, pp. 126–27.

Bussard, W. A., "It Pays to Build Design Models," *Petroleum Processing,* Vol. 12, Apr. 1957, pp. 90–93.

Cameron, D. G., "Travel Charts Analyze Layout and Materials Handling Problems," *Modern Materials Handling,* Vol. 9, No. 4, Apr. 1954, pp. 89–96.

———, "Travel Charts," *Modern Materials Handling,* Jan. 1952, p. 137.

Carter, H. B., "Why and How of Plant Layout," *General Electric Review,* Vol. 58, Mar. 1955, pp. 18–21.

Clark, B. L., "Scale Models Make Plant Layout a Sure Thing," *Factory Management and Maintenance,* Vol. 103, Feb. 1945, pp. 93–95.

Dasey, Homer H., "Better Layouts Quicker with Scale Models," *Factory Management and Maintenance,* Dec. 1944, p. 106.

———, "Case of the Cross-Eyed Waif," *Iron Age,* Vol. 171, No. 19, May 7, 1953, pp. 200–04.

———, "Save Time, Money with Three-Dimensional Planning," *Iron Age,* Vol. 168, No. 19, Nov. 8, 1951, pp. 133–35.

Davidson, R. L., "Can You Save Design Hours with 'Photo Blueprint'?," *Petroleum Processing,* Vol. 10, No. 3, Mar. 1955, pp. 348–53.

DeGroat, G. H., "Models are Tools not Toys," *American Machinist,* Vol. 100, July 2, 1956, pp. 701–16.

De Villeneuve, Louis, "Quantitative Flow Chart," *Proceedings of Second Biennial Packaging and Materials Handling Institute, University of Southern California,* 1952.

Disco, M. L., "Three Level Layout Boosts Assembly Capacity 65%," *Factory Management and Maintenance,* Vol. 106, May 1948, pp. 116–17.

Fanning, C. L., "Inexpensive Pictorial Plant Layout," *Tool Engineer,* Vol. 33, July 1954, p. 56.

Farr, Donald E., "Charts That Show Problems and Solve Them Too," *Modern Materials Handling,* Jan. 1955, p. 72.

Fischer, W. H., "Parking Lot Problems," *Plant Engineering,* Vol. 4, No. 1, Jan. 1950, pp. 34–35.

Footlik, I. M., "Making Building Efficient," *Modern Materials Handling,* Vol. 11, No. 3, March 1956, pp. 107–09.

Gaudreau, A. T., "Adapting Old Buildings to Modern Handling," *Plant Engineering,* Vol. 11, No. 9, Sept. 1957, pp. 132–6, 273.

———, "Planned for Handling Materials," *National Safety News,* Vol. 64, July 1951, pp. 22–25.

———, "Reducing Costs With Modernized Plant Layout," *Plant Engineering,* Vol. 6, No. 1, Jan. 1952, pp. 79–82; No. 2, Feb. 1952, pp. 92–94, 16, 132.

———, "Techniques and Types of Industrial Plant Layout," *Plant Engineering,* Vol. 5, No. 1, Jan. 1951, pp. 51–53.

Glover, C. W., "Materials Handling and Factory Layout," *Mechanical Handling,* Vol. 41, No. 1, Jan. 1954, pp. 23–29; No. 2, Feb. 1954, pp. 60–63.

Gould, J., "Mass-Production Layout Techniques in a Job Shop," *Factory Management and Maintenance,* Feb. 1946, pp. 97–99.

Green, R. C., "Reduce Costs With Scale Models," *Chemical Engineering,* Vol. 64, June 1957, pp. 235–37.

Green, R. C. and Shukis, S. P., "Reduce Costs With Scale Models," *Chemical Engineering,* Vol. 64, No. 6, June 1957, pp. 235–37.

Haldeman, J. S., "New Method For Producing 3-D Plaster Models," *Machinery,* Vol. 54, Mar. 1948, pp. 144–49.

Harju, J. B., "Plant Layout—Foundation of Industrial Plant Planning," *Consulting Engineer,* Vol. 8, No. 4, Oct. 1956, pp. 54–59.

Harmon, H. M., "Flow-Line Planning in Factory Layout," *Emmott,* 1948.

———, "Initial Stages of Factory Planning," *Mechanical World,* Vol. 122, Oct. 1947, pp. 383–84, 417–18.

———, "Materials Handling in Multi-Story Buildings," *Mechanical Handling,* Vol. 34, Oct. 1947, pp. 519–22.

———, "Planning Multi-Story Factories," *Mechanical World,* Vol. 123, Jan. 23, 1948, pp. 85–87.

———, "Plant Layout for Materials Handling," *Mechanical Handling,* Vol. 34, March 1947, pp. 125–28.

Harrington, D. E., "Architect and Plant Layout," *Mechanical Handling,* Vol. 39, No. 1, Jan. 1952, pp. 8–11.

Huffman, J. R., "Evaluation of Quantitative Techniques in Plant Layout," *American Society of Mechanical Engineers Paper No. 53,* July 2, 1953.

Jackson, H. E., "New Look in Plant Layout," *Mill and Factory,* Vol. 50, Apr. 1952, pp. 130–31.

Kellogg, E. C., "Plant Layout; Three Dimensions Help," *Iron Age,* Vol. 171, March 19, 1953, pp. 75–76.

Kimball, G. K., "Mold Buildings to Your Needs," *American Machinist,* Vol. 93, Dec. 1, 1949, pp. 89–92.

Klein, M., and Milberg, S. H., "Application of Linear Programming to Materials Handling," *Modern Materials Handling,* Vol. 10, No. 2, Feb. 1955, pp. 80–84.

Levy, M. L., "Let the Travel Chart Simplify Your Material Movement Problems," *Mill & Factory,* Vol. 48, May 1951, pp. 100–01.

Macy, F. D., "How to Evaluate a Plant Layout," *Petroleum Refiner,* Vol. 36, July 1957, pp. 162–68.

Mallick, R. W., "Are Your Plant Layout and Material Handling Coordinated?", *Production Series, American Management Association,* No. 162, 1945.

——, "Planning Ceramics Plants for Profit," *Ceramics Industry,* March 1949.

——, "Planning for Safety," *Mechanical Engineering,* Vol. 66, Dec. 1944, pp. 774–78.

Mallick, R. W., and Sansonetti, J. H., "Templet or Model for Plant Layout," *American Machinist,* Aug. 1946, pp. 101–104.

Manning, P. W., "Foundation for Layout-Materials Handling," *Modern Materials Handling,* Vol. 5, No. 5, May 1950, pp. 16–18, 29.

Metropolitan Life Insurance Co., "Factory Planning and Layout" (Policy Holders Service Bureau), New York, 1947, 35 pp.

Montoro, J. C., "Use of Models for Layout and Planning," *Iron and Steel Engineer,* Vol. 31, No. 9, Sept. 1954, pp. 154–60.

Muther, R., "How Plant Layout and Material Handling Should and Can Be Tied Together," *Advanced Management,* Vol. 18, Aug. 1953, pp. 28–30.

——, "How to Evaluate Alternative Layouts," *Factory Management and Maintenance,* Vol. 113, Feb. 1955, pp. 126–29.

——, "Managing the Plant Layout Function," *Advanced Management,* Vol. 20, April 1955, pp. 20–23.

Noy, P. C., "Make Right Plant Layout—Mathematically," *American Machinist,* Vol. 101, No. 6, Mar. 25, 1957, pp. 121–25.

Parks, C. H., "Disappearing Boards Show Plant Layout In Sections," *Factory Management and Maintenance,* Vol. 105, No. 81, Dec. 1947.

Parrett, R. E., "Preparation of Layouts Aided by Photostating," *Factory Management and Maintenance,* Vol. 106, Nov. 1948, pp. 70–71.

Paton, B. L., "Models as Design Tool," *Mechanical Engineering,* Vol. 78, No. 11, Nov. 1956, pp. 1019–23; *Petroleum Refiner,* Vol. 35, No. 11, Nov. 1956, pp. 161–64.

——, "Do Models Pay Out?", *Mechanical Engineering,* Vol. 78, Nov. 1956, pp. 1019–23.

Pioch, W. F., "Plant Model Insures Success in Layout Changes," *Factory Management and Maintenance,* Vol. 105, July 1947, pp. 130–32.

Richmond, M., "Standardized Procedure for Flow Planning," *Flow,* Vol. 11, No. 6, March 1956, pp. 64–67.

Robinson, T. B., "How Good is Your Layout Planning," *American Machinist,* Vol. 93, Aug. 25, 1959, pp. 79–81.

Roch, W. D., "Layout, Good to Better to Best," *Factory Management and Maintenance,* Vol. 113, Sept. 1955, pp. 130–31.

Rogers, S. A., "14 Cost Cutting Extras with Shop Layout Blueprints," *Factory Management and Maintenance,* Vol. 111, Oct. 1953, p. 145.

Roos, H. W., "Revised Layout Provides for Future Expansion," *Textile World,* Vol. 100, Apr. 1950, pp. 103–06.

Rowan, M. J., "How Materials Handling Affects Plant Layout," *American Machinist,* Vol. 92, Dec. 30, 1948, pp. 83–98.

——, "Right Layout and Good Handling Cut Overhead Ten Per Cent," *American Machinist,* Vol. 94, May 29, 1950, pp. 65–69.

Rowley, G. S., "Sectional Layout Board Permits Quick Changes," *Factory Management and Maintenance,* Vol. 101, Oct. 1943, p. 89.

Rylander, A. E., "Elements of Plant Layout," *Tool Engineer,* Vol. 27, No. 5, Nov. 1951, pp. 59–66.

——, "Introduction to Plant Layout," *Tool Engineer,* Vol. 19, Jan. 1948, pp. 17–24; Vol. 20, Feb. 1948, pp. 31–36; Vol. 21, Mar. 1948, pp. 41–46.

——, "Plant Layout," *Tool Engineer,* Vol. 12, June 1943, pp. 83–86; July 1943, pp. 85–89; Aug. 1943, pp. 90–94.

——, "Recent Trends in Plant Layout," *Western Machinery and Steel World,* Vol. 47, No. 1, Jan. 1956, pp. 79–84.

Schleusener, E., and Young, L., "Trimming Costs with Smart Layout," *Factory Management and Maintenance*, Vol. 114, Sept. 1956, pp. 102–105.

Seidel, J. J., "Scale Models Help Plan Equipment Replacement," *Chemical Engineering*, Vol. 64, Nov. 1957, p. 286.

Sideris, G., "Streamlining Plant Layout," *Electronics*, Vol. 31, Oct. 24, 1958, pp. 78–79.

Smith, W. P., "How Good Is This Layout," *Modern Materials Handling*, Vol. 9, No. 5, May, 1954, pp. 121–24.

———, "Travel Charting," *Journal of Industrial Engineering*, Jan. 1955, p. 13.

———, "Work Sampling—Fast Way to Get Facts on Handling," *Factory Management and Maintenance*, Vol. 111, May 1953, p. 70.

Speir, W. B., "Do-It-Yourself Models for Layout Studies," *Chemical Engineering*, Vol. 64, June 1957, p. 330.

Thuering, G. L., "How to Get Faster, Better, Less Expensive Plant Layout Drawings Without Drafting," *Factory Management and Maintenance*, Vol. 110, Oct. 1952, pp. 88–89.

Toles, G. E., "Circular Building Straightens Out Flow," *Mill and Factory*, Vol. 60, No. 5, May 1957, p. 121.

Tucker, C. T., "Three Ways to Lay Out a Personnel Dept.," *Factory Management and Maintenance*, Vol. 101, Sept. 1943, pp. 153–55.

Tucker, T. S., "How Photo-Drawings Work with Models," *Petroleum Processing*, Vol. 12, Apr. 1957, pp. 94–96.

Wallis, C. G., "Six Steps to Lower Layout Costs," *American Machinist*, Vol. 95, Apr. 2, 1951, pp. 96–97.

Weart, S. A., "Mechanical Methods for Determining Plant Layout," *Advanced Management*, Vol. 17, Apr. 1952, pp. 18–20.

———, "Take These Steps to Lay Out a Sub-Assembly," *Mill and Factory*, Vol. 55, Nov. 1954, pp. 110–12.

Wheeler, W. S., "Sectional Scale Model, With Complete Color Code," *Factory Management and Maintenance*, Vol. 106, Oct. 1948, pp. 104–05.

Woodward, R., "Process Plant Layout and Design," *Chemical and Metallurgical Engineering*, Vol. 48, May 1941, pp. 90–94.

Young, H. H., "Work Sampling," *Modern Materials Handling*, Oct. 1954, p. 118.

NO AUTHOR LISTED

"Designed for Point of Use Storage," *Factory Management and Maintenance*, Vol. 110, Apr. 1952, pp. B114–15.

"Disappearing Boards Show Plant Layout in Sections," *Factory Management and Maintenance*, Dec. 1947, p. 81.

"Elements of Plant Layout With an Outline of Procedure," *Tool Engineer*, Nov. 1951, p. 59.

"How to Use Templates for Plant Layouts," *Power*, Vol. 98, Apr. 1954, p. 146.

"Layout to Blueprint, No Draftsmen," *Factory Management and Maintenance*, Vol. 109, June 1951, pp. 88–89.

"Newest Concept in Plant Layout," *Factory Management and Maintenance*, Vol. 114, Oct. 1956, pp. 100–101.

"Photographs of Models in Place of Drawings," *Engineering News Record*, Vol. 154, No. 12, Mar. 24, 1955, pp. 47–48.

"Planning the Safe Plant," *National Safety News*, No. 69, Mar. 1954, pp. 9–10.

"Plant Design and Layout," *National Safety News*, Vol. 63, Mar. 1951, pp. 11–12.

"Plant Design and Layout," *National Safety News*, Vol. 67, Mar. 1953, p. 9.

"Plant Layout, Austin Company's Experience," *Architectural Forum*, Vol. 82, Feb. 1945, pp. 113–15.

"Plant Layout Efficiency," *Modern Materials Handling*, Vol. 8, No. 1, Jan. 1953, pp. 65–67.

"Plant Layout Made Easy Saves Dollars," *Factory Management and Maintenance,* Vol. 113, Feb. 1955, p. 103.

"Print Size Model, No Dustcatcher," *Factory Management and Maintenance,* Vol. 113, July 1955, p. 147.

"Reception Room Layout as It Should Be," *Plant Engineering,* Vol. 3, Nov. 1949, pp. 28–29.

"Scale Models By-pass Blue Prints," *Chemical Engineering,* Vol. 64, Nov. 1957, p. 158.

"Scale Models—Toys or Useful Planning Aids," *Flow,* Vol. 9, No. 6, Nov. 1954, pp. 68–71, 149–53.

"String Diagrams," *Modern Materials Handling,* Aug. 1953, p. 67.

"They Call It 'Peripheral'," *Factory Management and Maintenance,* Oct. 1956, pp. 114–15.

"Three Dimension Blueprint Saves Money," *Oil and Gas Journal,* Vol. 54, Aug. 20, 1956, p. 121.

"Use That Third Dimension," *Mill and Factory,* Vol. 58, Mar. 1956, p. 123.

"What's Lowest-Cost, One-Story, Small Building?", *Factory Management and Maintenance,* Vol. 112, No. 4, Apr. 1954, pp. 98–101.

"Windowless Plant with Breathing Walls," *Engineering News Record,* Vol. 144, No. 15, Apr. 13, 1950, pp. 32–33.

Appendix I

Conveyors

A. SUGGESTED GRADES FOR ROLLER CONVEYOR

The following grades are based upon ball bearing rollers of a size and diameter to suit the average conditions.

Grade in./ft.	Grade in %	Commodities	Remarks
.483	4	Wood cases	20# to 50#
.419	3½	Wood cases	50# to 150#
.300–.360	2½ to 3	Wood cases	150# to 250#
.839	7	Cartons	3# to 7#
.720	6	Cartons	7# to 15#
.601	5	Cartons	15# to 50#
.541–.601	4½ to 5	Crates	20# to 125#
.483	4	Barrels	Sugar type, filled
.181–.360	1½ to 3	Drums	150# and over
.483	4	Baskets	Wood runners
.181	1½	Tire molds	1500#
.839	7	Tires	Standard size
.601	5	Milk cans	Empty
.483	4	Milk cans	Full
.241–.483	2 to 4	Tote pans	Weight and condition
.483	4	Lumber	Standard boards
.483	4	Brick	Standard size
.360	3	Bobbin boxes	Filled
.419	3½	Bobbin boxes	Empty
.241	2	Rolls of paper	Concaved rolls
.181	1½	Heavy foundry molds	
.192	1.6	Sheet steel packs	20,000#
.276	2.3	Coils of steel	2 to 4 tons
.331–.360	2¾ to 3	Coils on curves	

Source: Mathews Conveyer Company, *Mathews Conveyer Handbook*, HB 58, p. 15.

B. ROLLER CONVEYOR CURVE WIDTH

4'-0" INSIDE RADIUS

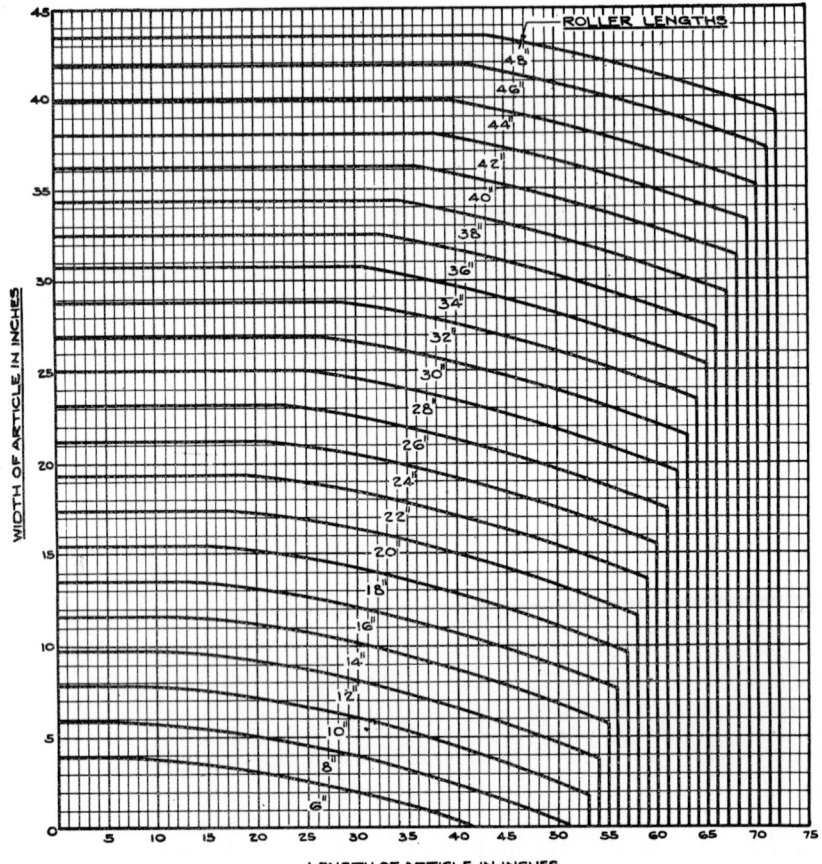

Chart for determining roller-conveyor width required to provide 3-inch clearance on standard curves of 4 ft. inside radius for various size articles. The above chart is based on guard rail clearance equal to roller length plus one inch. (By permission of the Mathews Conveyer Co.)

C. HORSEPOWER REQUIRED TO DRIVE EMPTY BELT CONVEYOR

Belt Speed, F.P.M.	25	50	Horizontal Length of Conveyor in Feet							
			100	200	300	400	500	600	800	1000

14" CONVEYORS

Belt Speed	25	50	100	200	300	400	500	600	800	1000
50	.12	.14	.17	.24	.31	.38	...	...	...	...
100	.24	.27	.34	.48	.62	.75	...	...	...	...
150	.36	.41	.51	.72	.92	1.13	...	...	...	...
200	.48	.55	.68	.96	1.23	1.51	...	...	...	...
250	.60	.69	.85	1.20	1.53	1.88	...	...	...	...
300	.72	.82	1.03	1.43	1.84	2.25	...	...	...	...

18" CONVEYORS

Belt Speed	25	50	100	200	300	400	500	600	800	1000
50	.15	.17	.22	.30	.39	.48	.56	.65	...	...
100	.30	.35	.43	.60	.78	.95	1.13	1.30	...	...
150	.45	.52	.65	.90	1.17	1.43	1.69	1.95	...	...
200	.61	.69	.87	1.21	1.56	1.90	2.25	2.59	...	...
250	.76	.86	1.09	1.51	1.95	2.38	2.81	3.24	...	...
300	.91	1.03	1.30	1.81	2.33	2.85	3.37	3.89	...	...
350	1.06	1.20	1.52	2.11	2.72	3.33	3.93	4.54	...	...
400	1.21	1.38	1.73	2.42	3.11	3.80	4.50	5.18	...	...

24" CONVEYORS

Belt Speed	25	50	100	200	300	400	500	600	800	1000
50	...	.23	.28	.40	.51	.63	.74	.85	1.08	1.30
100	...	.45	.57	.80	1.02	1.25	1.48	1.70	2.16	2.60
150	...	.68	.85	1.20	1.53	1.88	2.22	2.55	3.24	3.90
200	...	.91	1.14	1.59	2.04	2.50	2.96	3.41	4.32	5.20
250	...	1.14	1.42	1.99	2.55	3.13	3.70	4.26	5.40	6.50
300	...	1.37	1.70	2.39	3.07	3.75	4.43	5.11	6.48	7.80
350	...	1.60	1.98	2.79	3.58	4.38	5.17	5.96	7.56	9.10
400	...	1.82	2.27	3.18	4.09	5.01	5.91	6.82	8.64	10.4
450	...	2.05	2.55	3.58	4.60	5.64	6.56	7.67	9.72	11.7
500	...	2.27	2.84	3.98	5.11	6.26	7.39	8.52	10.8	13.0

36" CONVEYORS

Belt Speed	25	50	100	200	300	400	500	600	800	1000
50	...	.40	.50	.70	.90	1.10	1.30	1.50	1.90	2.30
100	...	.80	1.00	1.40	1.80	2.20	2.60	3.00	3.80	4.60
150	...	1.20	1.50	2.10	2.70	3.30	3.90	4.50	5.70	6.90
200	...	1.60	2.00	2.80	3.60	4.40	5.20	6.00	7.60	9.20
250	...	2.00	2.50	3.50	4.50	5.50	6.50	7.50	9.50	11.5
300	...	2.40	3.00	4.20	5.40	6.60	7.80	9.00	11.4	13.8
350	...	2.80	3.50	4.90	6.30	7.70	9.10	10.5	13.3	16.1
400	...	3.20	4.00	5.60	7.20	8.80	10.4	12.0	15.2	18.4
450	...	3.60	4.50	6.30	8.10	9.90	11.7	13.5	17.1	20.7
500	...	4.00	5.00	7.00	9.00	11.00	13.0	15.0	19.0	23.0
550	...	4.40	5.50	7.70	9.90	12.1	14.3	16.5	20.9	25.3
600	...	4.80	6.00	8.40	10.8	13.2	15.6	18.0	22.8	27.6

Source: Material Handling Engineering, *Directory & Handbook,* 1960–61.

D. HORSEPOWER REQUIRED TO CONVEY ANY MATERIAL HORIZONTALLY

Tons Per Hour	CENTER TO CENTER LENGTH IN FEET									
	50	100	150	200	250	300	500	700	1000	1400
50	.3	.4	.5	.5	.6	.7	1.0	1.3	1.7	2.3
100	.6	.8	.9	1.1	1.2	1.4	2.0	2.6	3.5	4.7
150	.9	1.1	1.4	1.6	1.8	2.0	3.0	3.9	5.2	7.0
200	1.2	1.5	1.8	2.1	2.4	2.7	3.9	5.2	7.0	9.4
250	1.5	1.9	2.3	2.7	3.0	3.4	4.9	6.4	8.7	11.7
300	1.8	2.3	2.7	3.2	3.6	4.1	5.9	7.7	10.5	14.1
350	2.1	2.7	3.2	3.7	4.2	4.8	6.9	9.0	12.2	16.4
400	2.4	3.0	3.6	4.2	4.8	5.5	7.9	10.3	13.9	18.8
450	2.7	3.4	4.1	4.8	5.5	6.1	8.9	11.6	15.7	21
500	3.0	3.8	4.5	5.3	6.1	6.8	9.8	12.9	17.4	23
550	3.3	4.2	5.0	5.8	6.7	7.5	10.8	14.2	19.2	26
600	3.6	4.5	5.5	6.4	7.3	8.2	11.8	15.5	21	28
650	3.9	4.9	5.9	6.9	7.9	8.9	12.8	16.7	23	31
700	4.2	5.3	6.4	7.4	8.5	9.5	13.8	18.0	24	33
800	4.8	6.1	7.3	8.5	9.7	10.9	15.8	21	28	38
900	5.5	6.8	8.2	9.5	10.9	12.3	17.7	23	31	42
1000	6.1	7.6	9.1	10.6	12.1	13.6	19.7	26	35	47
1100	6.7	8.3	10.0	11.7	13.3	15.0	22	28	38	52

Source: Material Handling Engineering, *Directory & Handbook,* 1960–61.

E. HORSEPOWER REQUIRED TO ELEVATE LOADS THROUGH LIFT IN FEET

Tons per Hour	LOAD ELEVATION IN FEET											
	5	10	15	20	25	30	40	60	80	100	150	200
25	.14	.26	.39	.51	.64	.76	1.02	1.52	2.03	2.53	3.79	5.05
50	.26	.51	.76	1.01	1.27	1.52	2.02	3.03	4.04	5.05	7.58	10.1
100	.51	1.01	1.52	2.02	2.53	3.03	4.04	6.06	8.08	10.1	15.2	20.2
150	.76	1.52	2.28	3.03	3.79	4.55	6.06	9.09	12.1	15.2	22.7	30.3
200	1.01	2.02	3.03	4.04	5.05	6.06	8.08	12.1	16.2	20.2	30.3	40.4
250	1.27	2.53	3.79	5.05	6.32	7.58	10.1	15.2	20.2	25.3	37.9	50.5
300	1.52	3.03	4.55	6.06	7.58	9.09	12.1	18.2	24.2	30.3	45.5	60.6
400	2.02	4.04	6.06	8.08	10.1	12.1	16.2	24.2	32.3	40.4	60.6	80.8
500	2.53	5.05	7.58	10.1	12.6	15.2	20.2	30.3	40.4	50.5	75.8	101.
600	3.03	6.06	9.09	12.1	15.2	18.2	24.2	36.4	48.5	60.6	90.9	121.
700	3.53	7.07	10.6	14.1	17.7	21.2	28.3	42.4	56.6	70.7	106.	141.
800	4.04	8.08	12.1	16.2	20.2	24.2	32.3	48.5	64.6	80.8	121.	162.
900	4.55	9.09	13.6	18.2	22.7	27.3	36.4	54.5	72.7	90.9	136.	182.
1000	5.05	10.1	15.2	20.2	25.3	30.3	40.4	60.6	80.8	101.	152.	202.

Source: Material Handling Engineering, *Directory & Handbook,* 1960–61.

F. SPEEDS AND CAPACITIES FOR VARIOUS MATERIALS AND BELTS

Belt Width	Weight per Cu. Ft. of Material	CAPACITY IN TONS PER HOUR — Belt Speed—F.P.M. 100	150	200	250	300	350	400	450	500	550	600	Cross-Section of Load Square Feet	Cubic Feet per Hour @ 100 F.P.M.	Cubic Yards per Hour @ 100 F.P.M.	*Bushels per Hour @ 100 F.P.M.
14	30	9	14	19	24	28							.108	648	24	315
	50	16	24	32	40	47										
	75	24	35	47	60	71										
	100	32	47	63	79	95										
	125	40	60	80	100	120										
	150	47	71	95	120	140										
18	30	16	24	32	40	48	56	64					.180	1070	40	520
	50	27	40	53	67	80	94	105								
	75	40	60	80	100	120	140	160								
	100	53	80	110	135	160	190	215								
	125	67	100	135	170	200	235	270								
	150	80	120	160	200	240	280	320								
24	30	29	44	59	73	88	105	120	130	145			.330	2000	73	960
	50	49	73	98	120	145	170	195	220	245						
	75	73	110	145	185	220	255	295	330	365						
	100	98	145	195	245	295	345	390	440	490						
	125	120	185	245	310	370	430	490	550	610						
	150	145	220	295	365	440	515	590	660	735						
36	30	70	105	140	175	210	245	280	315	350	385	420	.780	4700	173	2260
	50	115	175	235	290	350	410	465	525	585	640	700				
	75	175	260	350	435	525	610	700	790	875	960	1050				
	100	235	350	465	585	700	815	935	1050	1160	1280	1400				
	125	290	435	585	730	870	1020	1170	1310	1460	1600	1750				
	150	350	525	700	875	1050	1225	1400	1570	1750	1920	2100				
48	30	130	195	265	330	395	460	525	590	655	720	790	1.460	8750	325	4200
	50	220	330	440	545	655	765	875	985	1090	1200	1310				
	75	330	490	655	820	985	1150	1310	1480	1640	1810	1970				
	100	440	655	875	1095	1310	1530	1750	1970	2190	2410	2630				
	125	550	820	1090	1370	1640	1920	2190	2460	2740	3010	3280				
	150	655	985	1310	1640	1970	2300	2630	2950	3280						

Source: Material Handling Engineering, *Directory & Handbook*, 1960-61.

G. BELT CONVEYOR HORSEPOWER CALCULATIONS *

1. LIVE LOAD

Total load of articles being conveyed for entire length of conveyer.

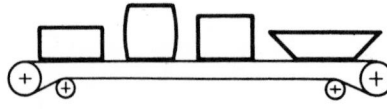

2. WEIGHT OF BELT ...

Both top and bottom.

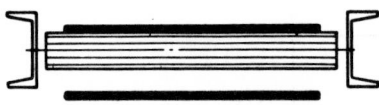

APPROX. WEIGHT OF ROLLERS

	6"	12"	18"	24"	30"	36"	42"	48"
1⅞"-#16GA.	1.4	2.2	3.0	3.9	4.8	5.6	6.4	7.4
1.9"-#12GA.	2.4	3.9	5.3	6.7	8.2	9.6	11.0	12.4
2⅛"-#16GA.	1.2	1.9	2.6	3.3	4.0	—	—	—
2¼"-#16GA.	2.0	3.2	4.3	5.4	6.5	7.6	8.8	9.9
2½"-#14GA.	2.4	3.8	5.2	6.6	8.0	9.4	10.8	12.3
2½"-#11GA.	4.4	6.0	7.6	9.1	10.6	12.1	13.7	15.2
2½"-#10GA.	4.7	6.4	8.1	9.8	11.5	13.2	14.9	16.6
2⁹⁄₁₆"-#7GA.	5.0	8.0	11.0	14.0	17.0	20.0	23.0	26.0

4. INCLINES

Total *Live Load* on the incline portion only, multiplied by the sine of the angle of incline gives the added pull necessary.

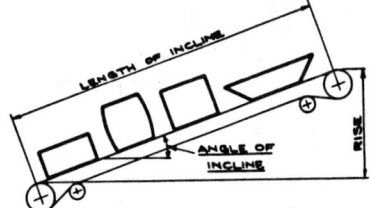

Maximum recommended incline receiving from gravity, 10° with plain cotton or stitched canvas belts, 12° with rubber filled, or crepe top belts. With the use of three-pulley devices or other means of starting the article up the incline the maximum incline for satisfactory conveying without undue slippage is 12° for plain cotton or stitched canvas, 15° for rubber filled belts, and 25° for crepe top

Tread rollers should be spaced closer on the steeper inclines, especially with heavier articles. At least two rollers under the article being conveyed is good practice.

SINE OF VARIOUS ANGLES

ANGLE	SINE	ANGLE	SINE
5°	.09	20°	.34
10°	.17	22°	.37
12°	.21	24°	.41
14°	.24	26°	.44
16°	.28	28°	.47
18°	.31	30°	.50

APPROX. WEIGHT OF BELTS PER FOOT

BELT WIDTH	3-PLY 28-OZ.	4-PLY 28-OZ.	4-PLY 32-OZ.	ADD FOR ⅛6 COVER
6"	.5	.6	.8	.2
12"	1.0	1.2	1.6	.4
18"	1.4	1.8	2.4	.7
24"	1.9	2.4	3.2	.8
30"	2.4	3.0	4.0	.9
36"	2.9	3.7	4.8	1.1
42"	—	—	5.6	1.3
48"	—	—	6.4	1.5

CREPE TOP IS CONSIDERED ⅛6

3. WEIGHT OF ROLLERS ...

Including return idlers.

The same forces act on a decline belt; however, the motor in this case must resist the forces which require practically the same horsepower as the incline unit.

* By permission of the Mathews Conveyer Co.

Belt Conveyor Horsepower Calculations (continued)

5. DEFLECTORS . . .

Add 35% of the weight of the heaviest article.

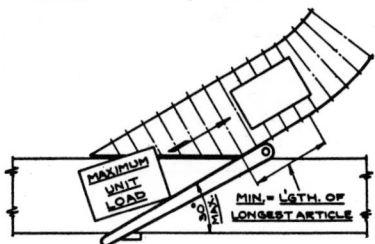

6. FOR THREE-PULLEY OR TWO-PULLEY DEVICES . . .

Add 5% of the load *preceding* the device.

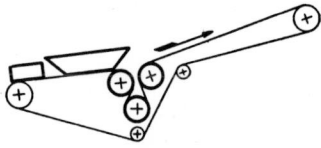

7. DRIVES

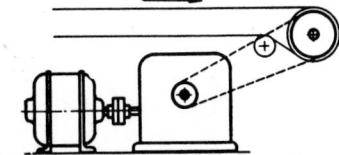

For single worm gear efficiency use the formula 100 minus ½ the ratio.

Example: Using ratio 30 to 1

$$100 \text{ minus } \frac{30}{2} = 85$$

For single worm gears with helix attachment, use the above formula for the worm ratio and deduct 5% more for the helix.

For double worm gears, use the single worm formula for both reductions.

Example: Using primary ratio of 20 to 1, and secondary ratio of 40 to 1, making a total of 800 to 1.

$$100 \text{ minus } \frac{20}{2} \text{ minus } \frac{40}{2} = 70$$

For parallel type planetary or spiral gear motors, use 90 to 95 per cent.

For open spur gear on chain reductions, use 90 to 95 per cent for each reduction.

8. FRICTION

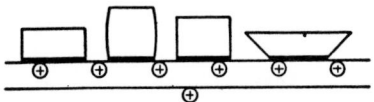

Ordinary belts on ball bearing rollers, 5%.
Ordinary belts on bronze or wood bearing rollers, 10%.

Wood slider bed—27½%.
Metal slider bed—30%.

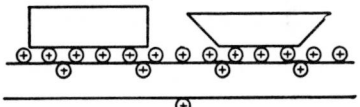

For live roller conveyers, with ball bearings—7½%.
For live roller conveyers, with bronze or wood bearings—15%.

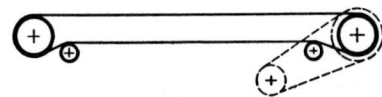

For head and tail pulleys, floating and tandem drives, add about 15 to 25 per cent for losses.

9. HORSE POWER CALCULATIONS

The final Horsepower may now be tabulated as follows, using as an example a belt conveyer under these conditions *(1) Total live load 1000 lbs. (2) Weight of belt, 200 lbs (3) Weight of rollers, 600 lbs. (4) Live load on incline, 200 lbs. Degree of incline, 12 (5) One deflector and maximum unit load 80 lbs. (6) One three-pulley device and total load preceding device, 200 lbs. (7) Worm gear type reducer ratio 50:1.

Speed—60 F. P. M.

Belt Conveyor Horsepower Calculations (continued)

Example Using 5% for ordinary belts.

		Lbs.
*1. Live Load	1000 lbs. x 5%	50
2. Belt	200 lbs. x 5%	10
3. Rollers	600 lbs. x 5%	30
4. Load on incline	200 lbs. x .21	42
5. Deflector	80 lbs. x 35%	28
6. 3-pulley	200 lbs. x 5%	10
	Total	170

Add for tail pulleys and for drive about 15% of above.

15% of 170 lbs. — 25.5 lbs. (use) 30
                                                ———
                                                200

Worm gear reducer drive efficiency at 50 to 1 ratio = 75%

$\dfrac{200 \text{ lbs.}}{75\%} = 267$ lbs. pull required at *input* shaft of reducer.

For motor Horsepower, use the formula

$$\frac{\text{Pull x Speed in F. P. M.}}{33,000}$$

or in this case—

$$\frac{267 \times 60}{33,000} = .485 \text{ H. P.}$$

Use the next largest size motor, or in this example ½ H.P. Add to above for any contingencies such as peak load—moisture, sand, etc.

Numbers 1 to 8 refer to preceding paragraphs.

10. BELT TENSION . . .

Commonly known as T1 on the tight side and T2 on the slack side of standard belts is necessary to maintain the required friction between belt and pulley in order to drive properly.

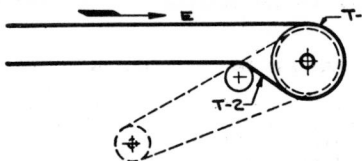

E = Effective Pull
T1 = Tight Side Tension
T2 = Slack Side Tension

TABLE OF FACTORS
SINGLE PULLEY

DEGREE	BARE		LAGGED	
WRAP	T-1	T-2	T-1	T-2
180°	1.85	.85	1.50	.50
200°	1.72	.72	1.42	.42
210°	1.67	.67	1.38	.38
215°	1.64	.64	1.36	.36
220°	1.62	.62	1.35	.35
240°	1.54	.54	1.30	.30

(E in the example cited would be 200 lbs. or the net pull required to move the belt. T1 and T2 affect only the strength of the belt and shafting and do not affect the horsepower required.

T1, for 210° wrap plain pulley in the example given would be 200 x 1.67 or 334 lbs.

T2 would be 200 x .67 or 134 lbs.

Lagged pulley 200 x 1.38 or 276 lbs. for T1 and 200 x 38 or 76 lbs. for T2.

11. TANDEM DRIVES . . .

Have a similar condition, but there are four factors, namely E, T1, T2 and T3.

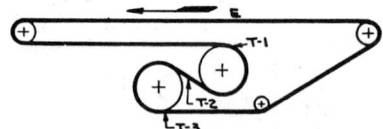

These factors depend on the degree of wrap and are commonly listed as follows:

TABLE OF FACTORS
TANDEM DRIVES

DEGREE	BARE PULLEYS		
WRAP	T-1	T-2	T-3
360°	1.26	.505	.201
380°	1.23	.485	.198
400°	1.21	.485	.196
420°	1.19	.475	.191
450°	1.16	.465	.187
500°	1.13	.452	.181

Belt Conveyor Horsepower Calculations (continued)

As an example for a tandem drive with E as 200 lbs. and a 420° total wrap, we would have:

T1 as 200 x 1.19 or 238 lbs.

T2 as 200 x .475 or 95 lbs.

T3 as 200 x .191 or 38.2 lbs.

Thus it is evident that there is considerably less tension created in a tandem drive than the standard single pulley drive for the same relative effective pull required.

Tandem drives, especially those having an extra rubber or crepe covering show some minor tendency to creep. This is particularly noticeable in crepe top belts where the crepe top becomes the surface against the second pulley. The pitch radius is figured to the center of the *fabric* of the belt, thus accounting for some of the creep.

We seldom consider lagging these pulleys due to the unequal wear of the lagging and the consequent return to a condition similar to the crepe top as mentioned.

12. BENDING MOMENTS . . .

Should be figured from the resultant forces due to T1 and T2 acting on all the pulleys.

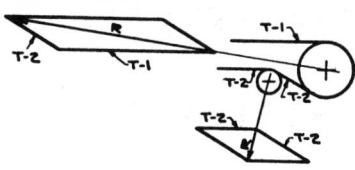

This resultant (R) may be laid out as a parallelogram and if made to scale with the forces in the proper direction will be sufficiently accurate for estimating.

Thus, in the example above, for a plain head pulley, T1 is 334 lbs. and T2 is 134 lbs., giving a resultant force acting on the shaft of 452 lbs.

For the snub pulley the resultant would be 70 lbs.

13. CHAIN PULL AND TORQUE

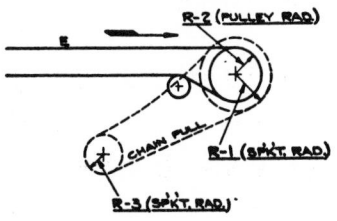

In figuring torque for the head shaft and torque and over-hung load on the reducer, use the following formulae.

Torque on head shaft $= E \times R2$

Chain pull on reducer $= \dfrac{E \times R2}{R1}$

Torque on Reducer $= \dfrac{E \times R2 \times R3}{R1}$

Examples using 200 lbs. for E, 4" for R2, 5" for R1 and 2" for R3.

Torque on head shaft 200 x 4" = 800" lbs.

Chain pull on reducer $\dfrac{200 \times 4}{5} = 160$ lbs.

Torque on reducer $\dfrac{200 \times 4 \times 2}{5} = 320$" lbs.

14. SCREW TYPE TAKEUPS

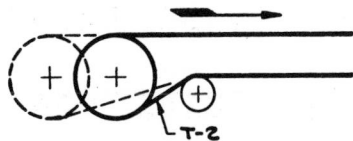

Normally the takeup adjustment is figured at 1% of the length of the conveyer. In other words, a 50'0" long conveyer should have an adjustment of .5 of a foot or 6".

Practically no adjustment is required on tandem drives, although we provide a few inches at each end for training the belt.

15. GRAVITY TAKEUPS

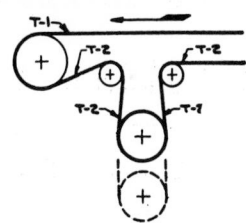

Belt conveyers over 200'0" long, or those subjected to wide changes in temperature, humidity, etc., should have automatic or gravity type takeups. The amount of weight would be two times T2 and in the example this would be 2 x 134 lbs. = 268 lbs.

16. BELT STRENGTHS

3 ply 28 oz. 22 lbs. per inch per ply.
3 ply 32 oz. 25 lbs. per inch per ply.
4 ply 28 oz. 27 lbs. per inch per ply.
4 ply 32 oz. 30 lbs. per inch per ply.

H. NET HORSEPOWER REQUIRED FOR BELT CONVEYORS *

Belt Speed in F.P.M.

Belt Pull in #	5	10	20	30	40	50	60	70	80	90	100	110	120
50	.008	.015	.030	.045	.060	.075	.090	.105	.120	.135	.150	.165	.182
75	.011	.023	.045	.068	.090	.113	.135	.158	.181	.203	.226	.248	.273
100	.015	.030	.060	.091	.121	.151	.181	.211	.241	.271	.301	.332	.364
125	.019	.038	.076	.113	.151	.188	.226	.264	.302	.339	.377	.415	.454
150	.023	.045	.091	.136	.181	.226	.271	.317	.362	.408	.453	.498	.545
175	.027	.053	.106	.157	.211	.264	.312	.370	.423	.476	.529	.582	.636
200	.030	.061	.121	.181	.242	.302	.362	.423	.484	.544	.605	.665	.727
225	.034	.068	.136	.204	.272	.340	.408	.476	.544	.612	.680	.748	.818
250	.037	.075	.151	.227	.302	.378	.454	.529	.605	.680	.756	.831	.909
275	.041	.083	.167	.250	.333	.416	.499	.582	.665	.749	.832	.915	1.00
300	.045	.091	.182	.272	.363	.454	.545	.635	.726	.817	.907	.998	1.09
325	.049	.099	.197	.295	.393	.492	.590	.688	.787	.885	.983	1.08	1.18
350	.053	.106	.212	.318	.424	.529	.635	.741	.847	.953	1.06	1.16	1.27
375	.057	.114	.227	.340	.454	.567	.680	.794	.910	1.02	1.13	1.25	1.36
400	.061	.121	.242	.363	.484	.605	.726	.847	.968	1.09	1.21	1.33	1.45
425	.064	.129	.256	.386	.514	.643	.772	.900	1.03	1.16	1.29	1.41	1.54
450	.068	.136	.273	.409	.545	.681	.817	.953	1.09	1.23	1.36	1.50	1.64
475	.072	.144	.288	.431	.575	.719	.863	1.01	1.15	1.29	1.44	1.58	1.73
500	.076	.152	.303	.454	.605	.757	.908	1.06	1.21	1.36	1.51	1.66	1.82
525	.079	.159	.318	.477	.636	.794	.954	1.11	1.27	1.43	1.59	1.75	1.91
550	.083	.167	.333	.500	.666	.832	.999	1.17	1.33	1.50	1.67	1.83	2.00
575	.088	.174	.348	.522	.696	.870	1.044	1.22	1.39	1.57	1.74	1.91	2.09
600	.091	.182	.364	.545	.727	.908	1.09	1.27	1.45	1.63	1.82	2.00	2.18

* By permission of the Mathews Conveyer Co.

I. TROLLEY CONVEYOR HORSEPOWER CALCULATIONS *

1. CHAIN PULL—Horizontal Straight

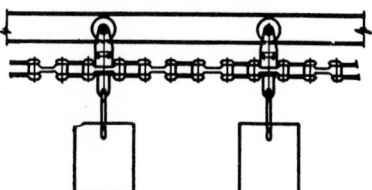

Weight of chain, trolley wheels, brackets, attachments and load multiplied by 2½% coefficient of friction, for Ball Bearings, 5% for Friction Bearings.

2. CHAIN PULL—Horizontal Bend

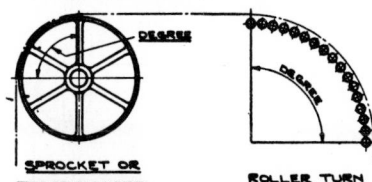

SPROCKET OR TRACTION WHEEL

DEGREE	FACTOR
22°-30'	1.5 %
30°	1.8 %
45°	2.0 %
60°	3.0 %
90°	4.0 %
180°	6.0 %

ROLLER TURN

DEGREE	FACTOR
22°-30'	2.0 %
30°	2.5 %
45°	3.0 %
60°	4.0 %
90°	6.0 %
180°	8.0 %

Multiply the chain pull at the end of the bend by the factors given.

3. CHAIN PULL—Vertical Bends

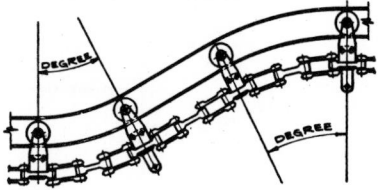

The increased friction necessary to negotiate a vertical bend must be added to the chain pull at the end of the bend. Use the following percentages:

DEGREE	PERCENT	DEGREE	PERCENT
15°	1¼%	45°	4%
22°-30'	2%	60°	5%
30°	2½%	90°	8%

4. LOAD DUE TO INCLINES

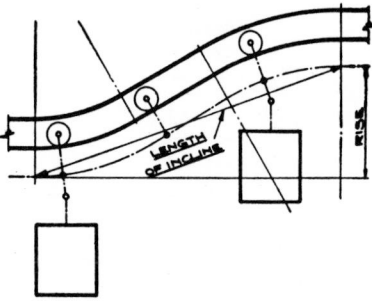

Multiply the number of loads on the incline by the rise and divide this by the inclined length. This gives direct chain pull. Then, add 5% of the accumulated total for friction.

The direct pull may be subtracted in the case of declines, or added in the case of inclines. The advantage in chain pull due to declines should be studied carefully to avoid subtracting from your calculations when the declined portion may be empty. The 5% friction must be added in either case.

5. DRIVES

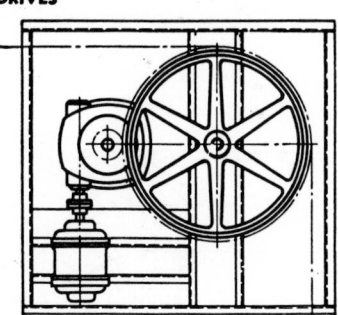

Add 10% of the total chain pull at this point for friction.

* By permission of the Mathews Conveyer Co.

Trolley Conveyor Horsepower Calculations (continued)

6. EXAMPLE

Weight of 4'-0'' of chain—4 x 3.1# · · · · · · · · · · · · · · · · 12.4#
Weight of 2 pairs wheels—4 x 2¼# · · · · · · · · · · · · · · · · 9.0#
Weight of 2 pairs T-B-1M brackets, 4 x 1# · · · · · · · · · · · · · 4.0#
Weight of 1—TA-1M attachment · · · · · · · · · · · · · · · · · · 1.5#
Weight of 1—TAD 4M attachment · · · · · · · · · · · · · · · · · · .8#
                                                                    27.7#
Live Load · 100.0#
                                                                   127.7#

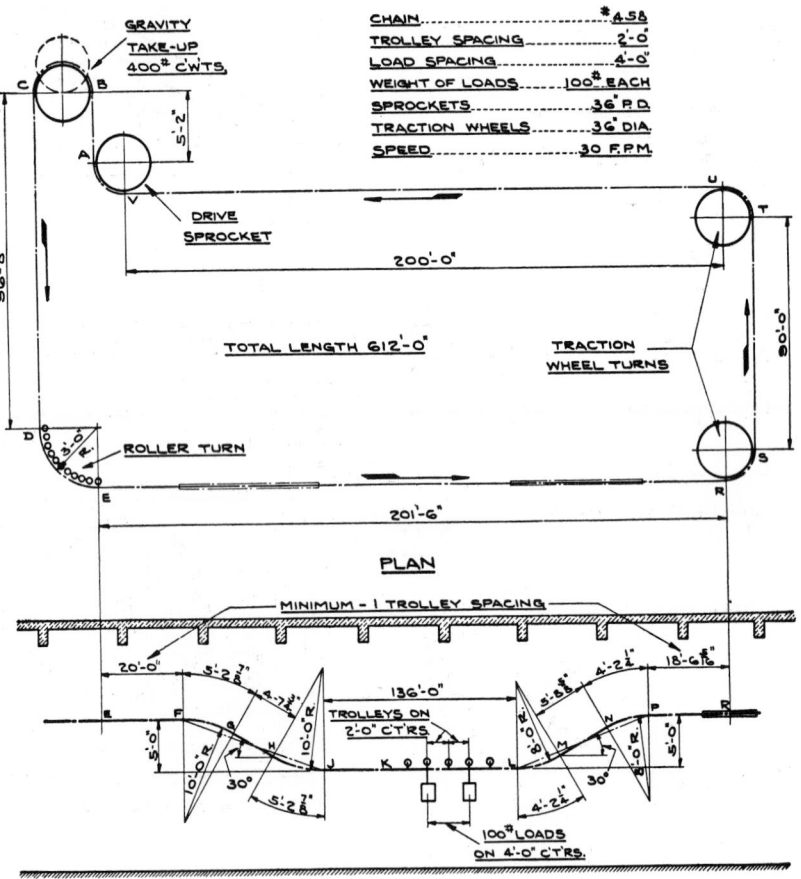

GRAVITY
TAKE-UP
400# CWTS.

CHAIN......................#4.58
TROLLEY SPACING...........2'-0"
LOAD SPACING..............4'-0"
WEIGHT OF LOADS.......100# EACH
SPROCKETS.................36" P.D.
TRACTION WHEELS.........36" DIA.
SPEED.....................30 F.P.M.

DRIVE
SPROCKET

200'-0"

TOTAL LENGTH 612'-0"

TRACTION
WHEEL TURNS

ROLLER TURN

36'-8"

30'-0"

201'-6"

PLAN

MINIMUM - 1 TROLLEY SPACING

20'-0"   5'-2⅝"   136'-0"   5'-8"   4'-2¼"   18'-6⅞"

TROLLEYS ON
2'-0" CT'RS.

30°   5'-2⅝"   4'-2¼"   30°

100# LOADS
ON 4'-0" CT'RS.

ELEVATION

NO LOADS FROM J TO K - 36'-0"
LOADING AREA K TO L - 100'-0"

Trolley Conveyor Horsepower Calculations (continued)

Average Weight per foot empty - - - - - - -7#
Average Weight per foot loaded - - - - - - 33#

CALCULATIONS

Initial tension due to take-up weights (assumed) 200#

A-B	5'-2" x 33# x 2½%=4.37	204.37
B-C	4'-8" x 33# x 2½%=3.79	208.16
	180° wheel turn 6% x 208.16=12.48	220.64
C-D	96'-8" x 33 x 2½%=80	301
D-E	4'-8" x 33 x 2½%=4	305
	90° roller bend 6% x 305=18	323
E-F	20'-0" x 33 x 2½%=17	340
F-G	5'-3" x 33 x 2½%=5	345
	Friction at F-G 2½% x 345=9	354
G-H	4'-8" x 33 x 2½%=4	357
H-J	5'-3" x 33 x 2½%=5	362
	Friction at H-J 2½% x 362=9	371

Decline 15'-1½" of chain 4—100# loads
5'-0" rise—15'-0" incline

$$\frac{4 \times 100\# \times 5'\text{-}0''}{15'\text{-}0''}=133 \qquad 238$$

	Friction 133 x 5%=7	245
J-K	36'-0" x 7 x 2½=6	251
K-L	100'-0" x 33 x 2½%=83	334
L-M	4'-2" x 33 x 2½%=4	338
	Friction at L-M 2½% x 338=8	346
M-N	5'-8" x 33 x 2½%=5	351
N-P	4'-2" x 33 x 2½%=4	355
	Friction at N-P 2½% x 355=9	364

Incline
$$\frac{4 \times 100\# \times 5'\text{-}0''}{15'\text{-}0''}=133 \qquad 497$$

	Friction 133 x 5%=7	504
P-R	18'-6" x 33 x 2½%=15	519
R-S	2'-4" x 33 x 2½%=2	521
	90° wheel 4% x 521=21	542
S-T	90'-0" x 33 x 2½%=74	616
T-U	2'-4" x 33 x 2½%=2	618
	90° wheel 4% x 618=25	643
U-V	200 x 33 x 2½%=165	808
V-A	2'-4" x 33 x 2½%=2	810
	Drive 10% x 810=81	891#
	Use 1000# drive series	

Speed 30 FPM Motor 1750 RPM.
Reducer ratio 82 to 1 Eff. 59%.
Spur gear reduction Eff. 90%.

$$\text{H.P.} = \frac{891 \times 30}{33000 \times 59 \times 90}=1.53 \text{ Use 2 H.P}$$

J. RADII AND INDIVIDUAL TROLLEY LOADS AT VERTICAL CURVES FOR TROLLEY CONVEYORS

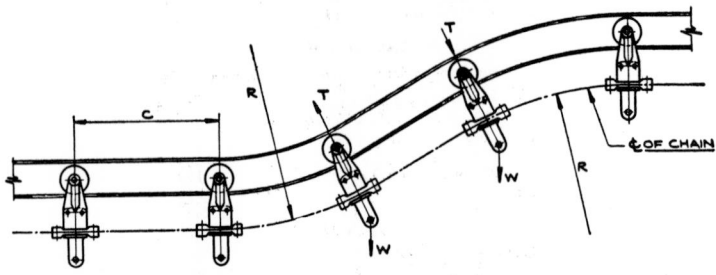

"T" = ADDED THRUST = CHAIN PULL MULTIPLIED BY FACTOR "K" BELOW.

"W" = HANGING LOAD, ADD OR SUBTRACT THRUST "T" TO HANGING LOAD "W" ON TROLLEY.

FOR MOMENTARY OVERLOADS DUE TO THRUST "T", TROLLEY WHEEL LOAD RATINGS MAY BE INCREASED 25 PER CENT.

FOR RADII NOT LISTED IN TABLE USE NEAREST RADII LISTED OR INTERPOLATE.

458-CHAIN		348-CHAIN		477-CHAIN	
C	R-MIN.	C	R-MIN.	C	R-MIN.
16"	6'-0"	12"	5'-0"	9.232"	13'-0"
24"	8'-0"	18"	6'-0"	13.848	14'-0"
32"	10'-0"	24"	7'-0"	18.464	15'-0"
40"	12'-0"	30"	8'-0"	23.080	16'-0"
48"	14'-0"	36"	9'-0"	27.696	17'-0"
				32.312	18'-0"

VALUES OF FACTOR "K"

VERTICAL RADIUS-R	8	12	16	18	20	24	27	28	32	36	40	44	45	48	52	54	56	60	63	64	68	72
1'-3"	.50																					
2'-0"	.34	.50																				
2'-6"	.28	.38	.50																			
2'-9"	.23	.35	.44	.50																		
3'-6"	.20	.28	.35	.39	.50																	
4'-0"	.17	.25	.32	.36	.43	.50																
4'-6"	.15	.23	.28	.33	.33	.45	.50															
5'-0"	.13	.20	.25	.30	.35	.40	.44	.48	.50													
6'-0"	.12	.18	.22	.25	.30	.34	.38	.41	.48	.50												
7'-0"	.10	.14	.19	.22	.27	.28	.32	.35	.40	.44	.48	.50										
8'-0"	.09	.11	.16	.19	.24	.25	.28	.30	.33	.37	.40	.43	.46	.48	.50							
9'-0"	.08	.10	.15	.17	.18	.23	.25	.25	.30	.34	.37	.38	.42	.43	.44	.48	.50					
10'-0"	.07	.09	.13	.15	.16	.21	.23	.23	.27	.30	.34	.35	.38	.40	.41	.44	.45	.48	.50			
11'-0"	.06	.08	.11	.13	.15	.19	.21	.22	.25	.27	.32	.33	.33	.36	.37	.41	.42	.44	.46	.48	.50	
12'-0"	.06	.08	.10	.12	.14	.17	.19	.19	.23	.24	.28	.29	.30	.33	.35	.35	.36	.40	.42	.44	.46	.48
13'-0"	.05	.07	.10	.11	.13	.15	.18	.19	.22	.23	.25	.27	.28	.30	.31	.32	.33	.38	.40	.42	.44	.46
14'-0"	.05	.07	.09	.11	.12	.14	.17	.18	.20	.22	.23	.25	.26	.28	.29	.30	.31	.36	.38	.40	.42	.44
15'-0"	.05	.06	.09	.10	.11	.13	.15	.16	.19	.21	.22	.24	.25	.26	.27	.28	.29	.34	.36	.38	.40	.42
16'-0"	.04	.05	.08	.09	.10	.12	.13	.14	.16	.19	.20	.22	.23	.24	.25	.26	.27	.32	.34	.36	.38	.40
17'-0"	.04	.05	.08	.09	.09	.12	.12	.13	.16	.18	.19	.20	.21	.23	.24	.25	.26	.30	.32	.34	.36	.38
18'-0"	.04	.05	.07	.08	.09	.11	.12	.12	.15	.17	.18	.20	.21	.22	.23	.24	.25	.28	.30	.32	.34	.36
19'-0"	.04	.05	.07	.08	.09	.11	.12	.12	.14	.16	.18	.19	.20	.21	.22	.23	.24	.26	.28	.30	.32	.34
20'-0"	.03	.05	.06	.07	.08	.10	.11	.12	.13	.15	.17	.18	.19	.20	.21	.22	.23	.24	.26	.28	.30	.32

TROLLEY SPACING IN INCHES

FOR ADDED CHAIN PULL AT EACH BEND ADD 5% FOR 60° BENDS, 3¾% FOR 45° BENDS, 2½% FOR 30° BENDS, ETC. THUS WITH INITIAL CHAIN PULL OF 1000# AND 2-30° BENDS ADD TO THE 1000#, 2 x 2½% = 5% OF 1000# = 50#

Appendix II

Trucks and Pallets

A. PROCEDURE FOR COMPARATIVE RATING FOR FORK LIFT TRUCKS *

Some manufacturers specify a number of pounds capacity with a particular length of load while others specify a number of pounds capacity at a given number of inches from the heel of the fork. Some give an inch-pound rating based on the distance of the load center from the heel of the fork, while others base their inch-pound rating on the distance from the center of the load to the center of the front axle.

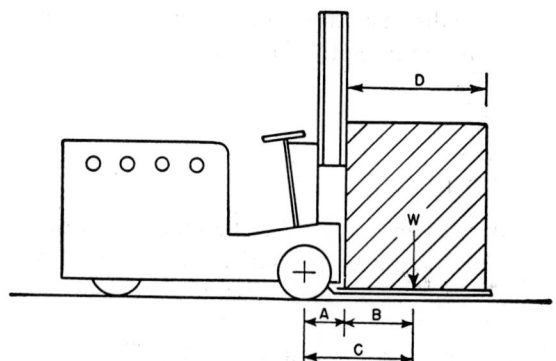

Here is one method of comparative rating:

With reference to the accompanying sketch, the symbols are interpreted as follows:

A = Distance from center of front axle to heel of fork measured in inches.

$B = \dfrac{D}{2}$ = Distance from heel of fork to center of load measured in inches.

$C = A + B$ = Distance from center of front axle to center of load measured in inches.

$D = 2 \times B$ = Length of Load.

W = Weight of load measured in pounds.

---

* Source: Material Handling Engineering, *Directory & Handbook,* 1960–61.

In order to calculate a load with a length other than that specified by the manufacturer, or to compare one truck with another of a different rating, it is necessary to obtain the "Inch-Pound Rating." The Inch-Pound Rating is W, the rated load; multiplied by C, the distance from the center of the front axle to the center of the load, i.e.

$$\text{Inch-Pound Rating} = W \times C$$

The inch-pound rating becomes a constant for that particular truck. Then, in order to figure (1) the maximum load length for any given load; or, (2) the maximum load for any given load length, the formula can be reversed to give this information, i.e.

$$(1) \quad C = \frac{\text{Inch-Pound Rating}}{W} \qquad\qquad (2) \quad W = \frac{\text{Inch-Pound Rating}}{C}$$

Example: A truck has a rating of 4,000# @ 30"—which means a 4,000# load which has its center 30" from the heel of the fork. The specifications show the distance from the center of the axle to the heel of the fork to be 15". By applying the formulas, the inch-pound rating may be arrived at:

$C = A + B = 15 + 30 = 45"$
Inch-Pound Rating $= W \times C = 4,000 \times 45 = 180,000$ inch-pounds

The rating of 180,000 inch-pounds then becomes a constant for the truck in question. Then, to determine how long a pallet or skid which will have a gross weight of 2,500# can be made, apply the formulas:

$$C = \frac{\text{Inch-Pound Rating}}{W} = \frac{180,000}{2,500} = 72"$$

$B = C - A = 72" - 15" = 57"$

$D = 2 \times B = 2 \times 57"$

$= 114"$ allowable load length

Or, as another example, it is desired to know the maximum safe load for a standard 84" rack, by applying the formulas:

$$B = \frac{D}{2} = \frac{84}{2} = 42" \qquad\qquad C = A + B = 15" + 42" = 57"$$

$$W = \frac{\text{Inch-Pound Rating}}{C} = \frac{180,000}{57"} = 3158\# \text{ gross weight allowed}$$

B. TYPICAL PALLET PATTERNS

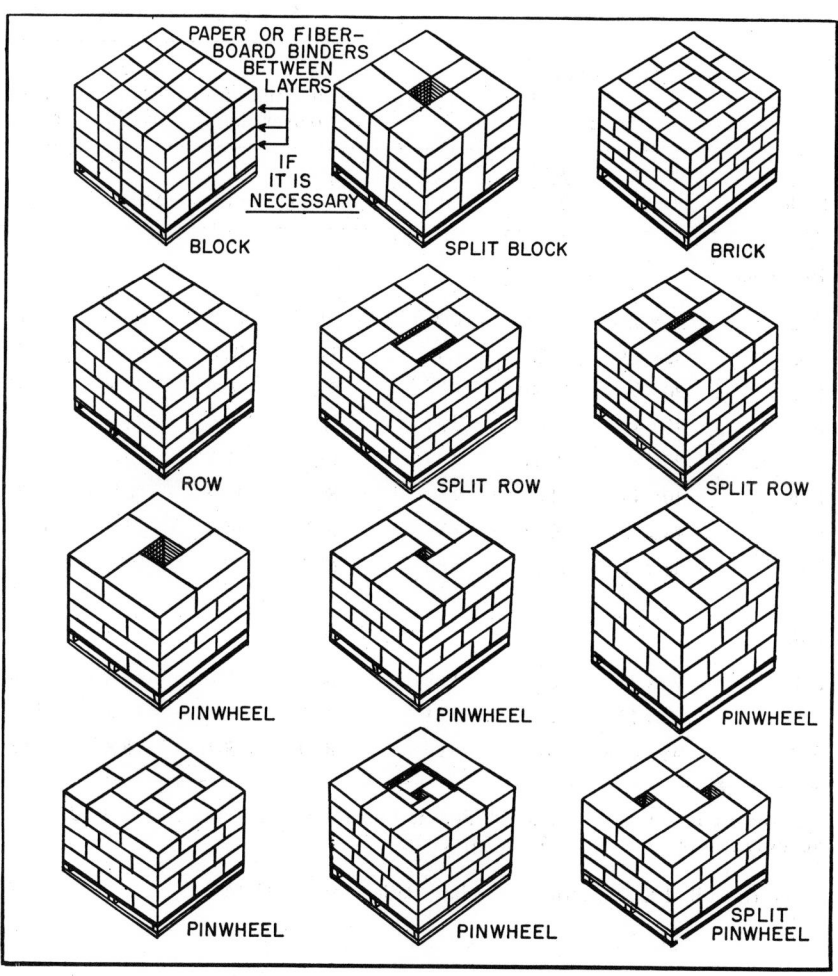

Source: Material Handling Engineering, *Directory & Handbook,* 1960–61.

C. AMERICAN STANDARD PALLET SIZES

A.S.A. Code	Standard Pallet Size and area ratios			Area Utilization Percent			
				1 in. clearance No overhang		1 in. clearance 1½ in. overhang	
	Dim.	Area Ft ^{2}	Ratio	Boxcar	Trailer	Boxcar	Trailer
Rectangular							
R–1	24 x 32	5.33	1.00	89.8	91.3	89.3	84.2
R–2	32 x 40	8.89	1.67	88.3	83.0	88.0	89.5
R–3	36 x 42	10.50	1.97	95.2	89.9	79.0	85.4
R–4	32 x 48	10.67	2.00	83.0	82.9	88.4	86.8
R–5	36 x 48	12.00	2.25	93.3	88.7	89.5	75.2
R–6	40 x 48	13.33	2.50	80.6	93.4	85.5	83.0
R–7	48 x 60	20.00	3.75	90.7	62.3	86.7	60.8
R–8	48 x 72	24.00	4.50	82.9	74.7	91.8	72.3
Square							
S–1	36 x 36	9.00	1.69	93.3	77.0	68.4	82.2
S–2	42 x 42	12.25	2.31	74.1	85.0	79.0	43.9
S–3	48 x 48	16.00	3.00	82.9	50.0	58.8	49.2

Based on 50-ton AAR standard Boxcar dimensions 50 ft 6 in. by 9 ft 2 in. and highway trailer dimensions 35 ft x 7 ft x 6 in.

Source: A.S.M.E., "American Standard Pallet Sizes" ASA MH 1.1.

D. TRAILER PALLET LOADING EFFICIENCY

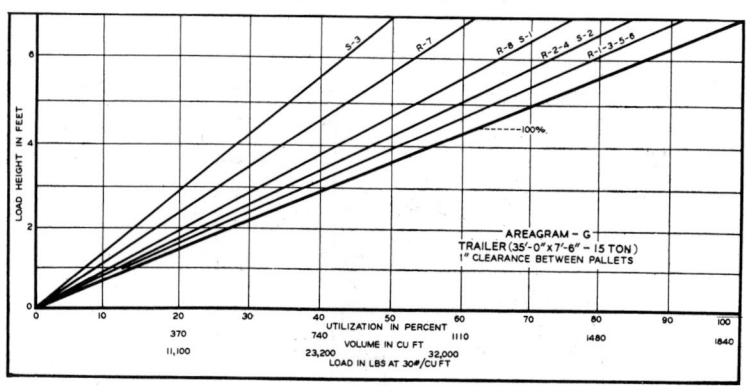

		Loading Pattern		No. Pallets In Trailer	% Of Area Utilization
Pallet	Size	Width (90")	Length (411")		
R-1	24" x 32"	2-32" 1-24"	16-24" 12-32"	44	91.3
		Alternate Pattern			
		3-24"	12-32"	36	74.7
R-2	32" x 40"	2-40"	12-32"	24	83.0
R-3	36" x 42"	2-42"	11-36"	22	89.9
R-4	32" x 48"	1-32" 1-48"	8-48" 12-32"	20	82.9
		Alternate Pattern			
		2-32"	8-48"	16	66.4
R-5	36" x 48"	1-36" 1-48"	8-48" 11-36"	19	88.7
		Alternate Pattern			
		2-36"	8-48"	16	74.7
R-6	40" x 48"	1-40" 1-48"	8-48" 10-40"	18	93.4
		Alternate Pattern			
		2-40"	8-48"	16	83.0
R-7	48" x 60"	1-60"	8-48"	8	62.3
R-8	48" x 72"	1-72"	8-48"	8	74.7
S-1	36" x 36"	2-36"	11-36"	22	77.0
S-2	42" x 42"	2-42"	9-42"	18	85.8
S-3	48" x 48"	1-48"	8-48"	8	50.0

Title row: **1" Clearance Between Pallet Loads — No Overhang**

Source: Material Handling Engineering, *Directory & Handbook,* 1960–61.

E. MINIMUM RIGHT ANGLE STACK AISLE WIDTH FOR FORK TRUCK—FOR ONE OR TWO WHEEL REAR STEER TRUCKS AND WITH MEDIUM WIDTH LOADS *

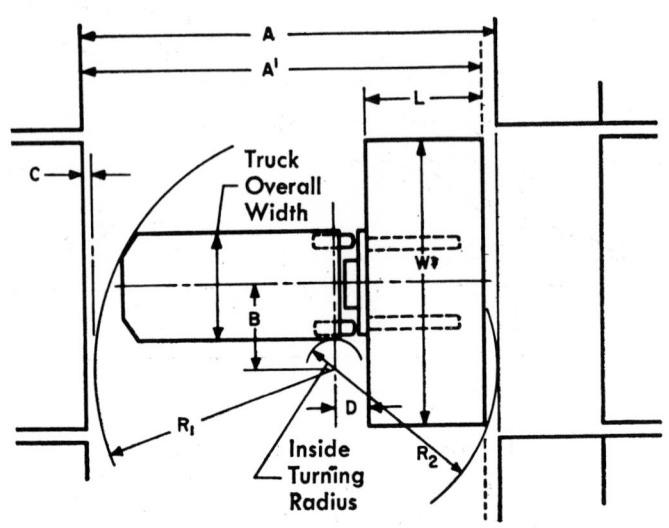

A = Minimum Aisle Width for Right Angle Stacking.

B = ½ Truck Overall Width Plus Inside Turning Radius.

C = Operating Clearance Best Suited for Individual Application and Steer Wheel Creep. (Consult Manufacturer.)

D = Distance from Face of Load to Centerline of Drive or Load Axle.

R_1 = Outside Turning Radius. (Empty Truck Under Power at Slow Speed.)

R_2 = Distance from Center of Turn to Indicated Load Corner

$$= \sqrt{(D + L)^2 + \left(\frac{W}{2} - B\right)^2}$$

L = Length of Load.

W = Width of Load.

When W is greater than $2B$ but not over $2(R_1 - B)$ use
$$A = R_1 + R_2 + C$$

If swing indicated by R_2 need not clear line of stack as shown dotted, then use:
$$A = R_1 + D + L + C$$

* Source: Material Handling Engineering, *Directory & Handbook,* 1960–61.

F. MINIMUM RIGHT ANGLE STACK AISLE FOR STRADDLE TYPE FORK TRUCK WITH SHORT NARROW LOADS ON REGULAR OR WING TYPE PALLETS *

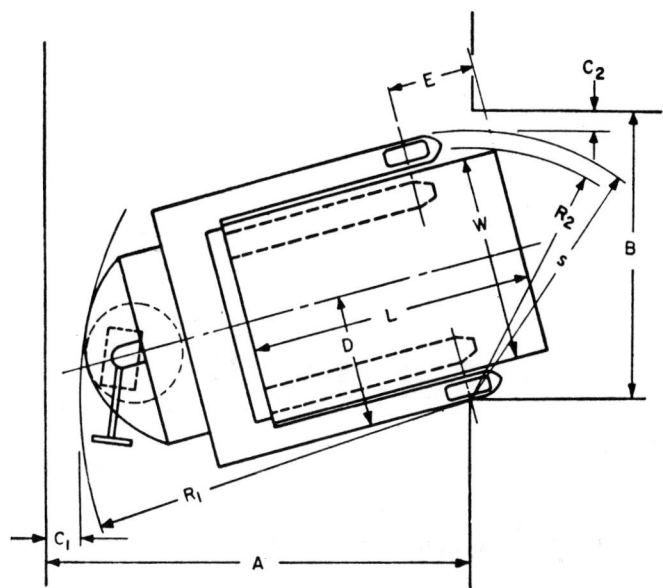

A = Minimum Operating Aisle Width.

B = Load Opening Width.

C_1 and C_2 = Operating Clearance Best Suited for Individual Application. (Consult Manufacturer)

D = ½ Truck Width.

E = Load Overhang.

L = Load Length.

W = Load Width.

R_1 = Outside Turning Radius.

S = Truck Rear Turning Radius.

R_2 = Distance from Center of Turn to Indicated Load Corner

$$= \sqrt{\left(D + \frac{W}{2}\right)^2 + E^2}$$

(1) $A = R_1 + C_1$

(2) When S is greater than R_2 use: $B = S + C_2$

* Source: Material Handling Engineering, *Directory & Handbook*, 1960–61.

Appendix III

Carrier Dimensions

A. DOOR OPENINGS IN BOX CARS AND AUTOMOBILE CARS

Dimension	Single Doors		Double Doors		End Doors	
	Min.	Max.	Min.	Max.	Min.	Max.
Clear width	5' 6"	6' 1"	7' 9"	15' 0"	8' 6"	9' 4"
Clear height	7' 8"	10' 6"	8' 0"	9' 11"	8' 6"	10' 1"

B. FREIGHT CAR DIMENSIONS, CAPACITIES AND WEIGHTS

Type of Car	A Length Over Strikers	B Inside Length		C Overall Width	D Inside Width		E Overall Height	F Inside Height		G Floor Height	Level Full Capacity	Tare Weight
	Avg.	Min.	Max.	Avg.	Min.	Max.	Avg.	Min.	Max.	Avg.	Av. Cu. Ft.	Avg. Lbs.
Flat	53' 0"	36' 0"	60' 0"	10' 3"	8' 6"	10' 6"	8' 7"	—	—	3' 11"	—	48,700
Gondola	43' 0"	33' 6"	65' 0"	10' 4"	7' 6"	9' 6"	10' 8"	4' 8" Avg.		3' 11"	1775	42,800
Hopper	35' 10"	34' 10" Avg.		10' 5"	10' 3" Avg.		14' 1"	—	—		2328	30,000
Box	41' 9"	40' 0"	50' 0"	10' 8"	8' 5"	9' 4"		7' 9"	10' 6"	3' 8"	3468	48,200
Auto-mobile	52' 3"	50' 6" Avg.		10' 8"	9' 2" Avg.		15' 1"	10' 4" Avg.		3' 7"	4798	53,300

Source: Material Handling Engineering, *Directory & Handbook*, 1960-61.

C. HIGHWAY TRAILER DIMENSIONS

Type of Trailer	A Overall Length	B Overall Width	C Inside Width	D Floor Height From Road	E Deflection Under Load	F Inside Height	G Overall Height
Platform	24' to 32'	7' 6" to 8' 0"	7' 4" to 7' 5"	49" to 56¼" Depending on Size of Tires Used on Trailer	As Much as 6" Varies According to Load and Position of Load	—	49" to 56¼"
Grain Haul	24' to 32'	to 8' 0"	7' 8" to 6' 10"			to 49½"	to 8' 10"
Dump Trailer	16' to 18'	7' 5" to 7' 6"	7' 2" to 7' 6"			to 52"	9' 0"
Livestock	24' to 34'	to 8' 0"	to 7' 5½"			to 7' 3"	Av. 12' 3"
Closed Van	20' to 34'	to 8' 0"				to 7' 3"	Av. 12' 6"
							Max. 12' 8½"

SINGLE AXLE

X (on trailers 17' to 24' long) = 2' 10¾"
X (on trailers 25' to 32' long) = 3' 10½"

TANDEM AXLE

Y (on trailers 23' to 30' long) = 7' 1¼"
Y (on trailers 31' to 34' long) = 8' 7¾"

Source: Material Handling Engineering, *Directory & Handbook*, 1960–61.

Appendix IV

Service Areas

A. WASHROOM PLANNING DATA *

Washfountain Capacities. Experience has established the following capacities for washfountains of the various sizes.

Fountain	Average Number Simultaneous Users	Average Number Total Users
54" Circular	8	40–50
36" Circular	5	25–30
54" Semi-circular	4	20–25
36" Semi-circular	3	15–20
Duo	2	10–12

Shower Capacities. Although varying widely under different conditions, the following ratio of showers to users is satisfactory for ordinary requirements:

Shower	Simultaneous Capacity	Average Number Total Users
Circular	5	40–50
Semi-circular	3	25–30

Water Consumption. The average rates of water consumption for washfountains and showers are as follows:

Washfountains	Gallons per Minute
54" Circular	7–9
36" Circular	4½–5½
54" Semi-circular	4½–5½
36" Semi-circular	2½–3
Duo	1½–2
Showers	2½ gallons per Showerhead

* Source: Bradley Washfountain Co., *Bradley Technical Manual.*

B–1. RECOMMENDED WASHROOM EQUIPMENT SPACING

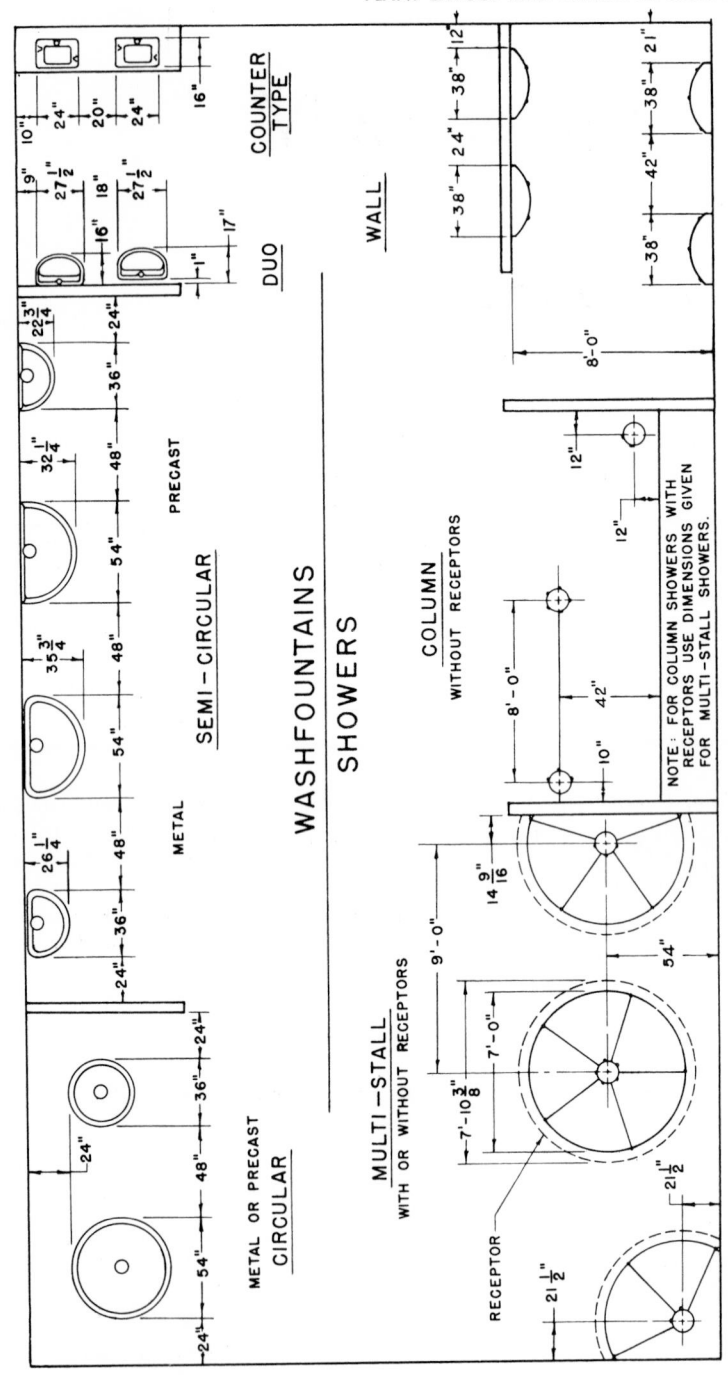

By permission of the Bradley Washfountain Co.

C. RECOMMENDED MINIMUM STANDARDS OF ILLUMINATION *

Interiors	Minimum Operating Foot-Candles
INDUSTRIAL	
Assembly	
Rough	30
Medium	100
Fine	500
Extra Fine	1000
Automobile Manufacturing	
Assembly Line	100
Frame Assembly	50
Body Manufacturing	
Parts	70
Assembly	100
Finishing and Inspecting	300
Cloth Products	
Cutting	300
Sewing	500
Pressing	300
Cloth Inspection	2000
Corridors and Stairways	20
Forge Shops and Welding	50
Foundries	
Rough Molding and Core Making	50
Fine Molding and Core Making	100
Inspection	
Rough	100
Medium	200
Fine	300
Extra Fine	500
Machine Shops	
Rough Bench and Machine Work	50
Medium Bench and Machine Work, Ordinary Automatic Machines, Rough Grinding, Medium Buffing and Polishing	100
Fine Bench and Machine Work, Fine Automatic Machines, Medium Grinding, Fine Buffing and Polishing	500, 1000
Packing and Boxing	50
Paint Shops	
Dipping, Simple Spraying, Firing	50
Rubbing, Ordinary Hand Painting and Finishing, Art, Stencil and Special Spraying	50
Fine Hand Painting and Finishing	100
Extra Fine Hand Painting and Finishing (Automobile Bodies, Piano Cases, etc.)	300

* These recommended values do not cover all situations. An excellent booklet giving more details, *Footcandles in Modern Lighting,* can be obtained from the General Electric Company.

Recommended Minimum Standards of Illumination (continued)

Interiors	Minimum Operating Foot-Candles
INDUSTRIAL	
Paper Manufacturing	
Beaters, Grinding, Calendering	30
Finishing, Cutting, Trimming, Paper Making Machines	50
Plating	30
Polishing and Burnishing	100
Power Plants, Engine Rooms—	
Boilers, Coal and Ash Handling, Storage Battery Rooms	30
Auxiliary Equipment, Oil Switches and Transformers	30
Engines, Generators, Blowers, Compressors	60
Switchboards	100
Stock Picking	30
Testing	
General	50
Extra Fine, Instruments, Scales, etc.	200
Upholstering—Automobile, Coach, Furniture	100
Warehouses	30–50
Woodworking	
Rough Sawing and Bench Work	50
Sizing, Planing, Rough Sanding, Medium Machine and Bench Work, Gluing, Veneering, Cooperage	100
Fine Bench and Machine Work, Fine Sanding and Finishing	200
COMMERCIAL	
Corridors and Stairways	20
Drafting Rooms	200
Dining Area	30–50
Library	
Reading Rooms	70
Stack Room	30
Loading and Unloading	30
Offices	
Bookkeeping, Typing and Accounting	100
Business Machines—Power Driven, (Transcribing and Tabulating) Calculators, Key Punch, Bookkeeping	150
Conference Room	50
Filing and Index References	100
Mail Sorting	100
Parking	1
Washrooms	30

Appendix V

Plant Layout Standards *

This standard was prepared under the direction of a committee of engineers from industry, the consulting field, the colleges and the Bureau of Ships of the U. S. Navy Department. It was approved as an ASME Standard on February 14, 1949, and is published in pamphlet form by the Society.

Templates. The Standard covers two-dimensional, one-plane templates and three-dimensional equipment models.

Template scale is, ¼ in. equals 1 ft., U. S. measure. This scale is standard with architects, engineers, furniture and equipment manufacturers, etc., for planning purposes. Equipment outlines are those which would be made around the periphery of a piece of equipment by a plumb line held 7 ft. above the floor, and passed around the outline of the machine. Projections such as wheels, handles, etc., are separately indicated as details not in the periphery.

Details on the template are those necessary to make it distinguishable and to locate important points. Kinds and relative weights of lines used are:

Fixed outline of machine tool or equipment—Thick solid line
Detail parts and substructures   —Thin solid line
Clearances for moving parts of machine
   tool or equipment   —Thick dash line
Overhead or underground elements—foun-
   dation pits, service clearances and other
   elements important to the template   —Medium dot-and-dash line
Center lines   —Thin dot-and-dash line

Clearances for movable parts, access and operation are shown in dash lines. Templates do not include storage, service or other space.

* From *Plant Layout Templates and Models*, developed, 1949, by the ASME Plant Layout Standards Committee, American Society of Mechanical Engineers.

Interferences are indicated by medium dot-and-dash lines and are included in final drawings.

Data on the templates includes: over-all length, width, height, including travel clearance but not operator or feed clearances. Weight and horsepower are given.

Specifications for identification are: name, model or style, size, user company identification marks or numbers.

Operator position is shown by a short heavy arrow. Other data included are controls, service provisions, power connection points, and similar indicators of necessary auxiliary operating facilities.

Templates should be printed on 110 lb., or more, index bristol or similar durable stock.* It is preferable to use colored stock:

Machine tools and other operating or production equipment   —Salmon

Office equipment and standard factory equipment—bins, racks,
   locker room equipment, toilet and washroom facilities   —Green

Materials handling equipment   —Yellow

Auxiliaries—pallets, skids, tote boxes, trays, pans, etc.   —Red

Models. Three-dimensional scale representations of equipment and facilities, called *models*, are made from wood, metal or plastic by appropriate processes, including tool and machine fashioning, die casting, and plastic production methods.

The scale is the same as that for templates, ¼ in. equals 1 ft., U. S. measure.

Details included are those sufficient, without distortion, to identify the model and show its important structural and operating features for ready identification of the equipment and indication of its operating requirements so far as plant layout is concerned. Control points and hazard areas are shown, with all controls and operating or moving parts located in neutral position, no moving parts being designed into the model unless it is impossible to show them in any other way.

Models are made in finishes and colors as near as possible to the actual item represented—including multiple finishes, as in office furniture.

Machine-tool model finishes should follow the recommendations of the National Machine Tool Builders Association. Machined surface can be shown by aluminum paint.

Control points should be shown by light buff paint, conforming to present-day practices for greater visibility and safety. The practice of

---

* Author's note: Templates are currently more commonly produced on transparent plastic film or sheet; see Chapter 15.

the individual company should be followed where models are used exclusively within a company.

Allowances and clearances should not be exaggerated. Accompanying templates should show these allowances for extreme operating and service conditions, but should not include any operator or facilities allowances, as stated above under discussion of templates. These accompanying templates should carry at least name or description and model number, and, if possible, type, size, maximum dimensions, center lines, weight, etc., and data on overhead and underfloor requirements.

Models should be durable, not easily damaged, have a lasting finish, and have sufficient weight to stay in position when placed, or be equipped with holes in the base for insertion of fastening pins.

All necessary identification markings—name, number, size, description, etc.—should be given in abbreviated form and in the most suitable place.

Models should be so designed as to be used with accompanying standard templates for the identical equipment. This provision facilitates drawing the layout on the floor plan.

Appendix VI

Building and Equipment Features

By permission of Cunningham-Limp Co.

TYPICAL LIGHT SOURCES

	Range of Colors Available for Creation of Varied Atmospheres	Effect on Appearance of Human Complexions	Aids in the Creation of a Warm Atmosphere	Aids in the Creation of a Cool Atmosphere	Brightness	Lends Itself to Dimming Applications	Initial Cost Per Lumen of Light Output	Energy Cost Per Lumen of Light Output	Lamp Life	Maintenance Cost	Undesirable Response to Voltage Fluctuation	Stroboscopic Effect	Restrike Time in Event of Momentary Power Interruption	Lends Itself for Use With High-Voltage Lighting Distribution	Deodorizing Ability	Germ Killing Ability	Sun Tanning Ability	Promotes Plant Growth
Incandescent	E	E	E	F	H	E	L	H	L	H	H	L	E	F	—	—	—	F
Fluorescent (Hot Cathode)	F	G	F	E	L	G	H	L	H	M	M	M	G	G	—	—	—	G
Fluorescent (Cold Cathode)	G	G	F	E	L	F	H	L	H	M	M	M	E	G	—	—	—	G
Mercury Vapor	P	F	P	G	M	P	H	L	H	L	L	H	P	G	—	—	—	G
Sun Lamp	—	—	—	—	—	—	—	—	M	—	M	—	P	—	—	—	G	—
Germicidal	—	—	—	—	—	—	—	—	H	—	M	—	—	—	F	E	—	—
Electro-Luminescent	G	G	F	G	L	G	H	H	H	—	M	—	E	F	—	—	—	—

TYPICAL LIGHTING FIXTURE MOUNTINGS

	Light Distribution	Initial Installed Cost	Ceiling Contrast	Appearance	Over-all Fixture Efficiency
Stem	E	M	L	F	E
Chain Hung	E	L	L	F	E
Surface	G	M	M	G	F
Semi-Recessed	G	H	M	G	G
Recessed	G	H	H	E	G
Luminous Ceiling	E	VH	L	E	F

TYPES OF POWER DISTRIBUTION SYSTEMS

	Initial Cost	Safety to Personnel	Lends Itself to Remote Control	Lessens Air-Conditioning Load	Lends Itself to Relocation of Switches
Std. 120 V. Power W/120 V. Switching	M	G	P	—	P
Std. 120 V. Power W/24 V. Switching	H	G	E	—	E
277/480 V. High Voltage W/277 V. Switching	L	F	P	—	P
277/480 V. High Voltage W/24 V. Switching	M	G	E	—	E
High-Frequency Power	H	G	—	F	—

TYPICAL EXTERIOR WALL MATERIALS

	COST						Resistance to Moisture Absorption	STRENGTH			
	Initial	Maintenance	Insulating Value	Fire Resistance	Durability	Appearance		Tensile	Load Bearing	Wind Resistance	Earthquake Resistance
Hollow Masonry Units Standard	L	M	G	G	G¹	G	F²	F¹	G	F¹	F¹
Lightweight	L	M	E	G	G¹	G	F²	F¹	G	F¹	F¹
Brick	M	L	F	E	E	E	G	G¹	G	G¹	G¹
Concrete, Precast Panels	M	L	F	E	E	F-G	E	E	E	E	E
Metal Panels Industrial Non-Insulated Steel Surface Protected	M	M	P	F	G	F	G	G	F	E	F
Aluminum	M	L	P	F	E	F	G	G	F	E	F
Industrial-Insulated	H	L	E	G	E	F	G	G	F	E	F
Architectural-Insulated	H	L	E	G	E	E	G-E	G	F	E	F

¹ Can be improved by reinforcing.
² Can be improved by painting.

SHIELDING

	Efficiency of Light Transmission	Light Control	Comfort	Initial Cost
White Louvers	G	G	G	L
Aluminum Louvers	F	E	VE	H
Prismatic Glass	E	E	G	H
Plastic	G	F	G	M
Ribbed Glass	E	E	E	L
Luminous	F	F	VE	H

H HIGH   E EXCELLENT
M MEDIUM   G GOOD
L LOW   F FAIR
     P POOR
V VERY

TYPICAL HEAT SOURCES

	Initial Cost of Equipment & Building	Operating Cost, Including Maintenance	Waste or Nuisance	Space Requirements, Storage & Handling	Convertibility to Other Fuels	Safety	Cleanliness	Reliability of Operation	Automatic Operation	Continuity of Supply of Fuel
Coal (Solid and Powdered)	H	L-M	H	H	E	G	P	G	G	G
Oil (Light to Heavy)	M	M-H	H	M	P-G	G	F	F	G	G
Natural Gas	L	L	M	L	P-G	G	G	G	E	G
Manufactured Gas	L	H	M	L	P-G	G	G	G	E	G
L.P. Gas	M	M-H	M	M	P-G	G	G	G	E	G
Water (Heat Pump)	M	M-H	L	L	P	E	E	G	E	F
Air (Heat Pump)	M	M-H	L	L	P	E	E	F	E	E
Atomic Energy	VH	H	VH	H	P	P	G	G	G	P
Solar	H	L-H	L	L-H	P	E	E	P	E	F
Electricity	L	H	L	L	P	E	E	G	E	E

TYPICAL STRUCTURAL ROOF DECKS

	COST		Weight	Fire Resistance	Durability	Appearance	Resistance to Moisture Absorption	Strength	Acoustical Properties		Insulating Value
	Initial	Maintenance							High Frequency	Low Frequency	
Wood	L	M	L	F	G	F	F	G	G	F	F
Metal Deck (Plus 1" insulation)	L	M	L	F	G	G	G	G	F	F	G
Gypsum — Poured in Place	L	M	M	G	G	G	P	F	G	F	G
Gypsum — Precast Plank	M	M	M	G	G	G	P	F	G	F	G
Insulating Plank	M	M	L	F-G	G	G	F	F	G	F	G
Lightweight Concrete on Permanent Steel Forms	M	M	M	G	G	G	G	G	F	F	G
Precast Concrete Tile	M	L	M-H	E	E	G	E	E	F	G	F
Reinforced Concrete	H	L	H	E	E	F-G	E	E	F	G	F

TYPICAL HEATING SYSTEMS

	Initial Cost	Maintenance Cost	Personnel Requirements	Space Requirements	Quick Response	Adaptability to Providing Cooled Air	Ventilation with Filtering & Fresh Air Make-up	Process Steam	Process Hot Water	Process Auxiliaries such as Compressors, Turbine Drives	Uniformity of Heat Distribution	Automatic Operation	Appearance	Safety	Cleanliness	Quietness of Operation	Effect on Building Construction
High Pressure Steam Boilers	H	H	H	H	E	G	G	E	E	E	—	G	—	F	—	F	—
H.P. Convectors	H	H	H	M	E	—	G	—	—	—	G	G	G	P	G	F	G
L.P. Convectors	M	M	M	L	G	—	G	—	—	—	G	G	G	G	G	G	G
H.P. Unit Heaters	H	H	H	L	E	—	G	—	—	—	F	G	F	P	G	F	G
L.P. Unit Heaters	M	M	M	L	E	—	G	—	—	—	F	G	F	G	G	F	G
H.P. Heating Coils—Ducted Air	H	H	H	M	E	—	G	—	—	—	G	G	G	F	G	G	F
L.P. Heating Coils—Ducted Air	M	M	M	M	G	—	E	—	—	—	G	G	G	G	G	G	F
H.P. Radiant Panels	H	H	H	L	P	—	—	—	—	—	E	G	E	P	G	G	P
L.P. Radiant Panels	M	M	M	L	P	—	—	—	—	—	E	G	E	G	G	E	P
Low Pressure Steam Boilers	M	M	M	M	G	G	G	P	G	P	—	G	—	G	—	G	—
Convectors	M	M	M	L	G	—	G	—	—	—	G	G	G	G	G	G	G
Unit Heaters	M	M	M	L	G	—	G	—	—	—	F	G	F	G	G	F	G
Heating Coils—Ducted Air	M	M	M	M	E	—	E	—	—	—	G	G	G	G	G	G	F
Radiant Panels	M	M	M	L	P	—	—	—	—	—	E	G	E	G	G	E	P
High Pressure Hot Water Boiler	H	H	H	H	E	G	G	G	E	P	—	G	—	F	—	G	—
H.P. Convectors	H	L	L	M	E	—	G	—	—	—	G	G	G	P	G	G	G
L.P. Convectors	M	L	L	L	G	—	G	—	—	—	G	G	G	E	G	E	G
H.P. Unit Heaters	H	L	L	L	E	—	G	—	—	—	F	G	F	P	G	G	G
L.P. Unit Heaters	M	L	L	L	G	—	G	—	—	—	F	G	F	E	G	G	G
H.P. Heating Coils—Ducted Air	H	L	L	M	E	—	G	—	—	—	G	G	G	F	G	G	E
L.P. Heating Coils—Ducted Air	M	L	L	M	G	—	G	—	—	—	G	G	G	E	G	E	E
H.P. Radiant Panels	H	L	L	L	P	—	—	—	—	—	E	G	E	P	G	G	P
L.P. Radiant Panels	M	L	L	L	P	—	—	—	—	—	E	G	E	G	G	E	P
Low Pressure Hot Water Boiler	M	M	M	M	G	G	G	P	G	—	—	G	—	E	—	E	—
Convectors	M	L	L	L	G	—	G	—	—	—	G	G	G	E	G	E	G
Unit Heaters	M	L	L	L	F	—	G	—	—	—	F	G	F	E	G	G	G
Heating Coils—Ducted Air	M	L	L	H	E	—	G	—	—	—	G	G	G	E	G	E	F
Radiant Panels	M	L	L	L	P	—	—	—	—	—	E	G	E	G	G	E	P
Direct Fired Oil Unit Heaters	L	M	L	M	G	—	G	—	—	—	F	G	F	F	G	F	G
Direct Fired Gas Unit Heaters	L	L	L	M	G	—	G	—	—	—	F	G	F	G	G	F	G
Direct Fired Gas Infrared Heaters	L	L	L	M	G	—	F	—	—	—	F	F	F	F	E	E	G
Heat Pump	L	M	L	M	F	E	G	—	—	—	—	G	—	G	—	F	—
Radiation	M	L	L	M	F	—	—	—	—	—	G	G	G	E	G	E	G
Unit Heaters	M	L	L	M	F	—	—	—	—	—	F	G	F	E	G	G	G
Heating Coils—Ducted Air	M	L	L	H	F	—	F	—	—	—	G	G	G	E	G	E	F
Electrical	L	L	L	L	E	E	G-F	G	—	E	E	—	G	—	E	—	—
Convectors	L	L	L	L	E	—	G	—	—	—	G	E	G	G	E	E	G
Unit Heaters	L	L	L	L	E	—	G	—	—	—	F	E	F	G	E	G	G
Radiant	L	L	L	M	E	—	F	—	—	—	P	E	G	F	E	E	G-F
Heating Coils—Ducted Air	L	L	L	L	E	—	G	—	—	—	G	E	G	G	G	G	G
Solar	H	H	L	H	P	—	F-P	—	—	—	—	F	—	G	—	G	P
Convectors	M	L	L	L	P	—	F	—	—	—	G	G	G	G	G	E	G
Unit Heaters	M	L	L	L	P	—	P	—	—	—	F	G	F	G	G	G	G

H HIGH
M MEDIUM
L LOW

E EXCELLENT
G GOOD
F FAIR
P POOR

Index